D1062089

Design of
Active-Site-Directed
Irreversible
Enzyme Inhibitors

Design of Active-Site-Directed Irreversible Enzyme Inhibitors

The Organic Chemistry of the Enzymic Active-Site

B. R. Baker
Department of Chemistry
University of California, Santa Barbara

John Wiley and Sons Inc., New York · London · Sydney

742284

Library of Congress Catalog Card Number: 67–17333
Printed in the United States of America

To my beloved Reba whose unceasing encouragement, stimulation, and insight continues to level the many depressive troughs of research.

Preface

Over the last 50 years three facts have emerged to serve as the basis for active-site-directed irreversible inhibitors that can specifically label an enzyme at or near the active-site by covalent bond formation: (a) enzymes are macromolecules that can form complexes with substrates and inhibitors (b) enzymes have functional groups on their surfaces that can be attacked by chemical reagents with the formation of a covalent linkage; and (c) neighboring group reactions can be accelerated as much as 10,000-fold over the same chemical reaction proceeding by a bimolecular process. When these three tenets are combined, the following concept emerges:

"The macromolecular enzyme has functional groups on its surface which logically could be attacked selectively in the tremendously accelerated neighboring group reactions capable of taking place within the reversible complex formed between the enzyme and an inhibitor substituted with a properly placed neighboring group" [B. R. Baker, *J. Pharm. Sci.*, **53**, 347 (1964)].

This concept has been undergoing exploration for the last six years in a rapidly growing number of laboratories. Because incorrect positioning of the covalent-forming group on the inhibitor can lead to compounds that will fail to form a complex with the enzyme—thus negating the neighboring group reaction—a definite *modus operandi* has gradually been developed which greatly improves the chances of the successful design of suitable inhibitors that will "label" at or near the active-site of a given enzyme. Such active-site labels have already proved useful in protein-structure studies. Although these active-site-directed irreversible inhibitors have not yet led to useful chemotherapeutic agents, the future for such discoveries appears to be based on scientifically sound premises; compared with a reversible inhibitor, an active-site-directed irreversible inhibitor has an extra dimension of specificity that is sufficiently sensitive even to selectively inactivate closely related isozymes.

An abundance of key references to current literature in the field is provided. I admit some prejudice in selecting a large number of references from my own laboratory, for these references have the continuity needed for the *modus operandi* that eliminates much of the unsuccessful guesswork in the design of labels for enzymic active-sites.

I gratefully acknowledge the financial assistance of the National Cancer Institute, U.S. Public Health Service, through Grants CA–05845, CA–05867, CA–06624, and CA–08695 for support of my researches and those of my colleagues on active-site-directed irreversible enzyme inhibitors; these researches and the opportunity to organize the material for a graduate course on this subject at the State University of New York at Buffalo led to my interest in writing this book. I am also indebted for constructive criticism to the many students who have worked with me in this area over the last six years and to Professors C. A. Bunton, T. C. Bruice, T. L. Hullar, and H. J. Schaeffer.

Santa Barbara, California   *B. R. Baker*
February 1967

Contents

Design of
Active-Site-Directed
Irreversible
Enzyme Inhibitors

I | General Considerations

The subject of enzyme inhibition is a broad one which can be divided into a number of areas. For example, the enzymologist may be interested in enzyme inhibitors to study enzyme function and mechanism; the pharmacologist studies those enzyme inhibitors that cause a unique response of possible medical interest in living whole-cell systems; the molecular biologist studies enzyme inhibitors in broken-cell systems in order to try to understand their function at a molecular level without the added complexities of inhibitor transport, inhibitor metabolism, and multiple-enzyme inhibition facing the pharmacologist; the physical bioorganic chemist studies inhibitors in purified enzyme systems in order to put the enzyme mechanism on a firmer physical organic basis; the protein physical chemist studies inhibitors in order to learn more about the function of secondary and tertiary structure in the protein. In order to design an enzyme inhibitor effective for protein structure or for chemotherapy, the investigator should be aware of developments in each of the above-mentioned disciplines—the depth of his awareness in each area being partially dependent upon his ultimate goal for the inhibitor.

In its simplest terms an enzyme E complexes with a substrate S and converts S to the product P as follows:

$$E + S \rightleftharpoons E \cdots S \rightleftharpoons E \cdots P \rightleftharpoons E + P \qquad (1\text{--}1)$$

An inhibitor I must, by definition, have an affinity for the enzyme as follows:

$$E + I \rightleftharpoons E \cdots I \qquad (1\text{--}2)$$

Since the inhibitor can complex reversibly with the enzyme to form an E$\cdots$I complex, less free enzyme E is then available for conversion of S to P; hence the resultant conversion is inhibited to a greater or lesser degree depending upon the relative concentrations of S and I and their relative equilibrium constant with E, namely K_s and K_i respectively.[1]

---

[1] The kinetics of these systems are described in a variety of books on enzymology such as in References 2–4.

Certain types of inhibitors I bearing a properly positioned leaving group X can form a reversible complex with the enzyme E····I—X then further react irreversibly[5,6] as follows:

$$E + I{-}X \; \underset{k_2}{\overset{k_1}{\rightleftharpoons}} \; \overset{\frown}{E\cdots I}{-}X \; \overset{k_3}{\longrightarrow} \; \overset{\frown}{E\cdots I} + X^{-}$$

In contrast to the reversible E····I complex in (1–2), which can redissociate to free inhibitor and active enzyme E, the irreversibly inhibited enzyme E····I in (1–3) can vary from inoperative to poorly operative. The rate of formation (k_3) of such a covalently linked enzyme-inhibitor complex is dependent upon the concentration of the E····I—X complex, the nucleophilicity of the enzymic group being alkylated, the relative reactivity of the leaving group X, and the ease of formation of the transition state in the S_N^2-type neighboring group reaction[6]; the concentration of E····I—X is in turn dependent upon the concentration of the inhibitor I—X and upon the reversible dissociation constant K_i of the enzyme-inhibitor complex.[7,8]

The reciprocal of the dissociation constant is a measure of the affinity of the enzyme for the inhibitor. The closer the structure of the inhibitor is to that of the substrate, the greater is the possibility that K_i will approach K_s; however, it is possible for K_i to be much smaller (greater affinity) than K_s with certain structural changes that are usually not directly predictable from the structure of the substrate. Although there is a greater possibility of obtaining an inhibitor by making a small structural change in the substrate, the possible utility of the resultant inhibitor for the design of irreversible inhibitors is sometimes not directly useful; the small structural changes are called isoteric replacements, for example, NH_2 for OH, S for O, S for C=C, or SO_2NH_2 for COOH.[9,10] Antimetabolites are enzyme inhibitors[9,10] having only a small change in structure; they have been classified as classical[11] antimetabolites. These small structural changes have such a limitation in the structural changes that can be made that their utility is considerably restricted. In contrast, nonclassical antimetabolites are

[2] J. B. Neilands and P. K. Stumpf, *Enzyme Chemistry*, John Wiley and Sons, New York, 1958.

[3] J. M. Reiner, *Behavior of Enzyme Systems*, Burgess Publishing Co., Minneapolis, Minn., 1959.

[4] J. L. Webb, *Enzyme and Metabolic Inhibitors*, Academic Press, New York, 1963.

[5] B. R. Baker, *Cancer Chemotherapy Reports* (U.S. Public Health Service), **4**, 1 (1959).

[6] B. R. Baker, *J. Pharm. Sci.*, **53**, 347 (1964).

[7] B. R. Baker, W. W. Lee, and E. Tong, *J. Theoret. Biol.*, **3**, 459 (1962).

[8] B. R. Baker and R. P. Patel, *J. Pharm. Sci.*, **52**, 927 (1962).

[9] R. O. Roblin, Jr., *Chem. Rev.*, **38**, 255 (1946).

[10] D. W. Wooley, *A Study of Antimetabolites*, John Wiley and Sons, New York, 1952.

[11] B. R. Baker, W. W. Lee, W. A. Skinner, A. P. Martinez, and E. Tong, *J. Med. Pharm. Chem.*, **2**, 633 (1960).

defined[11] as inhibitors that have large, but appropriate, structural changes; these large changes must obviously not interfere with the stereospecific requirements of the enzyme surface for complexing; that is, these large structural changes should be made in an area of the inhibitor that is not in contact with the enzyme when the inhibitor is complexed with the enzyme.[12]

It is obvious at this point that irreversible inhibitors have an extra dimension of specificity dependent on k_3 (1–3) that does not exist with reversible inhibitors.[13–15]. Furthermore, the affinity of the enzyme for the inhibitor is most usually due to the complexing ability of the enzymic active-site for a substrate and its mimic, the inhibitor. Thus when a neighboring group reaction occurs within an enzyme-inhibitor complex to give an irreversibly inhibited enzyme, this phenomenon is called active-site-directed irreversible inhibition. The *modus operandi* for design of irreversible enzyme inhibitors that operate by (1–3) and their further modification for additional specificity is the subject of this book.

ENZYME INHIBITORS IN CHEMOTHERAPY: THE 6-MERCAPTOPURINE STORY

Most useful drugs have been developed by the classical approach of Ehrlich namely, the empirical testing of more-or-less random chemicals on a living host; the host may or may not be infected with a parasite, depending on whether the investigator is seeking an antiparasitic agent or a pharmacologic effect on the host. The emergence of the Woods-Fildes antimetabolite theory,[16,17] after the discovery of the *p*-aminobenzoic acid (metabolite)-sulfanilamide (antimetabolite) relationship, gave impetus to a more rational approach to design of enzyme inhibitors that might be useful as drugs. The antimetabolite theory has fallen far short of its original promise[18,19] primarily because it cannot predict how to obtain selectivity of action. All enzyme inhibitors are akin to poisons, and therefore the heart of the chemotherapy problem resides in selectivity of action—a poisoning sufficiently selective to be useful. It is therefore relatively easy to get selectivity if the invading parasite must utilize an essential metabolic pathway that

[12] See Reference 5, p. 2.
[13] B. R. Baker, W. W. Lee, and E. Tong, *J. Theoret Biol.*, **3**, 459 (1962).
[14] B. R. Baker, *Biochem. Pharmacol.*, **11**, 1155 (1961).
[15] See Reference 6, p. 2.
[16] D. D. Woods, *Brit. J. Exp. Path.*, **21**, 74 (1940).
[17] P. Fildes, *Lancet*, **1**, 955 (1940).
[18] See Reference 9, p. 2.
[19] See Reference 10, p. 2.

is not employed by the host,[20] such as *de novo* synthesis of dihydrofolate.[21] However, it is a much more complex problem to obtain a selective inhibitor for a cancer cell, because the latter usually uses fewer enzymes than the host tissues.[22,23]

Increased understanding of biochemical pathways, particularly of nucleic acid biosynthesis in the past 20 years, has given additional impetus to the search for chemotherapeutically useful enzyme inhibitors on a more rational basis. However, once the candidate antimetabolite has been synthesized, it is usually evaluated in *in vitro* cell systems. In order for the candidate enzyme inhibitor to be effective in a host system, the candidate inhibitor must (a) be transported to and into the desired target cell from the site of administration, (b) not be metabolized too rapidly to an inactive form, and (c) show selective action only on the target enzyme in the target cell. If a candidate inhibitor is studied only for effectiveness in a host system, the jackpot of (a), (b), and (c) working at the same time will have to be achieved, a remote possibility predicated mostly on extremely good luck. Factor (c) can be eliminated as a first approximation by *in vitro* evaluation of the candidate compound on intact cells. Factor (b) can be studied in broken-cell systems in order to avoid the transport problem (a).

When a candidate inhibitor fails in a host system we usually do not know whether facet (a), (b), or (c) has failed. Therefore the design of an effective chemotherapeutic agent in a host system is more likely to be achieved by individual study of the three facets, followed by collective use.[24]

The emergence of the importance of nucleic acids for protein synthesis and cell division, as well as the biochemical pathways for the cellular synthesis of the monomeric nucleotides making up the nucleic acid polymers, have made this area of metabolism a prime target for chemotherapy of parasitic diseases.[25] One of the pioneer workers in this area, G. H. Hitchings, has been the most successful in uncovering a myriad of antimetabolites useful for parasitic diseases.[25,26] One of the discoveries by Hitchings et al., 6-mercaptopurine,[27] has been chosen for discussion. Because this antimetabolite is useful in the treatment of leukemia, it has probably been studied at the molecular level more than any other drug; its action involves

[20] See Reference 5, p. 2.
[21] G. H. Hitchings and J. H. Burchall, *Adv. Enzymol.*, **27**, 417 (1965).
[22] See Reference 5, p. 2.
[23] V. P. Potter, *Univ. Michigan M. Bull.*, **23**, 401 (1957).
[24] See Reference 13, p. 3.
[25] H. G. Mandel and J. F. Henderson, *Adv. in Pharmacol.*, **2**, 297 (1963).
[26] See Reference 21, p. 4.
[27] C. P. Rhoads, ed., "Symposium on 6-Mercaptopurine", *Ann. N. Y. Acad. Sci.*, **60**, 183 (1954).

most—if not all—the parameters that are likely to be encountered with an enzyme inhibitor *in vivo*.

Activation

6-Mercaptopurine (II) can act as a substrate[28] for the enzyme inosinic pyrophosphorylase,[29] which normally condenses hypoxanthine (I) with 5-phospho-D-ribofuranosyl-1-pyrophosphate (III) to give inosinate (IV); the product is thioinosinate (V). Since II is a slower substrate than hypoxanthine (I), II can also act as an inhibitor for the enzyme in the presence of

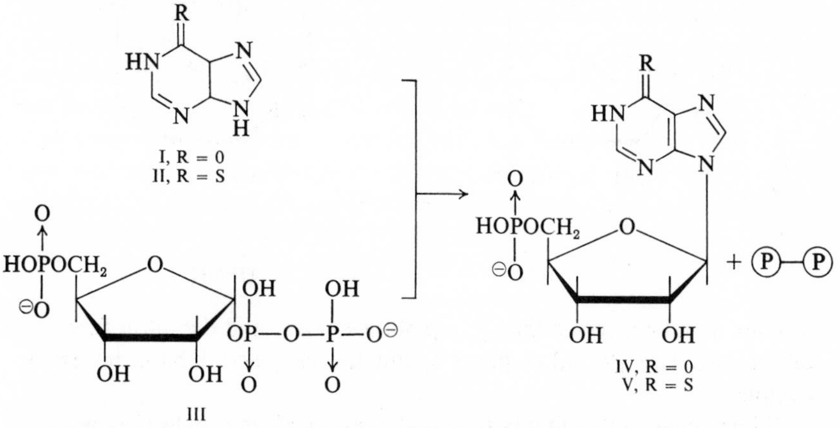

I[29,30]; this inhibition is apparently not critical in the cell, but thioinosinate is a potent inhibitor of a variety of enzymes utilizing nucleotidelike substrates.

Enzymes Inhibited by Thioinosinate

Inosinate (IV) is enzymatically oxidized by DPN, mediated by the enzyme inosinate dehydrogenase, to xanthylate (VI)—an intermediate to the nucleic acid precursor, guanylate. The enzyme has been isolated from bacterial sources[31,32] and from Ehrlich ascites tumour cells[33]; the rate of the enzymatic reaction is normally followed by the rate of change in optical density at 340 mμ as DPN is converted to DPNH.[32] The enzyme reaction is inhibited reversibly by thioinosinate (V)[31,33,34] The binding constant for the substrate for the Ehrlich ascites enzyme has been estimated

[28] R. W. Brockman, *Clin. Pharmacol. Therap.*, **2**, 237 (1961).
[29] C. E. Carter, *Biochem. Pharmacol.*, **2**, 105 (1959).
[30] M. R. Atkinson and A. W. Murray, *Biochem. J.*, **94**, 64 (1965).
[31] J. S. Salser, D. J. Hutchison, and M. E. Balis, *J. Biol. Chem.*, **235**, 429 (1960).
[32] B. Magasanik, H. S. Moyed, and L. B. Gehrina, *J. Biol. Chem.*, **226**, 339 (1957).
[33] M. R. Atkinson, R. K. Morton, and A. W. Murray, *Biochem. J.*, **89**, 167 (1963).
[34] A. Hampton, *J. Biol. Chem.*, **238**, 3068 (1963).

as 1.4×10^{-5} M[35]; thus the inhibitor binds to the enzyme about fourfold better than the substrate. With the enzyme from *Aerobacter aerogenes*, the amount of inhibition was observed to increase with increased time of contact between the enzyme and the inhibitor,[36] a phenomenon associated with irreversible inhibition. Hampton[36] has proposed that a mixed

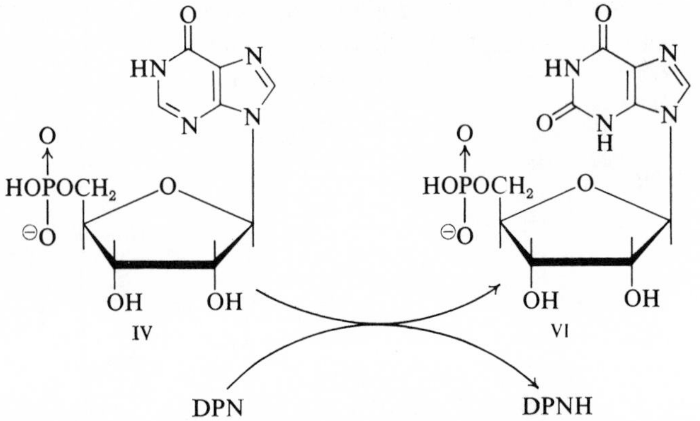

disulfide bond between a thiol group of the enzyme and the sulfur function of thioinosinate (V) takes place within the enzyme-inhibitor reversible complex.

Thioinosinate (V) inhibits the condensation of inosinate (IV) with L-aspartate,[37-39] mediated by the enzyme succinoadenylate kinosynthetase[40] which requires guanosine triphosphate as a cofactor for activation of the inosinate (IV).[40,41] Adenylate (VIII) is also an inhibitor of this enzyme.[42] The enzyme has been isolated from bacterial sources[43,44] and from mammalian tissues[45]; it is most easily assayed by the rate of change in optical density at 274 mμ as the product, succinoadenylate (VII), is formed.[44,46] With the *E. coli* enzyme, the apparent binding constant of inosinate (IV) is 5.4×10^{-5} M, and that of adenylate is 9.5×10^{-5} M,[42] an inhibitor-

[35] See Reference 33, p. 5.
[36] See Reference 34, p. 5.
[37] See Reference 31, p. 5.
[38] B. R. Baker, and P. M. Tanna, *J. Pharm. Sci.*, **54**, 845 (1965).
[39] J. D. Davidson, *Cancer Res.*, **20**, 225 (1960).
[40] I. Lieberman, *J. Biol. Chem.*, **223**, 327 (1956).
[41] H. J. Fromm, *Biochim. Biophys. Acta*, **29**, 255 (1958).
[42] J. B. Wyngaarden and R. A. Greenland, *J. Biol. Chem.*, **238**, 1054 (1963).
[43] See Reference 31, p. 5.
[44] See Reference 40, p. 6.
[45] See Reference 39, p. 6.
[46] See Reference 41, p. 6.

substrate ratio of 1.8; the inhibitor-substrate binding ratio for thioino-sinate (V) has been found to be 2.2.[47]

Succinoadenylate lyase,[48,49] the enzyme that reversibly converts suc-cinoadenylate (VII) to adenylate (VIII) and fumarate, is also inhibited by thioinosinate (V).[50-52] The binding ratio is 1 in the presence of a one

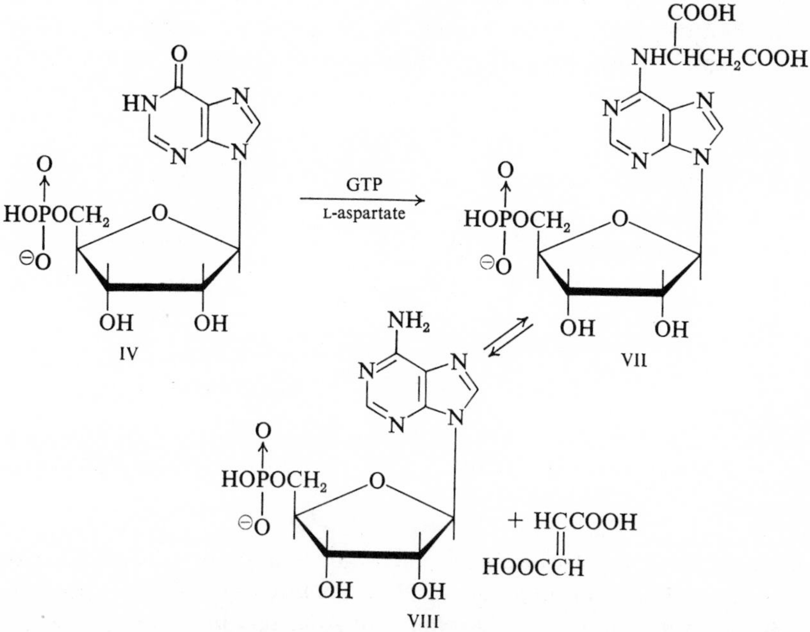

thirtieth equivalent of cupric ion, but binding of thioinosinate is reported to be poor in the absence of cupric ion[53]; the copper contaminant can arise as an impurity from the cupric sulfate used in one of the steps involved in the chemical synthesis of thioinosinate (V). There is considerable dif-ference of opinion over whether this enzyme is inhibited appreciably in the absence of cupric ion.

Thioinosine-5′-diphosphate has been observed to be an inhibitor of the RNA polymerase from *M. lysodeikticus* when adenosine-5′-diphosphate is used as the substrate[54]; the binding ratio of inhibitor to ADP was 0.02.

[47] See Reference 38, p. 6.
[48] C. E. Carter and L. H. Cohen, *J. Biol. Chem.*, **222**, 17 (1956).
[49] R. W. Miller, L. N. Lukens, and J. M. Buchanan, *J. Biol. Chem.*, **234**, 1806 (1959).
[50] J. S. Salser and M. E. Balis, *Federation Proc.*, **18**, 1806 (1959).
[51] A. Hampton, *Federation Proc.*, **21**, 370 (1962).
[52] M. R. Atkinson, R. K. Morton, and A. W. Murray, *Biochem. J.*, **92**, 398 (1964).
[53] W. A. Bridger and L. H. Cohen, *Biochim. Biophys. Acta*, **73**, 514 (1963).
[54] J. A. Carbon, *Biochem. Biophys. Res. Comm.*, **7**, 366 (1962).

Until it is established that some kinase can convert thioinosinate (V) to its diphosphate derivative, it cannot be assumed that this extremely potent block is of any chemotherapeutic significance in intact cells.

Purine biosynthesis is subject to feedback inhibition of its first step by purine nucleotides; glutamine ribosyl-pyrophosphate-5-phosphate amido-transferase,[55] the enzyme that converts the pyrophosphate, III, to 5-phosphoribosylamine (IX), is inhibited by a number of natural nucleotides[56] and by thioinosinate (V).[57] The apparent binding constant for III is

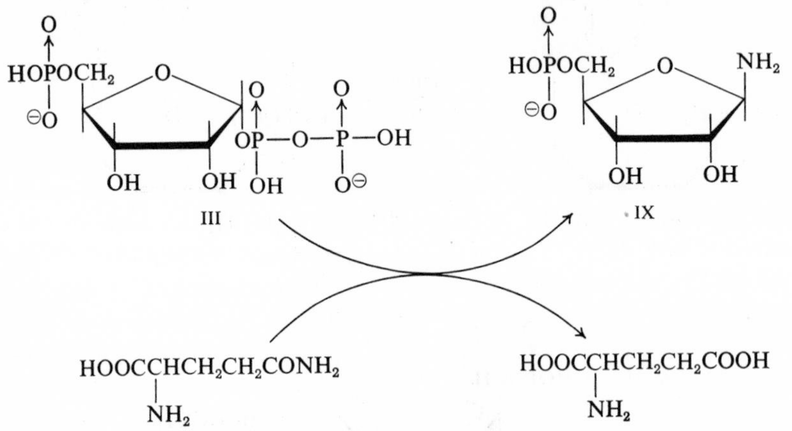

24×10^{-5} M; the best natural nucleotide inhibitor is adenylate with $K_i = 9 \times 10^{-5}$ M, an inhibitor-substrate binding ratio of 0.37. Inosinate (IV) and thioinosinate (V) have inhibitor-substrate binding ratios of 0.83 and 0.19, respectively.[57] Thus thioinosinate (V) is the best feedback inhibitor of this enzyme yet observed.

Of the six enzyme systems inhibited by 6-mercaptopurine (II), thioinosinate (V), or thioinosine-5'-diphosphate, which one is the most critical for cell growth? Such a question requires a study with intact, viable cells in which all the enzymes suspected of being inhibited and the activation enzyme for 6-mercaptopurine are operational in concert.[58]

Bennett et al.[59] observed with growing neoplasms in the mouse that an effective dose of 6-mercaptopurine inhibited incorporation of ^{14}C-glycine into nucleic acids but did not inhibit the incorporation of ^{14}C-adenine or

[55] S. C. Hartman and J. M. Buchanan, *J. Biol. Chem.*, **233**, 451 (1958).

[56] J. B. Wyngaarden and D. M. Ashton, *J. Biol. Chem.*, **234**, 1492 (1959).

[57] R. M. McCollister, W. R. Gilbert, Jr., D. M. Ashton, and J. B. Wyngaarden, *J. Biol. Chem.*, **239**, 1560, 2570 (1964).

[58] R. W. Brockman and S. Chumley, *Biochim. Biophys. Acta*, **95**, 365 (1965).

[59] L. L. Bennett, Jr., L. Simpson, J. Golden, and T. L. Barker, *Cancer Res.*, **23**, 1574 (1963).

[14]C-5-aminoimidazole-4-carboxamide; therefore the critical block must occur prior to the synthesis of 5-aminoimidazole-4-carboxamide ribotide. Further work in their laboratory[58] showed that the critical block did occur prior to the formation of formyl glycineamide ribotide; there are three enzymic steps in the conversion of 5-phospho-D-ribosyl-1-pyrophosphate (III) to formyl glycineamide ribotide. Although it is highly probable, it cannot be stated unequivocally that the critical block by 6-mercaptopurine is in the enzymic formation of 5-phospho-D-ribosylamine (IX) until the other two enzymes are investigated for inhibition by thioinosinate (V); however it is most unlikely that either the second or third enzyme in this sequence would be inhibited.

Cell Membrane Permeability

Since 6-mercaptopurine (II) is activated by enzymic conversion to its nucleotide, thioinosinate (V), and the latter is a lethal agent to cells, cannot cells be treated directly with thioinosinate (V)? Unfortunately, the ionized thioinosinate (V) penetrates cell walls only with difficulty[60] and then only by cleavage of the nucleotide to 6-mercaptopurine,[61] as has been observed with inosinate (IV) or adenylate (VIII).[62] Apparently cells have no active-transport mechanism for nucleotides and, furthermore, the charge on the nucleotide prevents passive diffusion through the cell wall. Therefore, thioinosinate (V) affects the growth of 6-mercaptopurine-sensitive cells only at extremly high concentration.

Resistance

Unfortunately, cell populations soon arise after treatment with 6-mercaptopurine that are resistant to the effect of the drug. There are apparently several different modes of resistance[63]; one mode of resistance, the mutational loss of the activating enzyme that converts 6-mercaptopurine (II) to thioinosinate (V) or hypoxanthine (I) to inosinate (IV), has been studied in considerable detail.[64]

In the cell that is resistant to 6-mercaptopurine (II) due to the loss of the pyrophosphorylase that converts II to thioinosinate (V), it should be noted that the critical feedback enzyme (III → IX) is still inhibited by thioinosinate (V) in broken-cell systems; as was pointed out in the previous section, thioinosinate cannot be used for inhibition of cell growth because

[60] See Reference 58, p. 8.
[61] A. R. P. Paterson and A. Sutherland, *Can. J. Biochem.*, **42**, 1415 (1964).
[62] P. M. Roll, H. Weinfeld, E. Carroll, and G. B. Brown, *J. Biol. Chem.*, **220**, 439, (1956).
[63] See Reference 39, p. 6.
[64] See Reference 58, p. 8 and earlier references cited therein.

it will not penetrate a cell wall without cleavage back to 6-mercaptopurine (II). This type of resistance can be overcome by means to be discussed in sections to follow.

Latentiation

Latentiation is defined as a drug form that is inactive *per se* but one that can be converted to an active form by some intracellular enzymatic reaction; the activation of 6-mercaptopurine (II) to thioinosinate (V) represents a special case of latentiation. Latentiation has been employed to overcome cellular resistance to 6-mercaptopurine (II) due to mutational loss of the activating enzyme.

It was noted in the section on cellmembrane permeability that thioinosinate (V) could not penetrate the cell wall intact because there is no

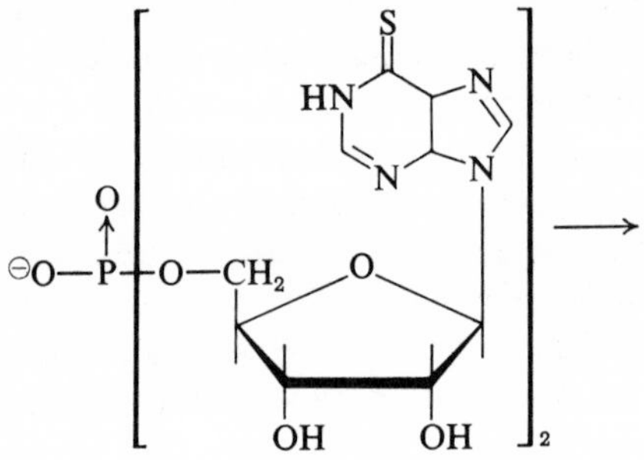

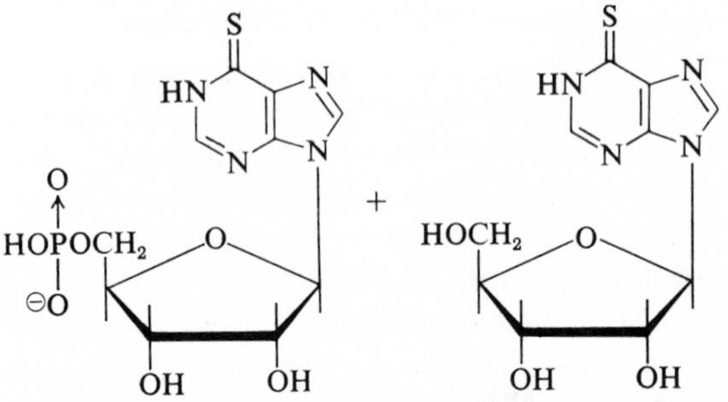

active-transport process for nucleotides, and the charged thioinosinate (V) could not penetrate the cell wall by diffusion. Di- and triester derivatives of thioinosinate (V) have been synthesized[65] relying on the fact that the less charged ester derivatives of V might penetrate the cell wall by passive diffusion, then be hydrolyzed to V by a nonspecific phosphoesterase;

[65] J. A. Montgomery, H. J. Thomas, and H. J. Schaeffer, *J. Org. Chem.*, **26**, 1929 (1961).

in this way, resistance could be overcome by activating the latent inhibitor to V by a different mechanism than the intracellular conversion of 6-mercaptopurine (II) to thioinosinate (V). The most successful of these derivatives on resistant cells was the thioinosine diester phosphate (X), which can penetrate the cell wall by passive diffusion presumably because only a single charge is present in X, and some of X may be nonionized; after penetration, X is presumably cleaved by a phosphoesterase to thioinosine (XI) and the desired thioinosinate (V).[66]

Alternate Inhibitors for Feed-back Inhibition of Purine Biosynthesis

In addition to 6-mercaptopurine (II) many other unnatural purines can inhibit the first step of purine biosynthesis after conversion of these unnatural purines to their nucleotides intracellularly. Because such a diverse lot of purines and nucleosides are inhibitory,[66-72] it would be unlikely that each one would be activated by the same enzyme that activates 6-mercaptopurine (II) to thioinosinate (V); if one of these purines or nucleosides were activated by a different enzyme, then the compound should be effective on cells which are resistant to 6-mercaptopurine (II) by virtue of their mutational loss of the pyrophosphorylase necessary for activating II.

Bennett et al.[73] screened a large number of purines and nucleosides against 6-mercaptopurine-resistant mammalian cells *in vitro*. They found that the most effective compound was 6-methylthiopurine ribonucleoside (XII), which also was as effective as 6-mercaptopurine (II) on the nonresistant cell line. Further study showed that XII was inhibiting the first step of purine biosynthesis after intracellular conversion to its nucleotide, most likely by means of the enzyme adenosine kinase. Furthermore XII was not cleaved by adenosine phosphorylase, nor was its nucleotide (XIII) cleaved by nucleotide pyrophosphorylases.

The intricate specificities of the host of enzymes involved in the feedback inhibition of purine biosynthesis are further noted by the effects of thioinosine (XI) and 6-methylthiopurine. The latter is not a substrate for adenine

[66] J. A. Montgomery, G. J. Dixon, E. A. Dulmadge, H. J. Thomas, R. W. Brockman, and H. E. Skipper, *Nature*, **199**, 769 (1963).

[67] See Reference 58, p. 8.

[68] J. S. Gots and E. G. Gollub, *Proc. Soc. Exp. Biol. Med.*, **101**, 641 (1954).

[69] G. A. LePage and M. Jones, *Cancer Res.*, **21**, 642 (1961).

[70] J. F. Henderson, *Biochem. Pharmacol.*, **12**, 551 (1963).

[71] R. W. Brockman, *Cancer Res.*, **23**, 1191 (1963).

[72] See Reference 57, p. 8.

[73] L. L. Bennett, Jr., R. W. Brockman, H. P. Schnebli, S. Chumley, G. J. Dixon, F. M. Schabel, Jr., E. A. Dulmakge, H. E. Skipper, J. A. Montgomery, and J. H. Thomas, *Nature*, **205**, 4978 (1965).

pyrophosphorylase and is thus not converted to the nucleotide; it is only one thousandth as effective on a nonresistant cell line as is 6-mercaptopurine, but it is slightly more effective than 6-mercaptopurine on the 6-mercaptopurine-resistant line. It is therefore probable that 6-methyl thiopurine is an extremely poor substrate of adenine pyrophosphorylase; only small amounts of XIII are formed by this enzyme. Also of interest is

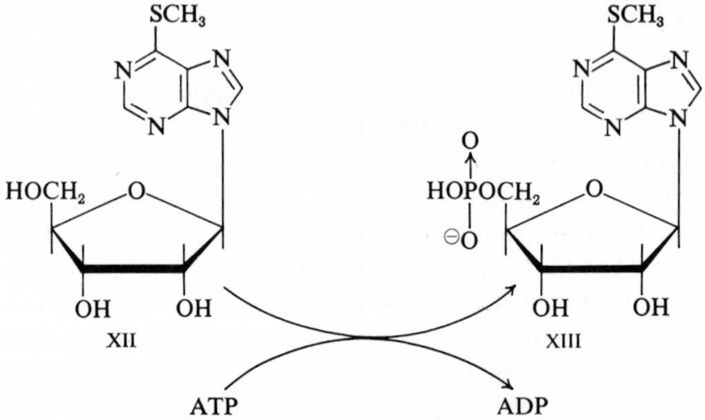

the fact that thioinosine (XI) is ineffective on a 6-mercaptopurine resistant cell line; thioinosine—in contrast to 6-methylthiopurine riboside (XII)—is not a substrate for adenosine kinase, and no kinase enzyme for inosine or guanosine that might use XI as a substrate could be found.[74] Therefore, thioinosine (XI) cannot be converted directly to thioinosinate by a kinase.

Cell Selectivity

Apparently thioinosinate (V) is a good feedback inhibitor of purine biosynthesis in any type of cell synthesizing purines *de novo*; then why does 6-mercaptopurine exert a preferential effect on some patients with leukemia and on some mouse tumors? Selectivity is probably the most moot point in chemotherapy and, unfortunately, has been studied the least. Selectivity most probably arises by an interplay of a myriad of activating and detoxifying enzymes that can metabolize 6-mercaptopurine.[75] Another possibility that many investigators accept is that the growth of a rapidly growing cell may be slowed more by a drug of this type than the growth of a slowly growing cell; such a proposal is difficult to prove or disprove experimentally, and in the author's opinion it will gradually fall by the wayside as the true mechanism of selectivity for each drug is found. The detoxifica-

[74] M. F. Utter in *The Enzymes*, second ed., by P. D. Boyer, H. Lardy, and K. Myrbäck, eds. Academic Press, New York, 1960, Vol. 2, p. 75.
[75] See Reference 5, p. 2.

tion mechanism of selectivity is an attractive one to consider as a possibility, though it has yet to be studied thoroughly.

Levels of the enzyme xanthine oxidase are low in many tumors as are some other catabolic enzymes for purines, pyrimidines, and aromatic amino acids.[76] Because 6-mercaptopurine is a substrate for xanthine oxidase[77]—the product being the nontoxic thiouric acid—the higher the level of xanthine oxidase in the cell, the less effective will be the 6-mercapto-purine; conversely, if no xanthine oxidase is present and if the cell contains the necessary activating enzyme, 6-mercaptopurine could be toxic to the cell.

Such a selective detoxification has been observed with 6-thioguanine[78] and with 5-fluorouracil[79]; a definite correlation existed between toxicity to a cell and its inability to degrade the drug by the requisite catabolic enzymes. If such a detoxification mechanism is blocked by an inhibitor, toxicity to the host should increase and selectivity should be lost; such an observation has been made by Heidelberger et al., in the case of uridine, which blocks 2'-deoxyuridine phosphorylase, the first enzyme on the catabolic route for detoxifying the anticancer agent, 2'-deoxy-5-fluorouridine.[80]

IRREVERSIBLE ENZYME INHIBITORS

Esterase Inhibitors

A major milestone in the study of the specificity of chemical reaction on an enzyme was the discovery[81–83] that diisopropyl phosphofluoridate (DFP) (XIV) was a specific

$$(CH_3)_2CHOP\text{—}F$$

with O above P and $OCH(CH_3)_2$ below

XIV

$$RO\text{—}P\text{—}X$$

with O above P and OR' below

XV

$$RO\text{—}P\text{—}X$$

with O above P and R' below

XVI

$X = -F, -CN, -OC_6H_4NO_2-p$
R and R' = alkyl

[76] See Reference 23, p. 4.

[77] H. G. Mandel, *Pharmacol. Rev.*, **11**, 759 (1959).

[78] E. C. Moore and G. A. LePage, *Cancer Res.* **18**, 1075 (1958).

[79] E. Harbers, N. K. Chaudhuri, and C. Heidelberger, *J. Biol. Chem.*, **234**, 1255 (1959).

[80] G. D. Birnie, H. Kroeger, and C. Heidelberger, *Biochemistry*, **2**, 566 (1963).

[81] M. Dixon and E. C. Webb, *Enzymes*, Academic Press, New York, 1958, pp. 376–386, 486–502

[82] E. D. Adrian, W. Feldberg, and B. A. Kilby, *Brit. J. Pharmacol.*, **2**, 56 (1947).

[83] J. F. Mackworth and E. C. Webb, *Biochem. J.*, **42**, 91 (1948).

reagent for the active-site of some esterases and proteolytic enzymes. A large number of related compounds (XV, XVI) have been found to have utility as insecticides and in clinical medicine.[84-86] Although these compounds (XIV–XVI) will react with a number of esterases and proteolytic enzymes by formation of a phosphoryl serine derivative in the active-site, these compounds are not general enzyme poisons, for other types of enzymes are not inhibited.[81] In the enzymatic hydrolysis of a substrate —whether an ester or amide—an acylated enzyme is an intermediate which rapidly deacylates with natural substrates to regenerate the enzyme; in contrast the phosphorylated enzymes formed from XIV–XVI dephosphorylate at such a slow rate to regenerate the enzyme that the action of these compounds can be considered as a selective inactivation at the active-site. It should be noted that only one of over 20 serine residues of chymotrypsin specifically reacts with DFP,[87] thus indicating the unique character of the single serine residue at the active site. That the serine is unique in the active site should not have been so surprising in the long history of investigation of these esterase inhibitors; in 1964—several years after the active-site-directed irreversible inhibitor concept discussed in the next section was conceived[88] and experimentally verified[89] and almost 20 years after the first paper on DFP—Main[90] was the first to propose and experimentally verify that compounds such as XIV–XVI first formed a reversible complex with the enzyme, then reacted with the "unique" serine. Thus the uniqueness of the one serine is that it is part of the catalytic site of the hydrolytic enzymes that are irreversibly inhibited by XIV–XVI. Regardless of the time factor involved in understanding the mechanism for phosphorylating the "unique" serine, the interaction of DFP with cholinesterase can be considered[91] to be the first example of active-site-directed irreversible inhibition that occurred by initial complexing with the active-site of the enzyme followed by a facile neighboring group reaction within the enzyme-inhibitor reversible complex.

[84] R. D. O'Brien, *Toxic Phosphorus Esters*, Academic Press, New York, 1960.

[85] B. C. Saunders, *Some Aspects of the Chemistry and Toxic Action of Organic Compounds Containing Phosphorus and Fluorine*, Cambridge University Press, London, 1957.

[86] D. F. Heath, *Organophosphorus Poisons*, Pergamon Press, New York, 1961.

[87] N. K. Schaeffer, S. C. May, and W. H. Summerson, *J. Biol. Chem.*, **206**, 201 (1954).

[88] See Reference 5, p. 2.

[89] B. R. Baker, W. W. Lee, E. Tong, and L. O. Ross, *J. Am. Chem. Soc.*, **83**, 3713 (1961).

[90] A. R. Main, *Science*, **144**, 992 (1964); A. Y. Moon, J. M. Stutevant, and G. P. Hess, *J. Biol. Chem.*, **240**, 4202 (1965).

[91] B. R. Baker, *J. Pharm. Sci.*, **53**, 347 (1964).

The Azaserine Story

The antibiotic, azaserine (XIX), was first isolated[92] from a culture of *Streptomycetes* and has been shown to be effective against various mouse tumors[93] as well as various bacteria.[92] Skipper et al.[94] demonstrated that azaserine caused a decrease in incorporation of ^{14}C-formate or ^{14}C-glycine into the purines of nucleic acids when injected into tumor bearing mice. While Buchanan et al.[95] were in the midst of their pioneer program on the metabolic pathways in the *de novo* synthesis of purines from ^{14}C-glycine, they sought to establish which enzyme on the *de novo* pathway was inhibited. They observed in a cell-free pigeon liver system that the enzymatic

$$\text{NH}_2 \quad\quad \text{O}$$
$$\text{HOOCCHCH}_2\text{CH}_2\text{CNH}_2$$

$$\text{NH}_2 \quad\quad \text{O}$$
$$\text{HOOCCHCH}_2\text{CH}_2\text{COH}$$

$$\text{O} \quad\quad\quad\quad \text{O} \quad\quad \text{O}$$
$$(\text{HO})_2\text{POCH}_2 \quad\_\text{O}\quad \text{NHCCH}_2\text{NHCH}$$
$$\text{OH} \quad\quad \text{OH}$$
XVII

$$\text{O} \quad\quad\quad\quad \text{NH} \quad\quad \text{O}$$
$$(\text{HO})_2\text{POCH}_2 \quad\_\text{O}\quad \text{NHCCH}_2\text{NHCH}$$
$$\text{OH} \quad\quad \text{OH}$$
XVIII

$$\text{NH}_2 \quad\quad \text{O}$$
$$\text{HOOCCHCH}_2\text{OCCHN}_2$$
XIX

$$\text{NH}_2 \quad\quad \text{O}$$
$$\text{HOOCCHCH}_2\text{CH}_2\text{CCHN}_2$$
XX

block caused an accumulation of formyl glycineamide ribotide (XVII)—indicating that the azaserine was blocking further transformation of XVII to purine nucleotides—and that the blockade could be reversed by addition of L-glutamine to the system.[96]

Since only two enzymes in the *de novo* synthesis of purine nucleotides

[92] Q. R. Bartz, C. C. Elder, R. P. Frohardt, S. A. Fusari, T. H. Haskell, D. W. Johannessen, and A. Ryder, *Nature*, **173**, 72 (1954).

[93] C. C. Stock, H. C. Reilly, S. M. Buckley, D. A. Clarke, and C. P. Rhoads, *Nature*, **173**, 71 (1954).

[94] H. E. Skipper, L. L. Bennett, Jr., and F. M. Schabel, Jr., *Federation Proc.*, **13**, 298 (1954).

[95] J. M. Buchanan et al. in *The Chemistry and Biology of Purines*, G. E. W. Wolstenholme and C. M. O'Connor, eds., J. and A. Churchill, London, 1957, p. 233.

[96] S. C. Hartman, B. Levenberg, and J. M. Buchanan, *J. Am. Chem. Soc.*, **77**, 501 (1955).

employ L-glutamine as a cofactor and because the accumulated product was past the first one (III → IX), it was quite clear to Buchanan et al.[97] that the effect of azaserine on the transferase that converts formyl glycineamide ribotide (XVII) to the amidine XVIII should be investigated; they observed that azaserine (XIX) was a good competitive inhibitor of this enzyme. Of even more interest was the observation that azaserine (XIX) could inactivate the enzyme irreversibly in two minutes at 38° in the absence of L-glutamine; this inactivation was slower in the presence of the substrate, L-glutamine. Similar inactivation results were obtained with 6-diazo-5-oxo-L-norleucine (XX), a molecule first synthesized as an analog of azaserine (XIX),[98] then later isolated from a *Streptomycetes* fermentation.[99]

Later work by the Buchanan group[100] showed that a single cysteine residue in the enzyme had reacted specifically with azaserine (XIX), as shown by hydrolysis and isolation of *S*-carboxymethyl-L-cysteine and also by chymotryptic digestion and identification of the peptides containing the labeled cysteine. The internal alkylation reaction within the enzyme-azaserine complex can be considered to be the first example of a *properly constructed classical-type antimetabolite causing specific active-site-directed irreversible inhibition.* Azaserine chemically reacts with other enzymes that transfer the amide group of L-glutamine to substrate,[101-103] but it is not a general enzyme poison.[100,103,104] Thus the unique specificity of this chemical interaction is dependent upon the nature of the active-site; that is, a complex is formed between enzyme and inhibitor followed by a rapid neighboring group reaction within the complex.

[97] B. Levenberg, I. Melnick, and J. M. Buchanan, *J. Biol. Chem.*, **225**, 163 (1957).

[98] H. A. DeWald and A. M. Moore, *J. Am. Chem. Soc.*, **80**, 3941 (1958).

[99] H. W. Dion, S. A. Fusari, Z. L. Jakubowski, J. G. Zora, and Q. R. Bartz, *J. Am. Chem. Soc.*, **78**, 3075 (1956).

[100] T. C. French, E. G. David, and J. M. Buchanan, *J. Biol. Chem.*, **238**, 2171, 2178, 2186 (1963).

[101] H. O. Kammen and R. B. Hurlbert, *Cancer Res.*, **19**, 622 (1959); H. O. Kammen and R. B. Hurlbert, *Biochim. Biophys. Acta*, **30**, 195 (1958); K. P. Chakraborty and R. B. Hurlbert, *Biochim. Biophys. Acta*, **47**, 607 (1961); R. Abrams, and M. Bentley, *Arch. Biochem. Biophys.*, **79**, 91 (1959); S. C. Hartman, *J. Biol. Chem.*, **238**, 3036 (1963).

[102] S. Ghosh, H. J. Blumenthal, E. Davidson, and S. Roseman, *J. Biol. Chem.*, **235**, 1265 (1960); S. Granick *J. Biol. Chem.*, **232**, 1101 (1958); P. R. Srinivasan, *J. Am. Chem. Soc.*, **81**, 1772 (1959); P. R. Srinivasan and A. Rivera, Jr., *Biochemistry*, **2**, 1059 (1963); J. Press and P. Handler, *J. Biol. Chem.*, **233**, 448 (1958); B. Levenberg, *J. Biol. Chem.*, **237**, 2590 (1962).

[103] J. M. Buchanan, S. C. Hartman, R. L. Hermann, and R. A. Day, *J. Cellular Comp. Physiol.*, **54**, (Suppl. 1) 139 (1959).

[104] See Reference 5, p. 2.

THE ACTIVE-SITE-DIRECTED IRREVERSIBLE ENZYME INHIBITOR CONCEPT

The Endo Mechanism

The observations of Buchanan's group on the selective irreversible inhibition by azaserine (XIX), discussed above, led Baker[105] to propose the concept of endo-alkylation. Enzymatic transferase reactions using a cofactor can be generalized in the following form:

$$S + FX \rightleftharpoons SX + F$$

where S is the substrate and F is the cofactor bearing a group X that is to be transferred to substrate. In order for the group X to be transferred to the substrate, the group X must be held in juxtaposition between F and S by the active-site of the enzyme, as shown in Fig. 1–1; if more than a single

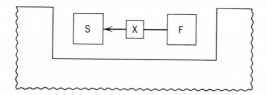

Fig. 1–1. A simplified diagram of the enzyme-catalyzed transfer of the group X from a cofactor F to the substrate S, both molecules being juxtapostioned at the active-site of the enzyme.

interatomic distance exists between S and X, then new bond formation to form SX will be difficult. When the group X is replaced by B, as shown in Fig. 1–2, an inhibitor results if B is a group that cannot be transferred.

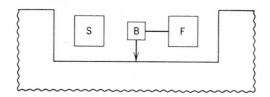

Fig. 1–2. A simplified diagram of endo-alkylation. A group, B, replaced the transfer group X, in Fig. 1–1. B can then alkylate some nucleophilic group within (endo) the active-site to form a covalent bond. From B. R. Baker, *J. Pharm. Sci.*, **53**, 347 (1964).

If the group B is the diazomethyl group of azaserine (XIX), then reaction with the SH group within the active-site occurs as shown by the arrow; the formation of this new covalent bond stops the dissociation of the

[105] See Reference 5, p. 2.

enzyme-inhibitor complex, and the active-site becomes selectively denatured. Because the alkylating group B has replaced the transfer group X, the alkylation most probably takes place *within the active-site (endoalkylation)*.

The active site may not be able to tolerate a group B that is bulkier than X because there may no longer be room for the juxtapositioning of S and FB; that such may be the case is indicated by the fact that the high homolog of azaserine, α-diazopropionyl-L-serine shows no biological activity.[106] This limitation on bulk greatly reduces the utility of the endo-alkylation concept because only small changes in structure of the substrate or cofactor can be made. It was proposed[107] that another small B group that might be useful for endo-alkylation would be the haloacetyl group; as will be described later, the $ClCH_2CO$ group has been found useful for endo-alkylation.

Since the azaserine inactivation was an alkylation within the active-site, the phenomenon was first termed "endo-alkylation" mechanism of irreversible inhibition.[107] The later detection of acylation reactions within an enzyme-inhibitor complex[108,109] required a more general expression; the term "active-site-directed irreversible inhibition" by the endo-mechanism was therefore suggested[110,111] because it covers any mode of covalent bond formation within the complex. Other terms coined for the phenomenon of covalent bond formation within an enzyme-inhibitor complex were "affinity labeling"[112] and irreversible inhibition by "bifunctional irreversible inhibitors."[113]

Bulk Tolerance in Enzyme-inhibitor Complexes

Hellerman et al.[114] observed that both glutarate (XXIII) and isophthalate (XXIV) effectively inhibited the glutamic dehydrogenase (GDH) catalyzed oxidation of L-glutamate (XXI) to a α-oxoglutatate (XXII) by DPN. Since isophthalate (XXIV) can fit the active site of GDH as well as the substrate, glutamate (XXI), it is apparent that glutamate must assume the staggered conformation of isophthalate when bound to the enzyme.[115] It is also apparent that the remainder of the benzene ring of isophthalate

[106] A. M. Moore, private communication.
[107] See Reference 5, p. 2.
[108] B. R. Baker and R. P. Patel, *J. Pharm. Sci.*, **53**, 714 (1964).
[109] See Reference 90.
[110] See Reference 108, p. 18.
[111] See Reference 6, p. 2.
[112] L. Wofsy, H. Metzger, and S. J. Singer, *Biochemistry*, **1**, 1031 (1962).
[113] W. B. Lawson and H. J. Schramm, *Biochemistry*, **4**, 377 (1965).
[114] W. S. Caughey, J. D. Smiley, and L. Hellerman, *J. Biol. Chem.*, **224**, 591 (1957).
[115] See Reference 114, p. 18.

(XXIV) constitutes a considerable change in gross measurement compared to the substrate, glutamate (IX).[116]

Inhibitors of the enzymatic oxidation of succinate to fumarate can vary considerably in gross measurements, providing the change is only at one

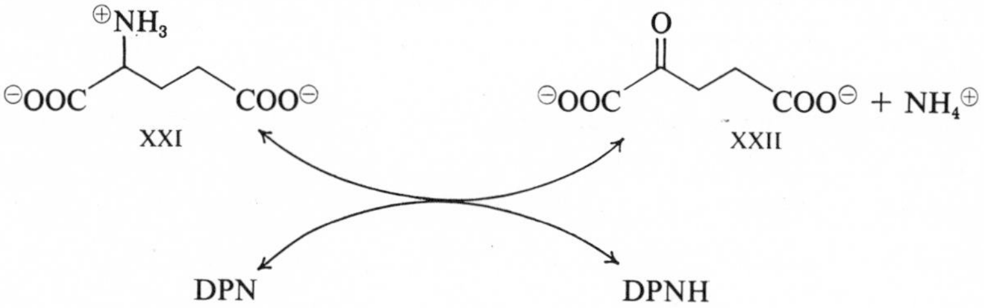

XXI XXII

XXIII

XXIV

α position of succinate; thus α-alkylsuccinic acids, even with large alkyl groups, competitively inhibit succinic dehydrogenase.[117]

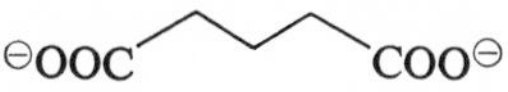

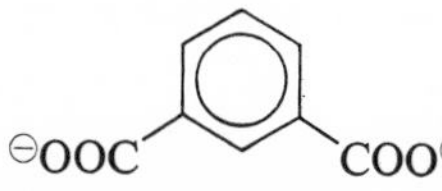

Phenoxyacetic acid (XXVII) has been observed to be a competitive inhibitor of lactic dehydrogenase (LDH); it was proposed that phenoxyacetate (XXVII) binds to LDH through its carboxylate group and an

XXV

XXVII

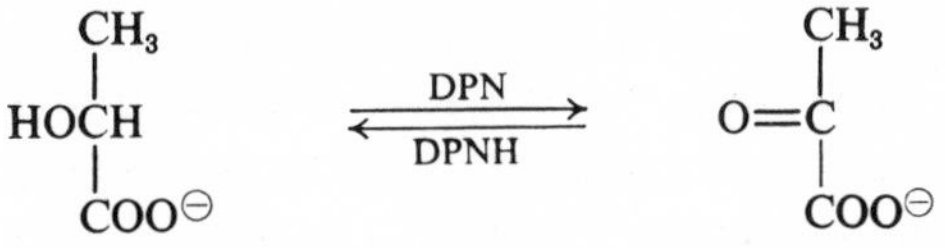

electron pair of the ether oxygen in the same way as the substrate, lactate (XXV) does.[118] When bulky groups were placed on the benzene ring of phenoxyacetate (XXVII), little change in binding occurred,[119] thus indicating that the benzene ring was not in contact with the enzyme

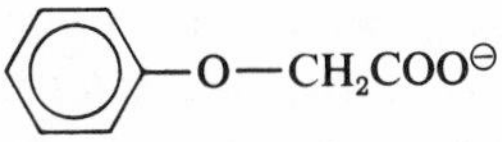

[116] See Reference 5, p. 2.
[117] W. Franke, E. Holz, and G. Tashen, *Ann.*, **608**, 168 (1957).
[118] P. Ottolenghi and O. F. Denstedt, *Can. J. Biochem. Physiol.*, **36**, 1075 (1958).
[119] See Reference 11, p. 2.

surface (see Fig. 1–3). Such a phenomenon has been termed bulk tolerance within the enzyme-inhibitor complex.

The Exo Mechanism

The demonstration of bulk tolerance within the enzyme-inhibitor complex as indicated in Fig. 1–3, combined with Buchanan's observations on selective irreversible inhibition by azaserine (XIX), led Baker[120] to propose the concept of exo-alkylation.

If the alkylating group B (Fig. 1–3) is on the side of the inhibitor not in contact with the enzyme and is placed so that it can bridge to some nucleophilic group on the enzyme surface, then covalent-bond formation

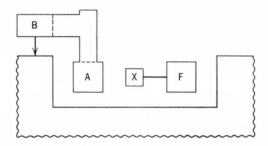

Fig. 1–3. A simplified diagram of an oversize (nonclassical) inhibitor. Note that the excess size above the horizontal dotted line of inhibitor faces away from the enzyme surface. When the alkylating group B can bridge to a nucleophilic site on the enzyme surface adjacent to the active-site, covalent-bond formation (arrow) occurs outside the active-site (exo-alkylation). From B. R. Baker, *J. Pharm. Sci.*, **53**, 347 (1964).

might take place (shown by arrow). The new bond formation outside the active site is termed exo-alkylation; such bond formation can stop dissociation of the enzyme-inhibitor complex in the same fashion as the endo-alkylation example with azaserine (XIX). In order to accommodate other modes of covalent bonding within an enzyme-inhibitor complex this phenomenon has been given the more general name of "active-site-directed irreversible inhibition" by the exo-mechanism.[121,122]

After Buchanan's first announcement of the irreversible inhibition of an enzyme by azaserine (XIX),[123] some four years elapsed before another example of an active-site-directed irreversible inhibitor appeared in the literature. In 1961, Baker et al.[124] presented data that 4-(iodoacetamido)-

[120] See Reference 5, p. 2.
[121] See Reference 108, p. 18.
[122] See Reference 6, p. 2.
[123] See Reference 97, p. 16.
[124] See Reference 89, p. 14.

salicylic acid complexes with glutamic dehydrogenase (GDH), then caused irreversible inhibition by the exo-alkylation mechanism. 4-(Iodoacetamido)-salicylic acid is believed to be the first example of an active-site-directed irreversible inhibitor deliberately designed as such; the earlier examples, DFP and azaserine, were found to be active-site-directed irreversible inhibitors when their biological activity was investigated. In 1962, five other laboratories[125-129] announced their independently conceived work on active-site-directed irreversible inhibitors and in 1963 a sixth laboratory announced another example.[130] Of these seven different examples, four were of the exo-alkylation type and three were of the endo-alkylation type. It is also of interest that five of the seven examples were irreversible inhibitors of chymotrypsin, one was an irreversible inhibitor of GDH, and one of a combining region of an antibody. These will be discussed in appropriate later chapters along with a number of more recent examples.

MAJOR TYPES OF ENZYME REACTIONS

There is a variety of ways to classify enzymes, such as by type of chemical reaction or by the number of substrates the enzymatic reaction requires; the latter classification system will be used, for it points up the type of information that is needed to design active-site-directed irreversible enzyme inhibitors. There are three major types: transferases, synthetases, and lyases.

$$S + FX \rightleftharpoons SX + F \quad \text{(transferase)} \qquad (1\text{-}4)$$

$$S_1 + S_2 \rightleftharpoons S_1 - S_2 \quad \text{(synthetase)} \qquad (1\text{-}5)$$

$$S_1 - S_2 \rightleftharpoons S_1 + S_2 \quad \text{(lyase)} \qquad (1\text{-}6)$$

The transferase enzymes use a cofactor F bearing a transfer group X; the cofactor may donate or accept the X group depending upon which direction the reaction is proceeding. An example of a transferase enzyme with a cofactor is inosinic dehydrogenase (p. 6) in which the cofactor, DPN, accepted a hydride ion from inosinate (IV); the cofactor DPN is then regenerated from DPNH by some other enzyme system such as oxidative phosphorylation. The production of inosinic dehydrogenase is somewhat

[125] G. Schoellman and E. Shaw, *Biochem. Biophys. Res. Commun.*, **7**, 36 (1962); *Biochemistry*, **2**, 252 (1963).

[126] See Reference 112, p. 18.

[127] W. B. Lawson and H. J. Schramm, *J. Am. Chem. Soc.*, **84**, 2017 (1962); see Reference 113, p. 18.

[128] G. Gundlach and F. Turba, *Biochem. Z.*, **335**, 573 (1962).

[129] A. Singh, E. R. Thornton, and F. H. Westheimer, *J. Biol. Chem.*, **237**, PC 3006 (1962).

[130] J. Kallos, *J. Mol. Biol.*, **7**, 104 (1963).

more complicated than this simple presentation is that the elements of water must be added to the 2,3- double bond of inosinate (IV)—presumably catalyzed by the enzyme—then a hydride removed from the 2- position by transfer to DPN, followed by proton removal from N-3.

An example of a transferase enzyme but with no cofactor is inosinic pyrophosphorylase (p. 5), where two substrates are reacted in an enzyme complex and two products are formed.

An example of a synthetase reaction is succinoadenylate kinosynthetase (p. 7) in which aspartate is condensed with inosinate (IV). Although no other organic product is formed from aspartate and inosinate, the reaction requires the removal of the elements of water; this is accomplished by activation of the 6-hydroxyl of inosinate as a phosphate ester by reaction with GTP, which, in turn, forms GDP. Thus this enzymic reaction takes place in two steps; strictly speaking both steps are transferase reactions.

An example of a lyase is the enzymic conversion of succinoadenylate (VII) to adenylate (VIII) and fumarate (p. 7); note that this particular enzyme reaction is reversible and that the reverse reaction is a synthetase reaction.

Figure 1–1 is a simplified diagram of a transferase enzyme. If S were DPN, F the hydrated inosinate, and X the hydride that must be transferred, then this diagram could represent the reaction that occurs with inosinic dehydrogenase; note that within the complex between the enzyme and the two substrates the hydride (X in Fig. 1–1) must be juxtaposed to the 4- position of the nicotinamide moiety of DPN in order that a facile transfer of hydride can occur in a neighboring group-type reaction within the enzyme-substrate complex.

Figure 1–1 can also be used to represent the transamidation reaction that occurs when L-glutamine reacts with the formyl ribotide (XVII) to give XVIII and glutamate (p. 15); this is accomplished by allowing S to represent XVII, F to represent the L-glutamyl moiety, and X to represent the amide—NH_2 group that is to be transferred. Note again the transfer group NH_2 must be properly juxtaposed in the enzyme-substrate complex.

Similarly Fig. 1–1 can be used to demonstrate a synthetase reaction such as succinoadenylate kinosynthetase (p. 7); if S is a 6-phosphoryl derivative of inosinate (IV), F is a succinyl moiety, and X is the α-amino group, then the α-amino group must be juxtaposed to the 6- position of the inosinate (IV) for a facile displacement of the phosphate-leaving group with resultant formation of a new C—N bond.

It is thus clear that the parameters of complex formation between an enzyme and a substrate or inhibitor must be considered, then explored experimentally, before an active-site-directed irreversible inhibitor can be successfully designed.

2 | Binding Between Groups on Proteins and Substrates or Inhibitors

GENERAL CONSIDERATIONS

In order for an active-site-directed irreversible enzyme inhibitor I—X to operate, it must first form a complex with the enzyme E; then a covalent bond forms within the enzyme-inhibitor complex, the formation of which is accelerated by the juxtaposed enzyme nucleophilic group and the leaving group X, as follows:

$$E + I—X \rightleftharpoons \overbrace{E\cdots I—X} \rightarrow \overbrace{E\cdots I} + X^-$$

Because an intermediate complex must be formed between the enzyme and the inhibitor, what are the binding forces that cause an affinity of the enzyme for the inhibitor? The binding groups on the enzyme can only arise from the nature of the 20 amino acids that reside in enzymes plus any metal ions firmly associated with each enzyme; in contrast, a much greater variation in types of groups can be built into the inhibitors. There are only four major types of interactions between enzyme and inhibitor, the strength of the complex being dependent upon the nature and strength of each bonding between the enzyme and the small molecule. Tremendous variation can occur in the strength of the enzyme-inhibitor complex formed, dissociations constants (K_i) varying from greater than zero to as low as 10^{-11} M for the interaction of aminopterin (4-amino-4-deoxyfolic acid) with dihydrofolic reductase[1] and 10^{-15} for the biotin-avidin complex.[2]

[1] J. R. Bertino, J. P. Perkins, and D. G. Johns, *Biochemistry* **4**, 839 (1965); W. C. Werkheiser, *J. Biol. Chem.*, **236**, 888 (1961).
[2] N. M. Green, *Biochem. J.*, **89**, 585 (1963).

The four major types of bonding are (a) anionic-cationic interactions, (b) hydrogen bonds, (c) charge-transfer complexes, (d) hydrophobic bonding and the accompanying van der Waals forces; mixed types such as a bond between a hydrogen acceptor and a π donor also occur.[3] Although maximum values of the energy involved in each type of binding can be estimated in most cases, the maximum energy possible would seldom be obtained since the binding operation is performed in water, and solvent can play a large part in some of the types of binding. This is an area in which much research is needed to determine binding energies in aqueous solution; even though Higuchi et al. have already made extensive studies on complex formation with polyfunctional molecules,[4] it is difficult to sort out the mode of binding.

The different types of bonding are summarized in Table 2–1. In certain special, but relatively rare, cases a reversible covalent linkage can form; for example, the carbonyl group of pyruvate[5] or pyridoxal phosphate[6] can form a reversible azomethine linkage with an environmentally weakened terminal amino group of a lysine. Similarly, biotin or lipoic acid can be covalently attached to certain enzymes by an acyl linkage.

PROTEIN GROUPS COMPLEXING WITH SUBSTRATES OR INHIBITORS

Anionic-Cationic Interactions

At first glance saltlike interactions would seem to be extremely strong, for up to 50 kcal/mole of energy could be involved. From two points of view, it is obvious that bonds with this much energy are not formed. First, it can be calculated from $-\Delta F = RT \ln(1/K_i)$ that 50 kcal/mole binding energy would give a K_i of about 10^{-38}; this value is many magnitudes lower than the most potent inhibitors ever observed, such as the aminopterin inhibition of folic reductase,[7] which has a K_i less than 3×10^{-11} M,

---

[3] The interaction of inhibitors with enzymes has been discussed at considerable length by J. L. Webb, *Enzyme and Metabolic Inhibitors*, Academic Press, New York, 1963, Vol. 1, pp. 193–318. His discussion is from a somewhat different viewpoint than presented here in Chapter 2, but the reader interested in problems of binding between groups on proteins and inhibitors would be well rewarded by study of Webb's interpretation.

[4] For a review of the studies by the Higuchi school, see T. Higuchi and K. A. Conners, *Advances in Analytical Chemistry and Instrumentation*, C. N. Reilly, ed., Interscience Publishers, New York, 1965, Vol. 4, pp. 117–212.

[5] J. M. Ingram and W. A. Wood, *J. Biol. Chem.*, **240**, 4146 (1965).

[6] E. H. Fischer in *Structure and Activity of Enzymes*, T. W. Goodwin, J. I. Harris, and B. S. Hartley, eds., Academic Press, New York, 1964, pp. 111–120.

[7] See Reference 1, p. 23.

Table 2–1. Protein Groups Complexing with Substrates and Inhibitors

Amino acids	Anionic-cationic	Hydrogen bond Donor	Hydrogen bond Acceptor	Charge-transfer Donor	Charge-transfer Acceptor	Hydrophobic bonding	van der Waals forces
A. *Basic*	yes					no	no
Arginine $(NHC-NH_3^{\oplus}$, $\|$, $NH)$		no	yes (?)	no	yes (?)		
Lysine $(-NH_3^{\oplus})$		no	yes (?)	no	yes (?)		
Histidine (HN—ring, N)		yes[a]	yes	yes	yes[b]		
B. *Acidic*	yes	yes	no	yes	no	no	no
Aspartate $(COO^{\ominus})$							
Glutamate $(COO^{\ominus})$							
C. *Amides* $(CONH)$	no	yes	yes	yes	yes	no	no
Asparagine							
Glutamine							
Polyamide backbone							
D. *Hydroxy containing* (*OH only*)		yes	yes	yes	yes	no	no
Serine	no						
Threonine	no						
Hydroxyproline	no						
Tyrosine	weak (?)						
E. *Sulfur containing*							
Cysteine (SH)	weak (?)	no (?)	yes	no (?)	yes	no	no
Cystine (S-S-)	no	yes	no	yes	no	no	no
Methionine (-S-)	no	yes	no	yes	no	no	no
F. *Alkyl*[c]	no	no	no	no	no	yes	yes
Leucine							
Isoleucine							
Valine							
Alanine							
Proline							
G. *Aryl*						yes	yes
Phenylalanine $(C_6H_5$ only$)$	no	no	no	yes	yes		
Tyrosine $(C_6H_4$ only$)$	no	yes	no (?)	yes	no (?)		
Tryptophane (indole ring, N H)	weak (?)[d]	yes	yes[e]	yes	yes[e]		

[a] Via nitrogen lone-electron pair.   [b] Via the π cloud of the ring.
[c] Glycine might be placed in this class, but other than polyamide binding, it will give little, if any, other bonding.
[d] The NH group is weakly acidic.   [e] Via NH group.

or the avidin-biotion complex[8] with $K_i = 10^{-15}$ M. Second, salts are mainly dissociated when dissolved in water; conversely, when the hydrated enzyme in water interacts with a hydrated ion in water, there may even be little association by a cationic-anionic interaction.

It is quite difficult to make even an intuitive guess about an association of an enzymatic cation (I) with an inhibitor anion (II) (or vice versa) to give the complex III, where the outside circles represent water molecules. The equilibrium will depend on whether there is a lower energy state in the solvated ions on the left side of the equation or in the salt interaction plus the energy of reassociation of water molecules (IV) on the right side of the equation.

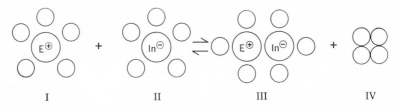

I   II   III   IV

Fig. 2–1. $E^{\oplus}$ is an enzyme with a cationic group and $In^{\ominus}$ is an inhibitor with an anionic group.

An anionic group on the enzyme might associate with an anionic group on an inhibitor by bridging with a divalent ion such as magnesium; magnesium ion is certainly required for many enzyme reactions involving phosphorylated substrates. The exact function of the metal ion in an enzyme reaction is difficult to assess; more than binding is probably involved, for some enzymes require a monocation such as potassium.

The enzymic amino acids containing a cationic group are arginine, lysine, and—at times—histidine. Both arginine and lysine have basic groups that are fully protonated at physiological pH, but the imidazole of histidine is a much weaker base with pK_a in the range of 6, varying with the enzymic environment of the imidazole.

The enzymic amino acids containing anionic groups are aspartate and glutamate; these carboxyl groups are usually fully ionized at physiological pH, although they also may be environmentally weakened.

The hydroxyl group of tyrosine and the thiol group of cysteine are weak acids that are more likely to form a hydrogen bond than a saltlike bond.

Hydrogen Bonds

Although hydrogen bonding between two compounds can be measured, the determination of the extent of hydrogen bonding in water must take

[8] See Reference 2, p. 23.

into consideration the water bonding problem. Consider the events that take place when an aqueous solution of an inhibitor with an acceptor

$$\overset{H}{E-D: \rightarrow HOH} + I-A \leftarrow :OH \rightleftharpoons E-D: \rightarrow A-I + \overset{H}{HOH \leftarrow OH}$$

$$\qquad V \qquad\qquad\qquad VI \qquad\qquad VII \qquad\qquad\qquad VIII$$

group A is mixed with an aqueous solution of an enzyme with a donor group D. Both the donor group and the acceptor group would presumably already be hydrogen-bonded with water, as indicated in V and VI; thus the hydrogen bond in complex VII will dissociate to an extent that depends upon the relative strengths of hydrogen bonds in the species V–VIII. At any rate, hydrogen bonds can have energies in the range of 2–5 kcal/mole; depending upon the equilibrium involving species V–VIII, this can vary down to zero.

In Table 2–1 the amino acids in proteins are listed; these are divided into seven groups, depending upon functionality. In Group A, arginine and lysine have strongly basic groups that are fully protonated near pH 7; therefore these groups are not likely to be donors for a hydrogen bond, but they could be acceptors. The imidazole of histidine with its pK_a near 6 would be an electron donor through the electron pair on free nitrogen; furthermore, the protonated species might be an electron acceptor.

In Group B the acidic amino acids have their carboxyl groups present in the anionic form near pH 7; the carboxylate could be the electron donor for a hydrogen bond, but it could not be an acceptor.

In Group C two types of amide functions are included, the side-chain carboxamides, such as those of glutamine and asparagine, and the poly-amide backbone of the protein. These types of bonds (IX–XI) should be

$$\begin{array}{ccc}
E-C\!\!=\!\!O: \rightarrow A-I & E-C\!\!=\!\!O & E-C\!\!=\!\!O \\
| & | & | \\
NH & NH \leftarrow :D-I & HN: \rightarrow A-I \\
| & | & | \\
\text{IX} & \text{X} & \text{XI}
\end{array}$$

considered. The oxygen of the amide could be a donor to an acceptor group on the inhibitor, as in IX; in contrast, the nitrogen electron pair would be such a poor donor, due to the effect of the electron-withdrawing carbonyl group, that a complex such as XI is not likely to form. The amide function can be an electron acceptor through the amide NH, as is indicated in X.

In Group D the alcoholic group of serine and threonine can be either a donor through the oxygen or an acceptor through the hydrogen. Because the phenolic hydroxyl group of tyrosine is acidic, the hydrogen of the hydroxyl group is more electron deficient than that of the hydroxylic hydrogen of serine; the hydrogen of the tyrosine hydroxyl should therefore be a better electron acceptor than the hydroxylic hydrogen of serine; conversely, the oxygen of tyrosine hydroxyl should be a poorer electron donor than the oxygen of the serine hydroxyl.

A similar argument can be advanced for the acidic thiol group of cysteine in Group E that was advanced for the acidic hydroxyl group of tyrosine, namely, the hydrogen of the thiol group should be a good acceptor, but the sulfur a poor donor—if it is a donor at all. The electron pair on sulfur in methionine or cystine could be the donors for a hydrogen bond, but it has no acceptor capacity.

With the aryl amino acids in Group G, a mixed hydrogen bond to the acceptor group on I—A might occur by π-donor action of the aromatic ring; the order of donor activity would be tryptophane > tyrosine > phenylalanine. This *mixed type* of bond will be discussed in more detail in a later section.

Charge-Transfer Complexes[9]

In addition to the donor-acceptor complexes involving hydrogen bonds, other donor-acceptor complexes can be formed between electron-rich donors and electron-poor acceptors; thus a complex *via* hydrogen bonding could be considered to be a special case of the general phenomenon of donor-acceptor complexes. In the most general sense, a donor-acceptor complex (DA) is formed by an electrostatic attraction between an electron donor (D) and an electron acceptor (A); the species DA can also be called a π complex. Additional stabilization of the DA complex occurs as a result

$$D + A \rightleftharpoons DA \rightleftharpoons D^+ A^- \tag{2-1}$$

of a minor amount of the resonance structure, the charge-transfer species $D^+ A^-$. In the charge-transfer field—in contrast to the enzyme field—the equilibrium constant K is measured as an association constant,[12] which is the reciprocal of K_i, the inhibitor-enzyme dissociation constant.

$$K_A = \frac{[DA]}{[D][A]} \tag{2-2}$$

The extent of formation of the electrostatic complex DA is obviously dependent upon the relative strengths of the two partners as donors and

[9] For more thorough discussions of charge-transfer complexes see References 10 and 11.

[10] L. J. Andrews and R. M. Keefer, *Molecular Complexes in Organic Chemistry*, Holden-Day, San Francisco, 1964.

[11] E. M. Kosower, *Molecular Biochemistry*, McGraw-Hill Book Company, New York, 1962, pp. 185–195.

[12] R. S. Milliken, *J. Am. Chem. Soc.*, **74**, 811 (1952).

acceptors respectively. The relative strengths of donors are indicated by their ionization potentials I_p as in equation (2–3); the relative strengths

$$D \xrightarrow{I_p} D^+ + e^- \tag{2–3}$$

$$A + e^- \xrightarrow{E_a} A^- \tag{2–4}$$

of acceptors are indicated by their electron affinities E_a as in Equation (2–4).[13]

An example of a charge-transfer complex is that derived from *N*-methyl-pyridinium iodide (XII); the electrostatic complex is depicted by XIII

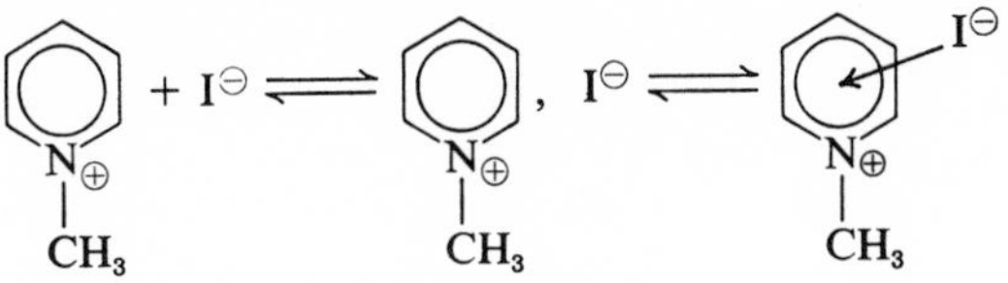

and the minor amount of the resonance structure in the complex is represented by XIV.[14] Another example is the benzene-iodine complex (XV) with the resonance structure XVI.[15]

Both the DA and D^+A^- species form a number of excited states when photoexcited at the proper wavelengths; thus ultraviolet or visible bands appear in the spectrum of DA at longer wavelengths; these charge-transfer bands do not obey Beer's law, nor are they directly dependent upon the concentrations of D and A initially introduced into the solution; they are dependent upon the DA and D^+A^- concentrations. Because the optical density due to the excited state of the complex is dependent upon the concentration of the complex, the association constant K can be determined by measuring the variation of the optical density of the charge-transfer band as a function of the concentration of A and D.[16,17] Furthermore, the larger K is the longer the wavelength of the charge-transfer band will be.[18]

[13] H. McConnell, J. S. Ham, and J. R. Platt, *J. Chem. Phys.*, **21**, 66 (1953).
[14] E. M. Kosower, *J. Am. Chem. Soc.*, **77**, 3883 (1955).
[15] H. A. Benesi and J. H. Hildebrand, *J. Am. Chem. Soc.*, **71**, 2703 (1949).
[16] See Reference 15, p. 29.
[17] For the possible complications that K measured in this way may not be the true association constant for D and A, see References 10 and 11, p. 28,
[18] See Reference 12, p. 28.

If 1-methyl pyridinium iodide (XII) does form a charge-transfer complex, then the position of the charge-transfer band should be sensitive to substitution by an electron-donating or electron-withdrawing group. Note in Table 2–2 that the electron-donating 4-methyl group causes

Table 2–2. Charge Transfer Bands of

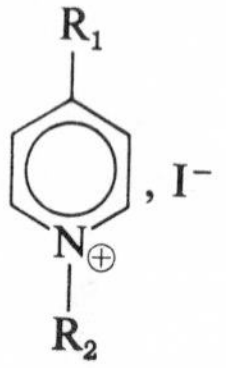

No.	R_1	R_2	$\lambda_{max}(m\mu)$	ϵ_{max}	Solvent
XVII	$CH_3{}^a$	CH_3	359	1230	$CHCl_3$
XII	H^a	CH_3	374	1200	$CHCl_3$
XVIII	$COOCH_3{}^b$	C_2H_5	451	970	A^c
XIX	CN^d	CH_3	491	1000	CH_2Cl_2

[a] Data from E. M. Kosower and J. A. Skorcz, *J. Am. Chem. Soc.*, **82**, 2195 (1960).
[b] Data from Reference 11, p. 28.
[c] *cis*-1,2-Dichloroethylene.
[d] Data from E. M. Kosower, J. A. Skorcz, W. M. Schwarz, Jr., and J. W. Patton, *J. Am. Chem. Soc.*, **82**, 2188 (1960).

XVII to give a charge-transfer band at a shorter wavelength than does XII. Furthermore, note that the increasingly electron-withdrawing groups, carbomethoxy (XVIII) and cyano (XIX) give compounds with charge-transfer bands of increasing wavelength; however, the ϵ value changes little.

The wavelength of the charge-transfer band of ionized species is extremely sensitive to solvent; the ultraviolet spectrum of 1-ethyl-4-carbomethoxypyridinium iodide was determined in a variety of solvents.[19] The wavelength of the charge-transfer band decreased in the following order: *cis*-dichloroethylene > acetonitrile > isopropyl alcohol > methanol > water. It would be of interest to determine whether or not the association constant K for the charge-transfer complex changes with solvent or whether the effect of water is only due to the effect of the solvent dipole on the transition energy of DA to the excited state.[20] From the standpoint of enzyme-inhibitor complexing, it would be of value to know

[19] E. M. Kosower, *J. Am. Chem. Soc.*, **80**, 3261 (1958).
[20] See Reference 19, p. 30.

the association constants in water of compounds in Table 2–1 particularly since a number of substrates and inhibitors have quaternary pyridinium structures.

In contrast, the position of the charge-transfer band with neutral donors and acceptors is usually not affected much by changes in solvent.[21] Therefore, with association constants of the charge-transfer type of neutral species, K, in an organic solvent would give a reasonable approximation to the expected K in water. In any case, when considering a charge-transfer complex between an enzyme and an inhibitor (or substrate) one must take into account that the DA complex will have less solvation than the solvated compounds D and A; therefore the reassociation of water molecules will also be a factor, as was discussed in the case of hydrogen bonding.

From Table 2–3 it can be seen that the better the molecule is as an

Table 2–3. Equilibrium Constants for

$$D + I_2 \rightleftharpoons D, I_2$$

D	K (molar)	Temperature	Solvent	Reference
C_6H_6	0.14	25°	CCl_4	a
$C_6(CH_3)_6$	1.35	25°	CCl_4	a
C_2H_5OH	0.47	20°	CCl_4	b
t-C_4H_9OH	0.95	25°	CCl_4	a
$(C_2H_5)_2O$	0.97	20°	CCl_4	b
$(C_2H_5)_2S$	210	20°	CH_2Cl_2	c
$C_2H_5SSC_2H_5$	5.6	20°	CH_2Cl_2	c
$(CH_3)_3N$	5700	20°	Heptane	d
$HCON(CH_3)_2$	1.13	20°	CH_2Cl_2	c
CH_3CONH_2	0.61	20°	CH_2Cl_2	c
$(n\text{-}C_4H_9O)_3PO$	21	20°	Heptane	e

[a] R. M. Keefer and L. J. Andrews, *J. Am. Chem. Soc.*, **77**, 2164 (1955).
[b] P. A. D. de Maine, *J. Chem. Phys.*, **26**, 1192 (1957).
[c] H. Tsubomura and R. P. Lang, *J. Am. Chem. Soc.*, **83**, 2085 (1961).
[d] Y. Yada, J. Tanaka, and S. Nagakura, *Bull. Chem. Soc. Japan.*, **33**, 1660 (1960).
[e] H. Tsubomura and J. M. Klingman, *J. Am. Chem. Soc.*, **82** 1314 (1960).

electron donor, the more favorable is complex formation with iodine. It should also be noted that in addition to aromatic π donors, an alcohol and an amine can also be donors; although alcohols and amines can also hydrogen bond to acceptors, it is definitely possible for mixed types of complexing between enzyme and inhibitor to occur, such as an alcohol donor on the enzyme to an electron-deficient π-cloud area of an inhibitor.

[21] See Reference 10 (pp. 122–124), p. 28.

Another example is the bond existing between the hydroxyl and vinyl groups of *o*-allylphenol (XX); of three different hydroxyl bands in the infrared, one has been attributed to the bonding between the hydroxylic hydrogen and the vinyl group[22]—a mixed hydrogen-bond charge-transfer complex. Thus in an enzyme-inhibitor complex an hydroxylic hydrogen of

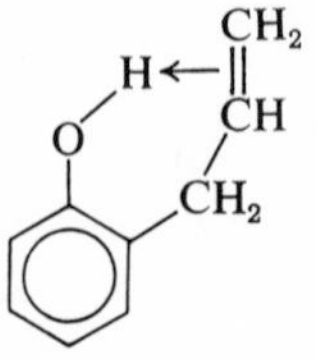

XX

an inhibitor could be an acceptor from the electron-rich π cloud of an enzymic indole as a donor.

The donors for a charge-transfer complex can be divided into two classes:

1. Electron-rich π cloud donors such as alkenes, alkynes, and aromatics substituted with electron-donating groups;

2. Lone-pair donors such as

$$R\text{—}\underset{\underset{H}{|}}{O}:,\quad R\text{—}\underset{\underset{R}{|}}{S}:,\quad RI:,\quad R_3N:,\quad R\text{—}\underset{\underset{R}{|}}{O}:\quad \text{and}\quad R\text{—}\underset{\underset{RS}{|}}{S}:,$$

the same groups that act as donors for hydrogen bonds.

From Table 2–4 it can be seen that the more electron deficient the acceptor is, the more favorable the complex formation will be. The acceptors for a charge-transfer complex can also be divided into two classes:

1. Electron-deficient π cloud acceptors, such as *s*-trinitrobenzene and tetracyanoethylene with strong electron-withdrawing groups, can be considered as π acids;

2. Weakly acidic hydrogens of molecules such as Br_3CH, alkyl-O—H, Ar—O—H, R-SH, imidazole-H are the same groups that act as acceptors in hydrogen bonds.

Of the charge-transfer complexes listed in Tables 2–3 and 2–4, it can be seen that one of the more favorable complexes is that derived from tetracyanoethylene and hexamethyl benzene with an association constant (K_a) of 263 in carbon tetrachloride; this is equivalent to a dissociation constant (K_i) of 3.8×10^{-3} M. In contrast, the benzene-tetracyanoethylene complex has $K_a = 2.0$ or $K_i = 5 \times 10^{-1}$ M; it could be expected that the phenol and indole moieties of tyrosine and tryptophane would be as good

[22] A. W. Baker and A. T. Shulgin, *J. Am. Chem. Soc.*, **80**, 5358 (1958).

or better donors than hexamethyl benzene. Although it is not known what these association constants would be in water, it would be worth determining. The association constants for charge-transfer complexes will probably be small with the types of groups involved on enzymes; however this type of interaction could make a definite contribution to binding between enzyme and inhibitor, particularly when combined with the hydrophobic bonding that could exist with a benzene-benzene interaction.

Table 2–4. Equilibrium Constants for

$$C_6(CH_3)_6 + A \rightleftharpoons C_6(CH_3)_6, A$$

A	K (molar)	Temperature	Solvent	Reference
I_2	1.35	25°	CCl_4	a
s-$C_6H_3(NO_2)_3$	5.7	20°	CCl_4	b
Tetracyanoethylene	263	22°	CH_2Cl_2	c

a L. J. Andrews and R. M. Keefer, *J. Am. Chem. Soc.*, **74**, 4500 (1952).
b R. Foster, *J. Chem. Soc.*, 1075 (1960).
c R. E. Merrifield and W. D. Phillips, *J. Am. Chem. Soc.*, **80**, 2778 (1958).

A closer approximation of what may occur with a charge-transfer complex between an enzyme and an inhibitor has been revealed by the elegant studies of Shifrin[23,24] on intramolecular charge transfer with a series of nicotinamide derivatives (XXI).

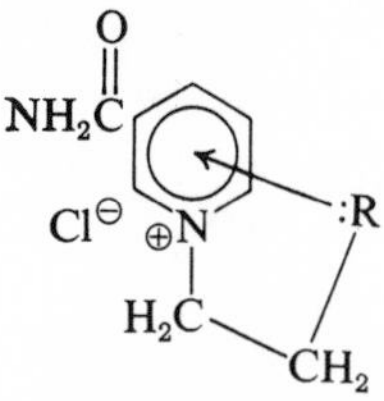

XXI

The ethyl bridge between an aryl R group and the pyridine does not allow the rings to lie in parallel planes for maximum charge transfer; actually they are 39° off the parallel. Even so, more charge-transfer complex was formed with XXI than with the two separate entities, 1-methylnicotinamide perchlorate and R—CH_2CH_3. (The intramolecular charge-transfer spectra was measured by difference spectra between XXI and the two separate entities at the same concentrations.) This type of

23 S. Shifrin, *Biochemistry*, **3**, 829 (1964).
24 S. Shifrin, *Biochem. Biophys. Acta*, **96**, 173 (1965).

intramolecular charge-transfer complexing more closely approximates the situation in an inhibitor-enzyme complex because—in addition to possible charge-transfer complexing—there would most probably be additional binding forces between the enzyme and inhibitor at the same or different areas of the inhibitor.

Since the acceptor moiety is constant in all of the compounds in Table 2–5, then as a first approximation, the energy of the charge-transfer bond

Table 2–5. Intramolecular Charge-transfer Complexes with

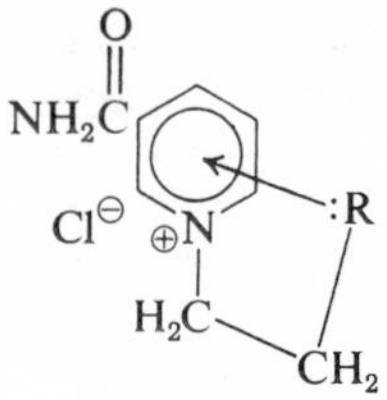

No.	R	$\Delta - \lambda_{max}(m\mu)^a$	$\Delta\epsilon$	Solvent
XXII	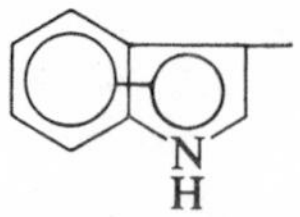	325	1000	H_2O
XXIII	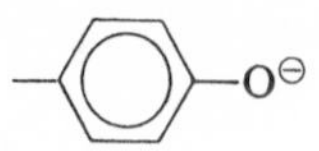 —⟨O⟩—$O^{\ominus}$	320	700	H_2O (pH 13)
XXIV	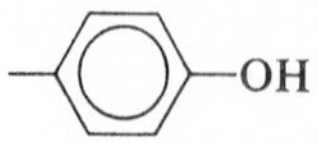 —⟨O⟩—OH	297	1000	H_2O
XXV	—SCH_3	300	900	H_2O
XXVI	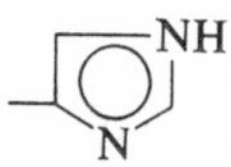	295 none	900 0	H_2O H_2O (pH 1)
XXVII	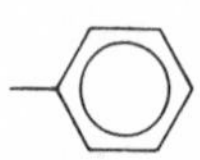 —⟨O⟩	283	1000	
XXVIII	—$\underset{\oplus}{N}(C_2H_5)_3$	none	0	H_2O

Data from S. Shifrin, Biochemistry, **3**, 829 (1964).

[a] Difference spectrum against equimolar concentrations of 1-methylnicotinamide perchlorate and RCH_2CH_3.

is dependent upon the ionization potential of the donor moiety; therefore, the longer the wavelength of the charge-transfer band, the better donor the donor moiety will be. Although it is difficult to measure the energy of the electrostatic bonding in the ground state, the results indicate clearly that these charge-transfer complexes can form in water and also indicate the order of donor ability.

The indole ring (XXII) (Table 2–5), as can be anticipated, is the best donor, with a charge-transfer band at 325 mμ. The phenol ring (XXIV) is less effective than indole as a donor unless the phenol is converted to the anion (XXIII) in 0.1 N sodium hydroxide.[25] The unionized phenol, the free electron pair of methylthio (XXV), and imidazole (XXVI) are about equal donors in neutral solution; the imidazole in its protonated form at pH 1 no longer shows a charge-transfer band, indicating that the lone pair of electrons on the imidazole nitrogen is the donor. Benzene (XXVII) is somewhat weaker as a donor than phenol (XXIV), due to the electron-donating properties of the hydroxyl group. The triethyl ammonium group, as a model for the ϵ-amino group of a lysine that would be protonated at physiological pH, shows no donor properties—as expected.

The interaction of phenol and indole side chains with the nicotinamide was also verified by fluorescence spectroscopy. Thus the compounds XXII–XXVIII serve as models for the relative donor properties of tryptophane, tyrosine, methionine, histidine, and phenylalanine as well as indicating the expected lack of donor properties by a protonated amine. It would be of interest to determine whether R=carboxylate, R=carboxamide, or R=OH could be electron donors (see Table 2–1, 3) by use of the Shifrin approach.

If the imidazole of XXVI—by virtue of the lone electron pair on nitrogen—were involved in an electrostatic complex with the nicotinamide in the ground state, then this lone electron pair should have less affinity for a proton than is normally observed for an imidazole; Shifrin found that histamine had pK_a = 6.0, but the imidazole of XXVI had pK_a = 5.5, direct evidence for an electrostatic complex in the ground state.

If the benzene ring of XXVII becomes a better donor when an electron-donating group is introduced (XXIV), then there should be a linear relationship between the reciprocal of the λ_{max} for the charge-transfer band (ν_{ct}) and the ionization potential of the substituted benzene; Fig. 2–2 shows the linearity observed by Shifrin. Similarly, there should be a straight-line relationship between ν_{ct} and the Hammett sigma constant; this was observed as shown in Fig. 2–3. These figures then allow the predic-

---

[25] A remote possibility exists that this difference in 0.1 N sodium hydroxide may be a salt effect; such a possibility could readily be checked with 0.1 N sodium chloride at neutral pH.

tion of ν_{ct} or (λ_{max}) to be estimated if the ionization potential of the donor is known by other measurements.

Although the spectrophotometric measurement of charge complex is the easiest method, other methods such as the solubility method of Higuchi[26] and the kinetic method of Bender,[27] have been used for measuring the complex in special cases. The solubility method does not distinguish between the different types of donor-acceptor complexes or even neces-

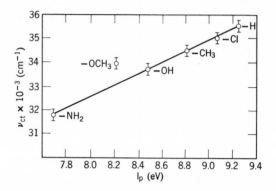

Fig. 2–2. A plot of the intramolecular charge-transfer band at its maximum (ν_{ct}), *versus* the ionization potential (I_p) of the substituted benzene of

From S. Shifrin, *Biochim. Biophys. Acta*, **96**, 173 (1965).

sarily between donor-acceptor complexes and hydrophobic bonding. The kinetic method of Bender is a special case where 3,5-dinitrobenzoate ion slows the rate of alkaline hydrolysis of *N*-(indole-3-acryloyl)imidazole; it was shown by kinetic analysis that the substrate was complexed to 3,5-dinitrobenzoate ion and that the complex was relatively unreactive towards hydroxide ion or *n*-butylamine. An association constant of 21.5 M^{-1} was obtained from the effect of variation of 3,5-dinitrobenzoate ion on the apparent rate constant; when checked by the spectrophotometric procedure at pH 7 and 420 mμ, an association constant of 23.6 M^{-1} was obtained. Although good agreement was obtained by both methods, the

[26] See Reference 4, p. 24.
[27] F. M. Menger and M. L. Bender, *J. Am. Chem. Soc.*, **88**, 131 (1966).

hydrolysis kinetics were also performed spectrophotometrically at 390 mμ; therefore, one cannot necessarily distinguish between the contribution of excited species and the contribution of the coulombic species to the association constant, even though the amount of excited species is probably negligible. The contribution by the coulombic species could be readily determined by repeating some of the kinetics by the pH-stat method in the dark. If the K_a determined by the pH-stat method agrees with the K_a

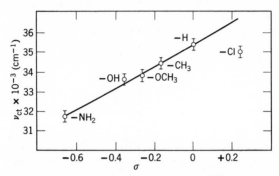

Fig. 2–3. A plot of the frequency of the intramolecular charge-transfer band at its maximum (ν_{ct}), *versus* the Hammett σ constant for the R group of

From S. Shifrin, *Biochim. Biophys. Acta*, **96**, 173 (1965).

determined by the excitation of the charge-transfer complex, then the excited state makes no significant contribution to the K_a; if the K_a's are different, then it should be possible to determine the relative contribution of the coulombic species and the excited species to the K_a in the spectrophotometer method at 420 mμ.

With the preceding evidence for charge-transfer complexes, what groups on an enzyme could be a donor or acceptor for a charge-transfer complex with a substrate or inhibitor? Consider the donor and acceptor groups that could be on the enzyme (Table 2–1).

In Group A, the arginine and lysine omega groups are protonated at physiological pH and therefore are not donors, in view of the lack of charge transfer with the triethyl ammonium group in XXVIII (Table 2–5). However, the imidazole of histidine can be a donor through the nitrogen lone pair, as is the case with XXVI (Table 2–5); note that in the protonated form the imidazole is not a donor. In contrast, in group A it may be possible that the protonated omega group of arginine and lysine could be acceptor groups, but no evidence is available. The electron-deficient π cloud of the imidazole of histidine should certainly be an acceptor—and a protonated imidazole even better—but measurements in water are again needed. A Shifrin type of study of the relative ability of these groups to act as acceptors when placed on a side chain of indole or phenol as donors would be most useful.

The acidic amino acids in Group B (Table 2–1) are fully ionized at physiological pH, therefore the anionic form must be considered. The anionic carboxylate is electron-rich and should therefore be a good donor, but not an acceptor.

The amides in Group C (Table 2–1) could be electron donors through an electron pair of oxygen; however, the lone electron pair on nitrogen will be a much poorer donor due to the effect of the electron-withdrawing carbonyl group. Note in Table 2–3 that N,N-dimethylformamide and acetamide can serve as donors. The hydrogen of the amide NH should serve as an acceptor because it does so in amide hydrogen bonding. Again direct measurements in water are needed.

The hydroxyl group of threonine, serine, and tyrosine (Group D, Table 2–1) can serve as a donor through the electron pair of the oxygen; note ethanol and *t*-butyl alcohol in Table 2–3. This hydroxyl group could also act as acceptor, but the tyrosine hydroxyl should be a better acceptor because the hydroxylic hydrogen is more acidic than that of serine and threonine.

The sulfur amino acids in Group E (Table 2–1) are strikingly different among themselves. The methionine sulfur should be a stronger donor than the cystine sulfur, as is the case with diethyl sulfide and diethyl disulfide, in Table 2–3. Because the SH group of cysteine is acidic, the electron pair on sulfur should be a poorer donor than that of the methylthio; however, if the SH group were sufficiently acidic—because of its environment in the protein—it could be a donor as an anion. In contrast, the thiolic hydrogen should be a good acceptor on the order of the tryosine hydroxylic hydrogen because of the acidity of the respective SH and OH groups. In contrast, the sulfur function of methionine or cystine should not be an acceptor.

The aryl amino acids of Group G (Table 2–1) should be donors with an order of effectiveness noted in Table 2–5; that is, tryptophane > tyrosine > phenylalanine. Conversely, the π clouds of these three aromatic rings should have the opposite order of effectiveness as acceptors; an exception is the imino hydrogen of tryptophane, which is weakly acidic and should therefore be an acceptor.

Hydrophobic Bonding and van der Waals Forces

Hydrophobic bonding and van der Waals forces are considered together because they will occur together in an enzyme-inhibitor or enzyme-substrate complex. Consider the model in Fig. 2–4; two molecules A and B containing hydrocarbon groups are dissolved separately in water; then the solutions are combined. When A and B are dissolved in water they become surrounded by water molecules; this process requires energy to change the water-hydrogen-bond structure with those water molecules directly in contact with the hydrocarbon surface of A and B. When the solutions are mixed, the A and B molecules can form a complex with the

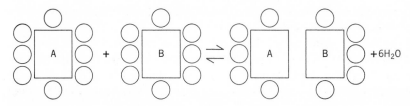

Fig. 2–4. A simplified diagram of hydrophobic bonding. The circles represent water molecules; A and B are molecules containing hydrocarbon groups along the right face of A and the left face of B.

regeneration of originally bonded water molecules; as is the case in Fig. 2–4, part of the energy required to dissolve A and B in water will be regained in the complex, namely, from the water structure re-formed from the six molecules of water no longer in contact with A and B.

The highly energetic process of hydrophobic bonding has a maximum energy release of 700 cal/mole of $> CH_2 \cdots CH_2 <$ interaction.[28] Furthermore, there can be an additional affinity of A and B dependent upon van der Waals forces, or dipole-dipole interaction; the van der Waals forces can also have a maximum bonding energy of 700 cal/mole of $> CH_2 \cdots CH_2 <$ interaction.[29] Thus simple hydrocarbon bonding could have as much as 1.4 kcal/mole of methylene on the substrate or inhibitor or about one power of ten in the dissociation constant; a simple butyl group could therefore give a maximum binding of 5.6 kcal/mole or a factor of about 10^{-4} in the dissociation constant. When hydrophobic bonding can be found with inhibitors, it is a most useful phenomenon, as will be described in later chapters.

[28] B. Belleau and G. Lacasse, *J. Med. Chem.*, **7**, 768 (1964); E. J. Cohn, and J. T. Edsall, *Proteins, Amino Acids, and Peptides*, Reinhold Publishing Corp., New York, 1943, Chapter 9; G. Nemethy and H. A. Scheraga, *J. Phys. Chem.*, **66**, 1173 (1962).
[29] L. Salem, *Can. J. Biochem. Physiol.*, **40**, 1287 (1962); B. Belleau and G. Lacasse, *J. Med. Chem.*, **7**, 768 (1964).

When these hydrophobic groups are on the enzyme surface, the alkyl amino acids in Group F (Table 1–1), such as leucine and valine, are examples of amino acids that could give a hydrophobic interaction with a substrate or inhibitor; most of the hydrophobic amino acids will be in the inner, less available hydrophobic core of an enzyme and are actually involved in proper folding of the protein to its tertiary structure, a part of the folding energy being contributed by the hydrophobic interaction between these amino acids.[30]

With the aromatic amino acids in Group G, hydrophobic interactions should also be possible, but there would be a flatter interaction than there is with the aliphatic hydrocarbon interaction; the free energy of hydrophobic bonding of benzene is maximally 4.6 kcal/mole.[31] By considering the number of carbon atoms and the relative polarity, one can guess that phenylalanine and tryptophane could show more hydrophobic bonding energy than tyrosine; furthermore, the enzyme-inhibitor complex between an aryl amino acid of Group G and an aryl group on the inhibitor could be further tightened by other forces, such as charge transfer or van der Waals forces.

Other groupings that could give hydrophobic bonding are the tetramethylene group of lysine, the trimethylene group of arginine, the methyl and ethylene groups of methionine, the ethylene group of glutamate, etc.

Mixed Types

The first three types of bonding shown in Table 2–1, namely anionic-cationic, hydrogen bond, and charge transfer, have in common an

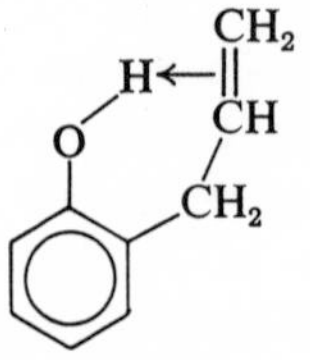

XX

electrostatic attraction of an electron-rich donor for an electron-poor acceptor, the order of maximum energy of bonding being in that order. Because all three are donor-acceptor types, there exists the possibility of mixed types; an example was mentioned earlier, namely *o*-allyl phenol (XX), where the π cloud of the vinyl group can donate to the electron-deficient hydroxylic hydrogen atom[32] (see also Table 2–3). Benzene as a

[30] C. Tanford, *J. Am. Chem. Soc.*, **84**, 4240 (1962).
[31] G. Nemethy and H. A. Scheraga, *J. Chem. Phys.*, **36**, 3382 (1962).
[32] See Reference 22, p. 32.

donor forms a complex with hydrogen chloride in heptane with $\triangle F$ about 2 kcal/mole. The donor properties increase about 0.1 kcal/mole per methyl group as additional methyl groups are substituted on the benzene ring (a good correlation between the ionization potential (I_p) and donor ability of the aromatics has been noted).[33] Thus an electron-rich carboxylate anion should be able to form an electrostatic bond by electron donation to (a) a cation, (b) to a hydrogen that can participate in hydrogen bonding, or (c) to a π base that can participate in charge transfer.[33] Other combinations are readily apparent and are indicated in Table 2–1.

SUBSTRATE AND INHIBITOR GROUPS COMPLEXING WITH ENZYMES

General Considerations

In Table 2–1 were listed the 20 amino acids in proteins and the types of bonding that they can undergo. The same type of bonding with any of the groups in Table 2–1 can occur if these groups are on substrates or inhibitors; for example, a carboxylate on a substrate can bond in the same way as a carboxylate on an enzyme. In addition to the 11 functional and two heterocyclic groups in Table 2–1, there are other functional groups listed in Table 2–6 with suggested modes of bonding.

Functional Groups

A variety of functional groups are listed in Table 2–6 with suggested modes of binding; although all possible functional groups have not been listed— particularly those unstable to water—the general concepts in this table should permit us to make predictions of binding of groups that are not listed. In many cases measurements have not been made; in these cases it would be useful to measure the proposed bonding forces—or lack thereof —intramolecularly as done with *o*-allyl phenol (XX)[34] or with 1- substituted nicotinamides (XXI).[35]

It should be pointed out that a multi-atom functional group, such as an amide or a phosphate, can have several modes of binding simultaneously. For example, with the —CONH— group, the hydrogen can be an acceptor and the oxygen a donor—the type of bonding responsible for the helical portions of proteins. A more complex example is the phosphate

---

[33] For complexes between inorganic acids as acceptors and aromatics as donors, see H. C. Brown and J. J. Melchiore, *J. Am. Chem. Soc.*, **87**, 5269 (1965); D. Cook, *J. Chem. Phys.*, **25**, 788 (1955).

[34] See Reference 22, p. 32.

[35] See References 23 and 24, p. 33.

Table 2–6. Functional Groups on Substrates and Inhibitors Complexing with Proteins

Functional group	Anionic-cationic	Hydrogen bond Donor	Hydrogen bond Acceptor	Charge-transfer Donor	Charge-transfer Acceptor	Hydrophobic Bonding[a]
A. *Cationic groups*[b]	*yes*	*no*	*yes?*	*no*	*yes?*	*no*
$R_3NH^\oplus$						
$R_4N^\oplus$						
$RNHNH_3^\oplus$						
$RNH\overset{\underset{\displaystyle |}{NH_2}}{C}{=}NH_2{}^\oplus$						
$R\overset{\underset{\displaystyle |}{NH_2}}{C}{=}NH_2{}^\oplus$						
$R\overset{\underset{\displaystyle |}{OR'}}{C}{=}NH_2{}^\oplus$						
$ArN{\equiv}\overset{\oplus}{N}$						
$R\overset{\underset{\displaystyle |}{SR'}}{C}{=}NH_2{}^\oplus$						
$R_3S^\oplus$						
B. *Anionic groups*[b]	*yes*	*yes*		*yes*		*no*
$RCOO^\ominus$			no		no	
$R\overset{\overset{\displaystyle O}{\parallel}}{C}S^\ominus$			no		no	
$R\overset{\overset{\displaystyle S}{\parallel}}{C}S^\ominus$			no		no	
$RSO_3{}^\ominus$			no		no	
$RSO_2{}^\ominus$			no		no	
$ROSO_3{}^\ominus$			yes[c]		yes?[c]	
$RPO(O^\ominus)_2$			no		no	
$ROPO(O^\ominus)_2$			yes[c]		yes[c]	
$R{-}AsO(O^\ominus)_2$			no		no	
C. *Weak bases*	*no*	*yes*		*yes*		*no*
RNH_2			yes		yes	
R_3N			no		no	
$R_3N \rightarrow O$			no		no	
$RCONHNH_2$			yes		yes	
D. *Weak acids*	*weak?*		*yes*		*yes*	*no*
ArOH		yes		yes		
RSH		no?		no?		
$RNH\overset{\overset{\displaystyle S}{\parallel}}{C}NR_2$		no?		no?		

Table 2–6. (*continued*)

Functional group	Anionic-cationic	Hydrogen bond Donor	Hydrogen bond Acceptor	Charge-transfer Donor	Charge-transfer Acceptor	Hydrophobic Bonding[a]
$\overset{S}{\overset{\|}{R}}CNHR'$		no?		no?		
$\overset{S}{\overset{\|}{R}}OCNHR'$		yes?[c]		yes?[c]		
$R_2C=NOH$		no?		no?		
$\overset{O}{\overset{\|}{R}}CNHOH$		yes		yes		
R_2CHNO_2		yes		yes		
$RNHC\equiv N$		no?		no?		
$RNHNO_2$		yes		yes		
E. *Neutral Sulfur groups*	no					no?
R_2S		yes	no	yes	no	
$R—S—S—R$		yes	no	yes	no	
R_2SO		yes	yes?	yes	yes?	
R_2SO_2		no?	no	no?	no	
RSO_2Hal		no?	no?	no?	no?	
$ROSO_2R$		yes[c]	no	yes[c]	no	
$RN=C=S$		yes?	no	yes?	no	
F. *Neutral nitrogen groups*	no					no
$RONO$		yes[c]	no	yes[c]	no	
$RONO_2$		yes[c]	no	yes[c]	no	
R_3CNO_2		yes	no	yes	no	
R_3CNO		yes	no	yes	no	
$RC\equiv N$		yes?	no	yes?	no	
$RCONHR$		yes	yes	yes	yes	
$RCONR_2$		yes	yes[d]	yes	yes[d]	
$\overset{S}{\overset{\|}{R}}CNR_2$		no?	no	no?	no	
$ROCONH_2$		yes	yes	yes	yes	
$R—N=N—R$		yes	no	yes	no	
$R—\overset{O}{\overset{\uparrow}{N}}=NR$		no?	no	no?	no	
$R—N\equiv C$		yes?	no	yes?	no	
$RCON_3$		yes	yes[d]	yes	yes[d]	
G. *Neutral phosphorus groups*	no					no
R_3P		yes	no	yes	no	
$R_3P \rightarrow O$		no?	yes[e]	no?	yes[e]	
$(RO)_3P$		yes	no	yes	no	

Table 2–6. (*continued*)

Functional group	Anionic-cationic	Hydrogen bond Donor	Hydrogen bond Acceptor	Charge-transfer Donor	Charge-transfer Acceptor	Hydrophobic Bonding[a]
$(RO)_3P \rightarrow O$		yes[c]	yes[e]	yes[c]	yes[e]	
$RP(OR)_2$, $\overset{O}{\underset{\uparrow}{}}$		yes	no	yes	no	
$RP(OR)_2$, $\overset{O}{\underset{\uparrow}{}}$		yes[c]	yes[e]	yes[c]	yes[e]	
$R_2P\!-\!NH_2$, $\overset{O}{\underset{\uparrow}{}}$		no?	yes	no?	yes	
$(RO)_2PNH_2$, $\overset{O}{\underset{\uparrow}{}}$		yes[c]	yes	yes[c]	yes	
$(RO)_2PNR_2$, $\overset{O}{\underset{\uparrow}{}}$		yes[c]	yes[e]	yes[c]	yes[e]	
H. *Neutral oxygen groups*	*no*	*yes*		*yes*		*no*
ROH			yes		yes	
R_2O			no		no	
$RCOOR$			yes[d]		yes[d]	
$(RO)_2CO$			yes[d]		yes[d]	
$R_2C(OR)_2$			no		no	
$RCH\!=\!O$			yes[d]		yes[d]	
$R_2C\!=\!O$			yes[d]		yes[d]	
I. *Miscellaneous*	*no*					*yes*
$R\!-\!Hal.$		yes	no	yes	no	
$R_2C\!=\!CR_2$[f]		yes	yes	yes	yes	
aryl[g]		yes	yes	yes	yes	
alkyl		no	no	no	no	

[a] Including other relatively nonpolar forces such as van der Waals and dipole interactions.

[b] At physiological pH.

[c] Via ester oxygen.

[d] If R is sufficiently electron-withdrawing, the resultant carbonyl carbon may have sufficient positive character to be an acceptor; see mode of carbonyl binding to trypsin and chymotrypsin in Chapter 3.

[e] If R is sufficiently electron withdrawing, the resultant phosphorus atom may have sufficient positive character to be an acceptor; see B. C. Saunders, *Some Aspects of the Chemistry and Toxic Action of Organic Compounds Containing Phosphorus and Fluorine*, Cambridge University Press, Cambridge, England, 1957, pp. 188–191.

[f] An ethylene can be a donor or acceptor depending upon whether R groups on the ethylene are electron-donating or electron-withdrawing.

[g] Donor or acceptor properties can be increased by substitution with electron-donating or electron-withdrawing groups.

44

monoester group so prevalent in metabolic pathways; over 20 ways can be envisioned for phosphate binding (disregarding the enzyme partner groups), including binding with one, two, or three bonds to the enzyme.[36]

Heterocycles

In Table 2–7 are listed a few unsubstituted, monocyclic heterocycles and their possible modes of binding. This list is abbreviated because binding information on unsubstituted heterocycles is likely to be of little value; most useful heterocycles that complex with receptor and enzyme sites are substituted, and the substituents affect the binding capacity of the ring system tremendously. A good case in point is the pyrimidine ring, which is important as a constituent of nucleic acids and as the ring system for a number of useful drugs.

Pyrimidine (XXIX) is a weak base soluble in water that can form hydrophobic bonds with the C_2, C_4, C_5, and C_6 carbons. Pyrimidine

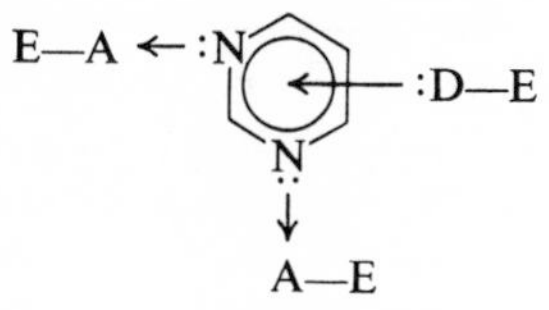

XXIX 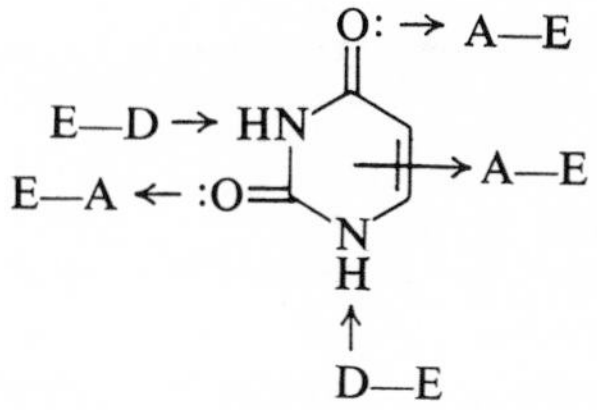   XXX

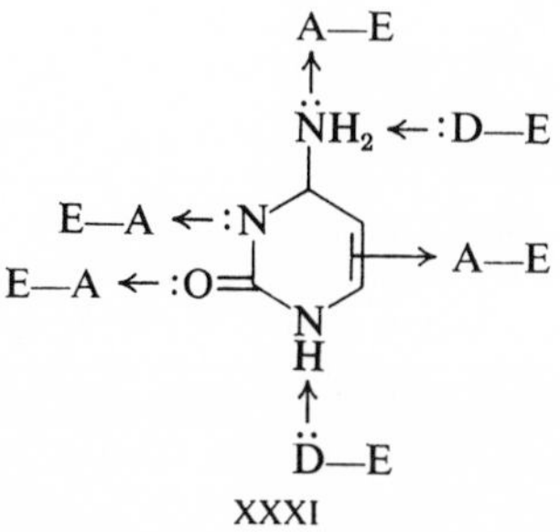

XXXI

(XXIX) is also an electron-deficient ring system and therefore its electron-deficient π cloud can accept electrons from a donor group on the enzyme. Furthermore, pyrimidine has an electron pair on each nitrogen, which, in contrast to the π system, can act as a point donor to an acceptor on the enzyme.

When the pyrimidine (XXIX) is substituted by the electron-donating hydroxyl group at its 2- and 4- positions, the resultant oxo tautomer, uracil (XXX), will have completely changed properties. The π system of the

[36] B. R. Baker, P. M. Tanna, and G. D. F. Jackson, *J. Pharm. Sci.*, **54**, 987 (1965).

ring becomes electron rich and can donate electrons to an acceptor group on the enzyme. Furthermore the two —CONH— groups can donate electrons from the oxygen and accept electrons to the hydrogen. Cytosine (XXXI) is both a weak acid and weak base, but compared to pyrimidine (XXIX) it is substituted by two electron-donating groups, amino and hydroxy. In addition to the types of bonds present in uracil (XXX), cytosine has two nitrogens that can be lone-pair donors and two amine hydrogens that can be acceptors.

Similar arguments can be advanced for the numerous known and unknown mono and polycyclic heterocycles, the mode of binding being tremendously influenced by substitution.

Table 2–7. Bonding of Some Monocyclic Heterocycles to Proteins

Heterocycle[a]	Anionic-cationic	Hydrogen bond[b] Donor	Hydrogen bond[b] Acceptor	Charge-transfer[b] Donor	Charge-transfer[b] Acceptor	Hydrophobic Bonding[c]
Imidazole	yes	yes	yes	yes	yes	poor
Furan	no	yes	no?	yes	no?	yes
Pyrrole	weak (?)	yes	no	yes	no	yes
Thiophene	no	yes	yes?	yes	yes?	yes
Pyrazole	weak (?)	yes	no?	yes	no?	poor
Triazole	weak (?)	yes	yes	yes	yes	no
Pyridine	weak (?)	yes	yes	yes	yes	poor
Pyrimidine	no	yes	yes	yes	yes	poor
s-Triazine	no	yes	yes	yes	yes	no?

[a] The bonding excludes active hydrogens such as the NH of pyrrole.

[b] It should be noted that the properties of a heterocycle can be modified by substitution of electron-donating or electron-withdrawing groups; see discussion.

[c] Also includes other nonpolar interactions such as van der Waals forces.

SUMMARY

It is clear that actually little is known about which specific groups on an enzyme *complex* with which groups on a substrate or inhibitor; however, the fact exists that these complexes do form, presumably through the types of bonding discussed in this chapter. The complexing constants can be measured, and perhaps x-ray crystallographic studies of inhibitors diffused on to enzyme crystals[37] will at least give an indication of which amino acid on the protein is adjacent to an inhibitor functional group; nevertheless,

[37] L. N. Johnson and D. C. Phillips, *Nature*, **206**, 761 (1965).

even the observation of an enzymic tryptophane being next to a specific group on an inhibitor will not necessarily differentiate hydrogen bonding from charge transfer from hydrophobic bonding.

It would be aesthetically and scientifically pleasing to know the exact bonding interactions; however, in actual practice, for the design of active-site-directed irreversible inhibitors, it is only necessary to know which groups on the substrate or inhibitor are complexing to the enzyme. This will be discussed in the next two chapters.

3 | Specific Mode of Binding to Enzymes
I. Proteolytic Enzymes

GENERAL CONSIDERATIONS

In Chapter 2 the possible binding forces that cause the affinity of an enzyme for an inhibitor were discussed. Although it is experimentally difficult at the present time to determine the actual groups on the enzyme that are involved in this binding, it is usually possible to determine which groups of a substrate or an inhibitor are involved in binding. The groups necessary for binding certainly vary from one enzyme to the next, this difference being part of the substrate specificity of the enzyme. How does one determine which groups on an inhibitor are involved in enzyme binding and how do these groups vary from one enzyme to the next? To answer these questions, the modes of binding to seven different enzymes have been arbitrarily chosen for illustrative purposes, two of which are discussed in this chapter.

CHYMOTRYPSIN

Chymotrypsin is one of a variety of proteolytic enzymes; over the years it has been one of the most studied enzymes because it is readily available in crystalline form and in recent years on a commercial basis. The amide groups most readily cleaved by chymotrypsin are those with the acyl end of the amide in the polypeptide derived from one of the aromatic amino acids, tyrosine, phenylalanine, or tryptophane.

After the discovery of Bergmann and Fruton[1] that simple esters and

---

[1] M. Bergmann and J. S. Fruton, *J. Biol. Chem.*, **118**, 405 (1937); *J. Biol. Chem.*, **124**, 321 (1938).

48

amides of *N*-acylated aromatic amino acids such as *N*-acetyl-L-phenylalaninamide could serve as substrates, it was shown that the reaction proceeds in two steps through an acylated serine residue. Histidine is also present in the active site, which catalyzes the acylation and deacylation of the serine residue as follows:

$$E + S \underset{k_{-1}}{\overset{k_1}{\rightleftharpoons}} E \cdots S \underset{k_{-2}}{\overset{k_2}{\rightleftharpoons}} \underset{+}{\overset{}{E-S'}} \underset{k_{-3}}{\overset{k_3}{\rightleftharpoons}} E \cdots P_2 \underset{k_{-4}}{\overset{k_4}{\rightleftharpoons}} E + P_2 \quad (3\text{-}1)$$

$$P_1$$

For most normal substrates, k_3 is considerably more rapid than k_2, although it is readily possible to reverse this order by choosing the proper substrate. Four types of measurements can then be made, K_m, k_2, and k_3 of a substrate, and K_i of an inhibitor. The elegant studies of Niemann and his coworkers have led to a generalized concept of binding areas on the substrate or inhibitor to the enzyme, as depicted in diagram I[2,3]; using this diagram they were able to establish what parameters are necessary for substrate properties and what parameters are necessary for inhibitor properties.

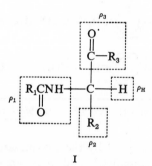

I

The general substrate structure in I has R_1, R_2, R_3, and H groups; the contact areas between these groups and the enzymes are arbitrarily depicted as ρ_1, ρ_2, ρ_3, and ρ_H, respectively. Soon after the announcement by Bergmann and Fruton of simple substrates—in contrast to natural polyamide substrates—for this enzyme, Neurath and his coworkers began studies with this enzyme.

ρ_3 Area

In Table 3–1 carbonyl variants are listed that complex to the ρ_3 area; it should be noted that K_m may not necessarily be the true dissociation

[2] G. E. Hein and C. Niemann, *J. Am. Chem. Soc.*, **84**, 4495 (1962).

[3] J. B. Jones, C. Niemann, and G. E. Hein, *Biochemistry*, **4**, 1735 (1965).

constant[4] because of the manner in which these particular measurements were made. Note that the ester (III) apparently complexed better than the amide (II) and that it is a faster substrate even though only semiquantitative data were determined. When the *N*-benzoyl group of III is replaced by *N*-acetyl (IV) the rate of hydrolysis is similar. The product of hydrolysis of IV, namely the carboxylate V can still complex to the enzyme about half as well as the ester (IV), but V is an inhibitor. Other functions of the carboxyl

Table 3–1. Parameters of the ρ_3 Binding Area of Chymotrypsin

No.	ρ_1	ρ_2	ρ_3	ρ_H	$K_i \times 10^3$ or $K_m \times 10^3 M$	k_2
II C_6H_5CONH-	$HO-$⬡CH_2-	$CONH_2$	L	42	fair
III C_6H_5CONH-	$HO-$⬡CH_2-	$COOC_2H_5$	L	3.9	good
IV CH_3CONH-	$HO-$⬡CH_2-	$COOC_2H_5$	L	74	good
V CH_3CONH-	$HO-$⬡CH_2-	COO^-	L	160	inhibitor

Data from S. Kaufman and H. Neurath, *Arch. Biochem.*, **21**, 437 (1948).

group that can be hydrolyzed by the enzyme are the *N*-methylamides,[5] hydrazides,[6] *N*-hydroxyamides,[7] and aryl amides,[8] *N*-(carboxamidomethyl) amides,[8] aryl esters,[8] and thio esters.[8] Most probably the carbonyl group is complexed to the enzyme, theoretically by either the oxygen of the

$C{=}O$ as a donor or the carbon of a polarized $\delta^+ C \overset{\frown}{=} O\delta^-$ as an acceptor.[9]

$$\overset{O}{\underset{\uparrow}{}}$$

Because molecules of type R_2P-X are also complexed to the enzyme

[4] G. E. Hein and C. Niemann, *Proc. Natl. Acad. Sci.*, (*U.S.*), **47** 1341 (1962).

[5] H. T. Huang and C. Niemann, *J. Am. Chem. Soc.*, **73**, 3223 (1951).

[6] R. Lutwack, H. F. Mower, and C. Niemann, *J. Am. Chem. Soc.*, **79**, 5690 (1957).

[7] D. S. Hogness and C. Niemann, *J. Am. Chem. Soc.*, **75**, 884 (1953).

[8] M. Dixon and E. C. Webb, *Enzymes*, Academic Press, New York, 1958, pp. 252–265.

[9] S. A. Bernhard, *J. Am. Chem. Soc.*, **77**, 1966 (1955).

and because the oxygen is a poor donor, although the $P \rightarrow O$ bond can polarize to $\delta^+ P—O^{\delta^-}$, the complexing via $E—D: \rightarrow \overset{\delta^+}{C}—\overset{\delta^-}{O}$ and $E—D: \rightarrow \overset{\delta^+}{P}—\overset{\delta^-}{O}$ is favored. Three such donors are present in the active site—the oxygen of the 195-serine hydroxyl and the one pair of electrons on the nitrogen of imidazole-57 and imidazole-40. Because the binding of substrates seems to be relatively pH independent,[10] the serine hydroxyl donor is preferred over the imidazole at this time. The binding of the carbonyl substrates and inhibitors of acetylchlorinesterase is quite definitively through the polarized electrophilic carbonyl carbon because an electron-withdrawing group attached to the carbonyl greatly enhances bonding; in contrast to chymotrypsin, this binding to acetylcholinesterase is pH dependent, the binding group having pK_a 7.2, presumably that of an imidazole.[11]

ρ_1 **Area**

In Table 3–2 are listed variants of the N-acylamide group, the ρ_1 binding area. Note that changing N-acetyl (IV) to N-benzoyl (III) still gives good substrate properties, but (III) gives better binding. A more detailed study on acylamido binding arises by comparing X–XIII; the aryl group (XII, XIII) gives better binding than an alkyl group (X, XI). As will be pointed out later (see Chapter 8), it is probable that methionine-192 on the enzyme is in the ρ_1 area; whether or not such is the case, it would be useful to vary the aryl group of XIII with electron-donating or electron-withdrawing groups to determine whether the aryl group complexes as an electron-acceptor, presumably from the electron pair on sulfur of methionine; also it would be useful to determine if hydrophobic forces are important by use of the hexahydrobenzamido or valeramido groups. In order to avoid R_1-ρ_2 interactions, this study should be performed on a trifunctional substrate[12] or inhibitor.

The phthalimido group (VI) or the unacylated α-amino group (VII)—present as NH_3^+ at physiological pH—lead to loss of substrate properties. Unfortunately, the ability of VI and VII to inhibit were not determined so that it cannot be stated whether or not binding, as well as substrate properties, were lost.

The hydrocinnamic ester (IX) still binds well to the enzyme, but it is a poorer substrate; therefore the α-acylamido group does aid substrate

---

[10] B. S. Hartley in *Structure and Activity of Enzymes*, T. W. Goodwin, J. I. Harris, and B. S. Hartley, eds., Academic Press, New York, 1964, p. 53.

[11] See Reference 10.

[12] J. P. Wolf, III, and C. Niemann, *Biochemistry*, **2**, 82 (1963).

Table 3–2. Parameters of the ρ_1 Binding Area of Chymotrypsin

No.	ρ_1	ρ_2	ρ_3	ρ_H	$K_i \times 10^3$ or $K_m \times 10^3$	k_2	Reference
III	C_6H_5CONH	HO—⟨benzene⟩CH_2— 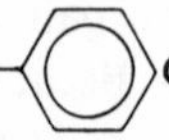	$COOC_2H_5$	L	3.9	good	a
IV	CH_3CONH	HO—⟨benzene⟩CH_2— 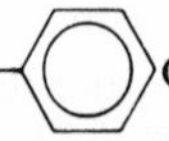	$COOC_2H_5$	L	74	good	a
VI	Phthalimido	HO—⟨benzene⟩CH_2— 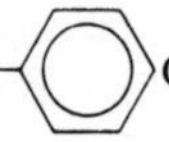	$COOCH_3$	L	0		a
VII	NH_3^+	HO—⟨benzene⟩CH_2— 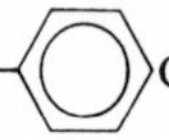	$COOC_2H_5$	L	0		a
VIII	C_6H_5CONH	$C_6H_5CH_2$—	$COOCH_3$	L	4.6	good	b
IX	H	$C_6H_5CH_2$—	$COOCH_3$ —		3.9	poor	b
X	CH_3CONH	HO⟨benzene⟩CH_2— 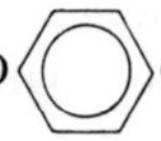	$CONHCH_3$	L	61 ± 7	inhibitor	c
XI	HCONH	HO⟨benzene⟩CH_2— 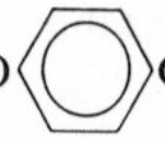	$CONHCH_3$	L	31 ± 8	inhibitor	c
XII	Nicotinamido	HO⟨benzene⟩CH_2— 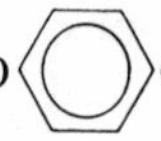	$CONHCH_3$	L	8.8 ± 1.0	inhibitor	c
XIII	C_6H_5CONH	HO⟨benzene⟩CH_2— 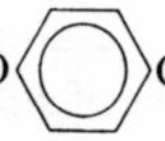	$CONHCH_3$	L	6.4 ± 1.6	inhibitor	c

[a] S. Kaufman and H. Neurath, *Arch. Biochem.*, **21**, 437 (1949).
[b] J. E. Snoke and H. Neurath, *Arch. Biochem.*, **21**, 351 (1949).
[c] W. E. M. Lands and C. Niemann, *J. Am. Chem. Soc.*, **81**, 2204 (1959).

properties, perhaps by forcing a conformational change[13] in the enzyme favorable for hydrolysis. It would appear that the carboxamido part of the α-acylamido function is actually detrimental to mere binding but that

[13] D. E. Koshland, Jr., Y. A. Yankeelov, Jr., and J. A. Thoma, *Fed. Proc.*, **21**, 1031 (1962).

the R group of the acylamido can bind; that is, the enzyme conformational change favorable for hydrolysis that may take place when an α-acylamido group is present derives its energy from the total binding energy of the substrate; the binding that would at first glance appear to be identical in VIII and IX actually could be a gain in binding by the phenyl group of the benzamido in the ρ_1 area but an equal loss in energy due to the conformational change, forced by the carboxamido function in the ρ_1 area to give better substrate properties with VIII. Along these lines it should be noted that replacement of the *N*-acetyl group of IV by *N*-tosyl gives a compound with k_2 eight times that of IV, but K_m was not recorded.[14]

ρ_2 Area

The binding in the ρ_2 area is apparently important for determining which amino acid in a protein has its amide group hydrolyzed by chymotrypsin. In Table 3–3 are listed some variants at the ρ_2 area. The early work of Neurath and coworkers clearly showed that the aryl amino acid esters (III, VIII, XIV) were better substrates than the aliphatic amino acid esters (XV–XVII). They noted that all the aliphatic amino acid esters—except serine (XVIII) which should have been measured as an inhibitor—could complex reasonably well with chymotrypsin but were poor substrates; in fact, the methionine derivative (XVII) complexed better than the aryl derivatives.

A more recent detailed study by Niemann and his coworkers compared compounds XIX–XXVIII, all of which were *N*-acetyl methyl esters. They also noted that an aryl amino acid derivative (XXVI) was by far the best substrate, but certain alkyl groups could bind as well (XXIII) or better than the aryl group of XXVI; however, XXIII was only about one quarter as good a substrate as XXVI and, furthermore, XXIII is an unnatural amino acid. As the alkyl group was increased from methyl (XX) to *n*-amyl (XXIII), binding became tighter but was not further tightened by *n*-hexyl (XXIV). This is clearly a hydrophobic binding phenomenon and the average —ΔF per methylene was 700 cal/mole; the tightest bonding observed in the series was with hexahydrobenzyl (XXVII), which complexed about seven times better than benzyl (XXVI) and nearly 4000-fold better than methyl (XX).

The methylthioethyl group of methionine (XVII) complexes about five times better than the benzyl group (VIII) in the benzamido series; also note that the methylthio group has the same hydrophobic character as a methyl group.[15] Therefore, we might expect that the methylthioethyl group should bind about as well as *n*-propyl; this is not the case because

[14] D. E. Hummel, *Can. J. Biochem. Physiol.*, **37**, 1393 (1959).
[15] T. Fujita, J. Iwasa, and C. Hansch, *J. Am. Chem. Soc.*, **86**, 5175 (1964).

Table 3-3. Parameters of the ρ_2 Binding Area of Chymotrypsin for Substrates

No.	ρ_1	ρ_2	ρ_3	ρ_H	$K_m \times 10^3\,M$	$k_2(\text{sec}^{-1})$	Reference
III	C_6H_5CONH—	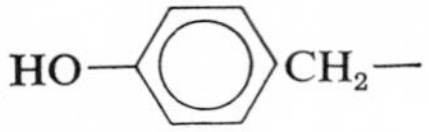 HO—⟨C₆H₄⟩—CH_2—	$COOC_2H_5$	L	3.9	good	[a]
VIII	C_6H_5CONH	$C_6H_5CH_2$	$COOCH_3$	L	4.6	good	[a]
XIV	C_6H_5CONH	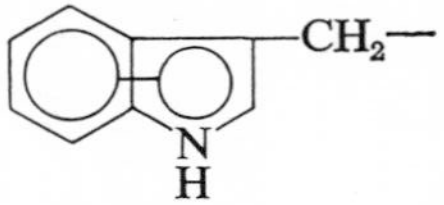 indolyl—CH_2—	$COOC_2H_5$	DL	4.8	good	[a]
XV	C_6H_5CONH	CH_3—	$COOCH_3$	L	10	poor	[a]
XVI	C_6H_5CONH	$(CH_3)_2CH$—	$COOCH_3$	L	4.6	poor	[a]
XVII	C_6H_5CONH	$CH_3SCH_2CH_2$—	$COOC_2H_5$	L	0.83	poor	[a]
XVIII	C_6H_5CONH	$HOCH_2$—	$COOCH_3$	L	—	0	[a]
XIX	CH_3CONH	H	$COOCH_3$	L	31	0.013	[b]
XX	CH_3CONH	CH_3	$COOCH_3$	L	739	1.27	[b]
XXI	CH_3CONH	C_2H_5	$COOCH_3$	L	53	1.05	[b]
XXII	CH_3CONH	$n\text{-}C_4H_9$	$COOCH_3$	L	6.7	2.7	[b]
XXIII	CH_3CONH	$n\text{-}C_5H_{11}$	$COOCH_3$	L	1.6	13.4	[b]
XXIV	CH_3CONH	$n\text{-}C_6H_{13}$	$COOCH_3$	L	2.94	6.23	[b]
XXV	CH_3CONH	$(CH_3)_2CHCH_2$	$COOCH_3$	L	3.76	4.98	[b]
XXVI	CH_3CONH	$C_6H_5CH_2$	$COOCH_3$	L	1.25	52.5	[b]
XXVII	CH_3CONH	$C_6H_{11}CH_2$	$COOCH_3$	L	0.19	15.2	[b]
XXVIII	CH_3CONH	$n\text{-}C_3H_7$	$COOCH_3$	L	10.2	2.7	[b]

[a] H. Neurath and G. W. Schwert, *Chem. Rev.*, **46**, 69 (1950).
[b] J. B. Jones, T. Kunitake, C. Niemann, and G. E. Hein, *J. Am. Chem. Soc.*, **87**, 1777 (1965).

benzyl (XXVI) binds eight times better than propyl (XXVIII) and methyl-thio (XVII) binds six times better than benzyl (VIII). The methylthio group is thus binding about 47 times better than *n*-propyl. It is therefore within the realm of possibility that the ρ_2 area of chymotrypsin has a hydrophobic group that also can be an electron acceptor for an electron pair of the sulfur. Such an amino acid requirement is fulfilled by tryptophane, the NH of which can be an electron acceptor, the ring of which can be an electron donor and which has hydrophobic properties (see Chapter 2); similarly, tyrosine could fulfill this requirement with its OH being an electron acceptor and its ring an electron donor with hydrophobic properties. However this explanation still does not account for cyclohexyl (XXVII) in its chair form being complexed to a flat amino acid such as tryptophane better than the flat benzene ring of XXVI; thus some other factor is also at play such as an aliphatic amino acid in the ρ_2 area, the conformation of the enzyme perhaps changing[16] for binding to one or the other amino acid depending upon the substrate. The suggestion of hexhydrobenzyl (XXVII) complexing with an aliphatic amino acid in the ρ_2 area with one conformation of the enzyme while benzyl (XXVI) complexes with an amino acid in the ρ_2 area in a different conformation would also explain why XXVI is a better substrate than XXVII; that is, the conformation binding an aryl amino acid in the ρ_3 area is more favorable for hydrolysis.[17]

ρ_H Area

When *N*-acetyl-L-phenylalanine methyl ester is converted to its α-methyl derivative, substrate properties are lost but inhibitory properties still remain.[18] One of the problems here is that α-methyl substitution greatly slows the rate of chemical hydrolysis. If an α-methyl-α-acylamido acid is converted to the more reactive *p*-nitrophenyl ester, k_2 is now observable, but k_3, the rate of hydrolysis of the acylated serine of the enzyme is still slow.[19] It can be concluded that an α-methyl group has no effect on binding properties; the effect on binding of higher alkyl or aralkyl groups on the α position has not been investigated.

The D isomers of substrates are inhibitors[18]; the inhibitory properties can be accounted for by the fact that a different rotomer of the inhibitor is binding. Because the ρ_2 area is usually determinant[18] as to the preferred rotomer—due to the strong binding in this area—this might not allow the carbonyl group (R_3) to complex in the ρ_3 area; because a ρ_3-R_3 interaction

---

[16] B. S. Hartley in *Structure and Activity of Enzymes*, T. W. Goodwin, J. I. Harris, and B. S. Hartley, eds., Academic Press, New York, 1964, p. 55.

[17] See Reference 16.

[18] See Reference 2, p. 49.

[19] W. B. Lawson and H. J. Schramm, *Biochemistry*, **4**, 377 (1965).

is necessary for substrate properties, it might be that the D isomers are complexed in a different way. Such a rotomer for a D isomer is shown in I*B*. Hein and Niemann[20] have also suggested conformation I*C* for the D isomer, with the explanation that a ρ_H substituent blocks entry of a group on the enzyme catalyzing the hydrolysis. Since the ρ_H region presumably does not contribute to binding, it should be possible to differentiate the I*B* rotomer from the I*C* rotomer by comparison of the effects of R_3 and R_1

on binding D isomers. In the *L*-tyrosine-*N*-methylamide series (Table 3–2) there is about a sevenfold difference in binding between *N*-acetyl and *N*-nicotinyl derivatives, the latter being better; in contrast, in the D-tyrosine series there is only a 1.5-fold difference with the D isomers being bound about as effectively as the nicotinyl-L-amide,[20] indicating the α-acylamido group of D isomers is in the ρ_H area. Better binding of the *N*-acetyl-D isomer compared to the *N*-acetyl-L isomer can be accounted for by the lack of an energy-requiring conformational change when the acylamido group is in the ρ_H area (compare VIII and IX in Table 3–2). The binding of *N*-acetyl-L-tyrosine ethyl ester is 50-fold better than the corresponding hydroxamide, but in the D series, the two isomers are about the same, being intermediate between the L ester and L-hydroxamide; these results can also be rationalized by rotomer I*C* if it is assumed that either rotomer I*B* or I*C* may bind, depending upon whether the α-acylamido group gives better binding to the ρ_1 area than the $R_3C{=}O$ group does to the ρ_3 area or vice versa.

Other Inhibitor Types

Removal of the α-acylamido of the substrate to give methyl hydrocinnamate (IX in Table 3–2) resulted in a decreased rate of enzymic hydrolysis but no appreciable net effect on binding. If the carbomethoxy group of IX is also removed along with a methylene group, the resultant toluene has $K_i = 13 \times 10^{-3}$ M[21] compared to IX with $K_m = 3.9 \times 10^{-3}$ M; thus the contribution to binding by the terminal CH_2COOCH_3 group of IX is only a factor of about three compared to toluene and most of the binding of IX is due to the phenyl binding in the ρ_2 area. Indole has $K_i = 0.80 \times 10^{-3}$

[20] D. T. Manning and C. Niemann, *J. Am. Chem. Soc.*, **80**, 1478 (1958).

M^{21} which is actually bound tighter than N-acetyl-L-tryptophane amide $(K_s = 5 \times 10^{-3} \ M)^{22}$ but less effectively than the corresponding ester $(K_s = 0.1 \times 10^{-3} \ M)^{22}$; thus, a large portion of the binding energy of tryptophane is also apparently due to the binding of the indole moiety to the ρ_2 area.

Table 3–4. Further Parameters of Binding to the ρ_2 Area of Chymotrypsin

Compound	$K_i \times 10^3 M$	$-\Delta F$(kcal/mole)	Reference
C_6H_6	25	2.08, 2.2	a, b
n-C_5H_{12}		3.06	b
Cyclohexene		2.81	b
Naphthalene		5.36	b
Indene		4.99	b
$CH_3C_6H_5$	13	3.47, 2.5	a,b
$CH_3CONHC_6H_5$	13		a
$C_6H_5NH_2$	7		a
$C_6H_5COO^-$	150		a
$C_6H_5CONH_2$	10		a
$C_6H_5CH_2NH_3^+$	22		a
$C_6H_5CH_2NHCOCH_3$	8		a
Indole	0.8	4.0	a
N—CH_3—indole	0.9		a
Quinoline	0.6		a
Isoquinoline	0.3		a
Adenine	neg.^{c}		a
Acridine	0.2		a
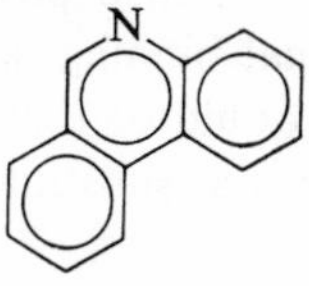	0.2		a
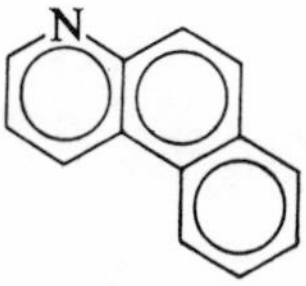	0.06	6.3	a

^{a} R. A. Wallace, A. M. Kurtz, and C. Niemann, *Biochemistry*, **2**, 824 (1965).
^{b} A. J. Hymes, D. A. Robinson, and W. J. Canady, *J. Biol. Chem.*, **240**, 134 (1965).
^{c} No inhibition at 5 mM; the K_i of benzene was determined at 8 mM.

[21] R. A. Wallace, A. N. Kurtz, and C. Niemann, *Biochemistry*, **2**, 824 (1963).
[22] See Reference 20, p. 56.

Further extensive work on ρ_2 area binding of inhibitors less functionalized than substrates were carried out by Niemann et al[23]; some of this data is summarized in Table 3–4, along with pertinent data of other workers. Note that benzene, pentane, and cyclohexene all bind in the same range; this is strong evidence that hydrophobic bonding can exist. If these compounds are complexing with a hydrophobic region, then repulsion of a charged species should occur whether or not the charge is positive or negative[24]; note that benzoate binds one eighth as effectively as benzene and benzylammonium ion about one half as effectively as toluene. Furthermore this repulsion of a charged group in a hydrophobic area should disappear when the charge is removed by derivatization[24]; note that benzamide is now a 2.5-fold better inhibitor than benzene and *N*-benzyl-acetamide about twofold better than toluene.

Note that indole, indene, *N*-methylindole, quinoline, and isoquinoline are all good inhibitors with K_i's on the order of $0.3–0.9 \times 10^{-3}$ M. Because indole and *N*-methylindole are electron-rich but quinoline is electron poor, the data again agrees best with hydrophobic bonding rather than any donor-acceptor bonding, whether of the charge-transfer, hydrogen-bond, or a mixed type. In contrast, the highly polar adenine is complexed much more poorly than benzene.

Benzo(c)quinoline and acidine are even slightly better inhibitors than isoquinoline and threefold better than quinoline; the best binding with ρ_2 nonfunctional inhibitors yet observed was noted with benzo(f)quinoline which gives a free energy of binding of 6.3 kcal/mole.

Because fewer functional groups are present on the inhibitors in Table 3–4 than on substrates, it really cannot be stated with certainty that the compounds are complexed completely in the ρ_2 area; it is also possible with the tricyclic systems, such as benzo(f)quinoline, that binding occurs in both the ρ_1 and ρ_2 areas. To answer these doubts it would be useful to synthesize and study compounds of types XXIX and XXX as substrates or

inhibitors, where the aryl group is one or more of the more potent bi- and tricyclic systems in Table 3–4.

[23] See Reference 21, p. 57.
[24] B. R. Baker, and B.-T. Ho, *J. Heterocyclic Chem.*, **2**, 335 (1965).

TRYPSIN

General Considerations

Trypsin catalyzes the hydrolysis of peptide or ester bonds formed from the carboxyl group of the basic amino acids, arginine and lysine.[25] The enzyme can be readily assayed by the rate of consumption of base at constant pH or more conveniently by a spectrophotometric procedure, which measures the appearance of the absorption of p-nitroaniline at 410 mμ when α-N-benzoylarginine p-nitroanilide is used as substrate.[26] Esters are split more rapidly than amides, which in turn are split more rapidly than peptides.[27] Acylation of the terminal basic group completely abolishes the reaction, indicating that the terminal ammonium group of lysine or the terminal guanidinium group of arginine is necessary for binding. In contrast acylation of the α-NH$_2$ facilitates the reaction, but the free α-NH$_3^{\oplus}$ group still allows the molecule to be a substrate. Complete removal of the α-nitrogen function results in the loss of substrate properties. These results are strikingly different than those seen with chymotrypsin, which best hydrolyses esters or amides of aromatic amino acids; as discussed in the previous section, the presence of an α-ammonium group abolishes substrate activity, but complete removal of the α-nitrogen function still allowed weak substrate properties for chymotrypsin.

A notable similarity in the catalytic site of trypsin and chymotrypsin has been described, namely almost the same amino acid sequence between the two histidine residues in the "histidine loop" which are separated by 15 amino acids in trypsin and 16 amino acids in chymotrypsin (Fig. 3–1).[28] Because the chemical reaction is identical, it is gratifying that the catalytic region is so similar; the difference between the two enzymes then resides in the bonding region for the tail of the α-amino acid, trypsin being specific for basic amino acid (except histidine) derivatives and chymotrypsin most effective on aryl amino acid derivatives.

Also with notable similarity to chymotrypsin, trypsin has a serine in the active site which is attacked by diisopropyl phosphofluoridate (DFP)[29]; however, the methionine-192 of chymotrypsin, which is the third amino acid from the serine-195, is replaced by glycine in trypsin and the sequence continues to differ from alanine-185 to serine-189 of chymotrypsin (Fig.

[25] H. Neurath and G. W. Schwert, *Chem. Rev.*, **46**, 69 (1950).

[26] B. F. Erlanger, N. Kokowsky, and W. Cohen, *Arch. Biochem. Biophys.*, **95**, 271 (1961).

[27] For a summary of substrate properties see M. Dixon and E. C. Webb, *Enzymes*, Academic Press, New York, 1958, pp. 252–269.

[28] B. S. Hartley in *Structure and Activity of Enzymes*, T. W. Goodwin, J. I. Harris, and B. S. Hartley, eds., Academic Press, New York, N.Y. 1964, pp. 47–60.

[29] G. H. Dixon, D. L. Kauffman, and H. Neurath, *J. Am. Chem. Soc.*, **80**, 1260 (1958).

3–1).[28] Because the ρ_1 area on chymotrypsin involves methionine-192 (see Chapter 8), we can now anticipate that the ρ_1 area binding (XXXI) might be different for trypsin. The ρ_2 area is definitely different because

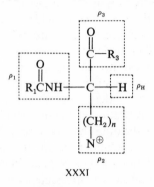

XXXI

trypsin requires a terminal cationic group for binding. The ρ_3 area might be anticipated to be similar because this is the catalytic area, but the only

ACTIVE SERINE SEQUENCES
Chymotrypsin-A

-Ala. Met. Ile. Cys. Ala. Gly. Ala. Ser. Gly. Val. Ser.-

Ser. Cys. Met. Gly. Asp. SER. Gly. Gly. Pro. Leu. Val. Cys.-
 (192)　　　　 (195)

Trypsin

-Asn. Met. *Phe.* Cys. Ala. Gly. Tyr. Leu. Glu. Gly. Lys. Asn.-

Ser. Cyst. *Gln. Gly.* Gly. Asp. SER. Gly. Pro.—Val. Cys.-

HISTIDINE LOOP
Chymotrypsin-A

-Thr. Gly. Phe. HIS. Phe. Cys. Gly. Gly. Ser. Leu. Ile. Asn.-
　　　　　 40

Glu. Asn. Try. Val. Val. Thr. Ala. Ala. HIS. Cys. Gly. Val. Thr.-
　　　　　　　　　　　　　　　 57

Trypsin

-*Ser.* Gly. *Tyr.* HIS. Phe. Cys. Gly. Gly. Ser. Leu. Ile. Asn.

Ser. Gln. Try.—Val. *Ser.* Ala. Ala. HIS. Cys. Tyr. Lys. Ser.

Fig. 3–1. Comparison of active-center sequences of trypsin and chymotrypsin. The active serine and histidine residues are capitalized; similarities in sequence are underlined with changes to a related functional amino acid italicized. (From Reference 28.)

a priori reason to assume that the ρ_H area is similar is that attack by the enzymic nucleophilic group might proceed from the direction of ρ_H area and be subject to steric effects as noted with chymotrypsin.

ρ_3 Area

Removal of the carboxamide function of α-N-tolylsulfonyl-L-arginine methyl ester (XXXV) to give XXXVI (Table 3–5) results in a 16-fold loss in binding, which is equivalent to 1.6 kcal/mole. Also note that the carbomethoxy group of XXXII binds better than the carboxanilide group of XLII, which in turn binds better than the carboxamide group of XXXIII. It follows that the C=O function is involved in binding. Whether an electron pair on the oxygen is an electron donor to an acceptor group on the enzyme or the polarized electrophilic carbon is an electron acceptor cannot be stated with any certainty at this time; this problem could be answered by synthesis and inhibitor evaluation of derivatives of lysine and arginine—where R_3 of XXXI is an aryl group that is electron rich and another that is electron poor.[30] Because the nitrophenyl ester of α-N-carbobenzoxy-L-lysine complexes about 27 times tighter than the methyl ester,[31] it would appear that the positively polarized carbonyl binds as an electron acceptor, but evaluation of ketone derivatives of XXXI could give a more definite answer.

ρ_1 Area

The ρ_1 area of binding to trypsin has been studied little compared to that to chymotrypsin. The relative contribution to binding by an R_1 group could be determined by measuring XXXVII (R_1 is H) as an inhibitor rather than a substrate. For example, it is clear that the α-ammonium group of XLIII can allow XLIII and XL to bind to the enzyme, but acylation makes the lysine derivatives better substrates; however a direct comparison for any contribution of the α-ammonium group to binding is not available.

The α-N-(o-, m-, and p-nitrobenzoyl)-L-arginine methyl esters have been measured as substrates,[32] but because these authors obtained a K_m that was about 100-fold larger than that reported for XXXII by others, some confusion could arise in trying to interpret these data. There is a need to vary the α-acyl group on L-argininamide and then to determine K_i by inhibition of the hydrolysis of the methyl or ethyl ester (XXXII), for N-benzoyl-L-argininamide has been found to have the same K_m when it

---

[30] See Reference 9, p. 50.
[31] M. L. Bender and F. J. Kézky, *J. Am. Chem. Soc.*, **87**, 4954 (1965).
[32] C. E. McDonald and A. K. Balls, *J. Biol. Chem.*, **229**, 69 (1957).

Table 3–5. Substrates and Inhibitors of Trypsin

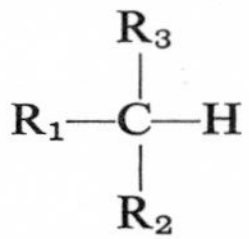

$$\begin{array}{c} R_3 \\ | \\ R_1\!-\!C\!-\!H \\ | \\ R_2 \end{array}$$

No.	R_1	R_2	R_3	$K_m \times 10^3$ or $K_i \times 10^3\ M$	$K_2(\text{sec}^{-1})$	Reference
XXXII	C_6H_5CONH-	$\overset{\oplus}{\underset{\|}{NH_2}}$ $NH_2CNH(CH_2)_3-$	$-CO_2alkyl$[a]	~0.08	27	d
XXXIII	C_6H_5CONH-	$\overset{\oplus}{\underset{\|}{NH_2}}$ $NH_2CNH(CH_2)_3-$	$-CONH_2$	2.1	0.36	d
XXXIV	C_6H_5CONH-	$\overset{\oplus}{\underset{\|}{NH_2}}$ $NH_2CNH(CH_2)_3-$	$-COO^{\ominus}$		inhibitor	e
XXXV	$p\text{-}CH_3C_6H_4SO_2NH-$	$\overset{\oplus}{\underset{\|}{NH_2}}$ $NH_2CNH(CH_2)_3-$	$-CO_2CH_3$	1.8	190	d,f
XXXVI	$p\text{-}CH_3C_6H_4SO_2NH-$	$\overset{\oplus}{\underset{\|}{NH_2}}$ $NH_2CNH(CH_2)_3-$	H	29	inhibitor	f
XXXVII	H	$\overset{\oplus}{\underset{\|}{NH_2}}$ $NH_2CNH(CH_2)_3-$	$-CO_2CH_3$	—	0	d

XXXVIII	HO	$\overset{\oplus NH_2}{NH_2CNH(CH_2)_3-}$	$-CO_2CH_3$	substrate	d
XXXIX	$C_6H_5CONHCH_2CONH-$	$\overset{\oplus NH_2}{NH_2CNH(CH_2)_3-}$	$-CONH_2$	substrate[b]	d
XL		$\overset{\oplus NH_3}{NH_3(CH_2)_4-}$	$CONH_2$	substrate[b]	d
XLI	$C_6H_5CONHCH_2CONH-$	$\overset{\oplus NH_2}{NH_3(CH_2)_4-}$	$CONH_2$	substrate[b]	d
XLII[c]	C_6H_5CONH-	$\overset{\oplus NH_2}{NH_2CNH(CH_2)_3-}$	$CONHC_6H_4NO_2-p$	0.94^c	0.61	g
XLIII		$\overset{\oplus NH_3}{NH_3(CH_2)_4-}$	$CONHC_6H_4NO_2-p$	0.36	0.003	g

[a] Methyl, ethyl, isopropyl, and cyclohexyl.
[b] Constants not determined.
[c] The D isomer was an inhibitor with $K_i = 0.8$ mM.
[d] H. Neurath and G. W. Schwert, *Chem. Revs*, **46**, 69 (1950).
[e] K. M. Harmon and C. Niemann, *J. Biol. Chem.*, **178**, 743 (1949).
[f] S. Benzer and B. Weisblum, *Nature*, **190**, 722 (1961).
[g] B. F. Erlanger, N. Kowkowsky, and W. Cohen, *Arch. Biochem., Biophys.*, **95**, 271 (1961).

acts as a substrate as it has K_i when it inhibits hydrolysis of the ester (XXXII).[33]

ρ_H Area

The D isomer of α-N-benzoylarginine p-nitroanilide binds to trypsin as an inhibitor as well as the L isomer (XLII) does as a substrate; because the carboxamide group of substrates is a complexing point to the enzyme, it follows that the carboxamide group of the D isomer of XLII is also complexed to the enzyme. It further follows, by the ρ formulation, that the L substrate has configuration XLIIA when complexed to the enzyme and

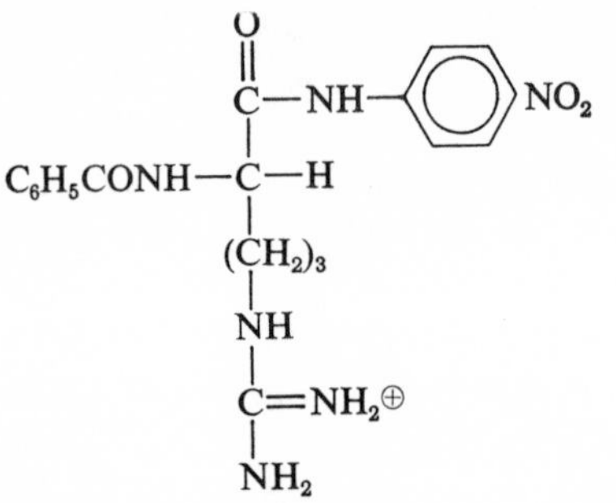

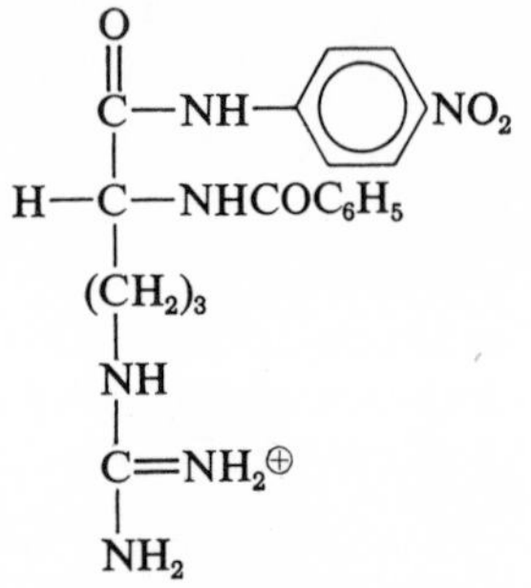

that the D inhibitor could have configuration XLIIIB; the large group in the ρ_H area could block the hydrolytic attack by the enzyme. The XLIIC conformation may be a possibility if the benzamido group contributes more to binding to the ρ_1 area than the carboxanilide group contributes in complexing to the ρ_3 area; a similar formulation was advanced for D inhibitors of chymotrypsin, but further studies are needed to determine if only the XLIIB conformation can bind, or if either conformation can bind depending upon the relative amounts of ρ_1 and ρ_3 binding.

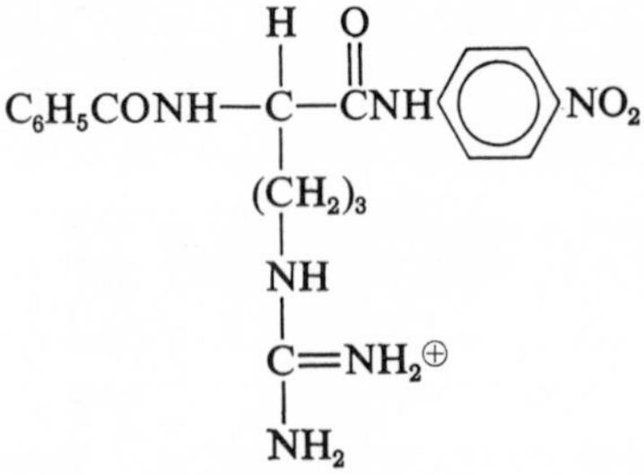

[33] S. A. Bernhard, *J. Am. Chem. Soc.*, 77, 1973 (1955).

ρ_2 **Area**

The ρ_2 binding area confirms specificity upon such proteolytic enzymes as trypsin and chymotrypsin; as noted earlier, only derivatives of lysine and arginine are hydrolyzed by trypsin. ω-Acylated lysine and arginine are not substrates, indicating the terminal cationic group is needed either for good substrate properties or binding or both; the lower homologs and histidine derivatives are inactive as substrates, thus showing a definite distance between the carbonyl and the cationic group is necessary for substrate properties.[34]

Excellent studies on inhibitors that bind in the ρ_2 area have been made by Shaw et al. and Inagami et al.; their results are summarized in Table 3–6. Inagami[35] noted that simple alkylammonium ions (XLIV–XLIX) were inhibitors with α-N-benzoyl-L-arginine ethyl ester as a substrate; maximum straight-chain binding was obtained at n-butylammonium, but n-hexylammonium was poorer than n-butyl and benzylammonium was better than n-butyl. A most interesting observation[36] was made that methyl-, ethyl-, and propylammonium ion failed to inhibit the trypsin-catalyzed hydrolysis of the relatively poor substrate, N-acetylglycine ethyl ester, but the latter was inhibited by n-butylammonium ion. Of even more pertinence the methyl-, ethyl-, and propylammonium ions accelerated the rate of hydrolysis of N-acetylglycine ethyl ester two to 10-fold but did not change K_m. They proposed that the alkylammonium binding caused a conformational change in the enzyme that brought the catalytic site closer to the carbonyl, thus accelerating the reaction. They also proposed that the arginine and lysine substrates had conformations LVIII and LIX, respectively when complexed to the enzyme; furthermore, there would be room for a propylammonium ion in the complex LX, but not a butylammonium ion, for the terminal methyl group of the latter would overlap the α-CH_2 group of N-acetylglycine ethyl ester. The rate of hydrolysis of N-acetylglycine ester could also be accelerated by methyl or ethyl guanidinium ion, but butyl guanidinium inhibited the reaction.[37] That an alkyl guanidinium ion can cause a conformational change in the enzyme was further verified by inactivation of the enzyme with iodoacetamide. The rate of inactivation by iodoacetamide was increased by a factor of 6 in the presence of methyl guanidinium ion, but inactivation was slowed in the presence of n-butyl guanidinium ion.[38]

These results give strong support to the concept that the alkylammonium

---

[34] See Reference 27, p. 59.

[35] T. Inagami, *J. Biol. Chem.*, **239**, 787 (1964).

[36] T. Inagami and T. Murachi, *J. Biol. Chem.*, **239**, 1388, 1395 (1964).

[37] T. Inagami, *J. Biol. Chem.*, **240**, PC3453 (1965).

[38] See Reference 37.

Table 3–6. ρ_2 Inhibitors of Trypsin

No.	Compound	K_i(mM)	$-\Delta F$ (kcal/mole)	$\Delta\Delta F/CH_2$ (kcal/mole)	Reference
XLIV	$CH_3\overset{\oplus}{N}H_3$	340^a	0.7		c
XLV	$C_2H_5\overset{\oplus}{N}H_3$	62	1.6	0.9	c
XLVI	$n\text{-}C_3H_7\overset{\oplus}{N}H_3$	8.7	2.8	1.2	c
XLVII	$n\text{-}C_4H_9\overset{\oplus}{N}H_3$	1.7	3.8	1.0	c
XLVIII	$n\text{-}C_6H_{13}\overset{\oplus}{N}H_3$	12	2.6		c
XLIX	$C_6H_5CH_2\overset{\oplus}{N}H_3$	0.6	4.4	3.7^b	c
L	$CH_3C(=NH_2)(\overset{\oplus}{N}H_2)$	36	1.9		c
LI	$C_6H_5C(=NH_2)(\overset{\oplus}{N}H_2)$	0.018	6.2		d
LII	$C_6H_5CH_2C(=NH_2)(\overset{\oplus}{N}H_2)$	15	2.4		d
LIII	$C_6H_{11}C(=\overset{\oplus}{N}H_2)-NH_2$	0.43	4.4		d
LIV	$p\text{-}NH_2C_6H_4C(=NH_2)(\overset{\oplus}{N}H_2)$	0.0083	6.7		d
LV	$p\text{-}EtOOCC_6H_4C(=NH_2)(\overset{\oplus}{N}H_2)$	Substrate			d
LVI	$C_6H_5NHC(=NH_2)(\overset{\oplus}{N}H_2)$	0.073	5.5		d
LVII	$C_6H_{11}NHC(=NH_2)(\overset{\oplus}{N}H_2)$	1.5			d

[a] Calculated from $-\Delta F = 0.7$ kcal.; the literature value of 34 is probably a typographical error.

[b] For the phenyl group.

[c] T. Inagami, *J. Biol. Chem.*, **239**, 787 (1964); α-N-benzoyl-L-arginine ethyl ester was used as substrate.

[d] M. Mares-Guia and E. Shaw, *J. Biol. Chem.*, **240**, 1579 (1965); α-N-benzoyl-DL-arginine-p-nitroanilide was used as substrate.

ions bind to the region on the enzyme where the alkylammonium tail of LVIII and LIX is bound; therefore the results in Table 3–6 can most probably be used to interpret the mode of binding of the alkylammonium tails of LVIII and LIX.

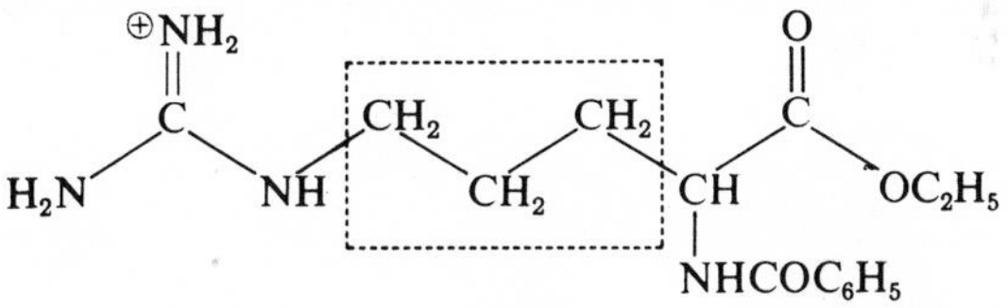

$$\overset{\oplus}{N}H_2$$

$$H_2N \overset{\|}{\underset{NH}{C}} \quad CH_2 \quad CH_2 \quad \overset{O}{\overset{\|}{C}}$$

$$CH_2 \quad CH \quad OC_2H_5$$

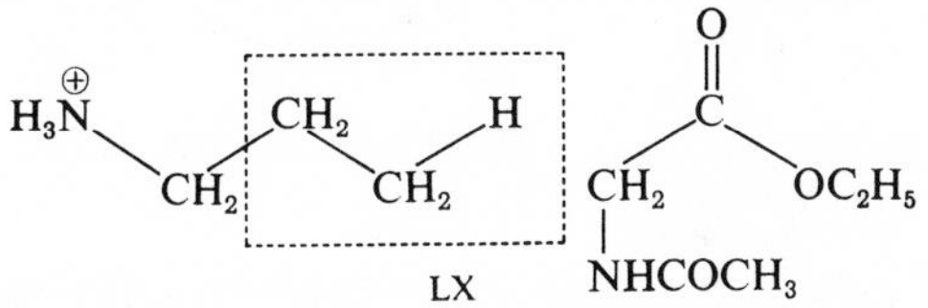

$$NHCOC_6H_5$$

LVIII

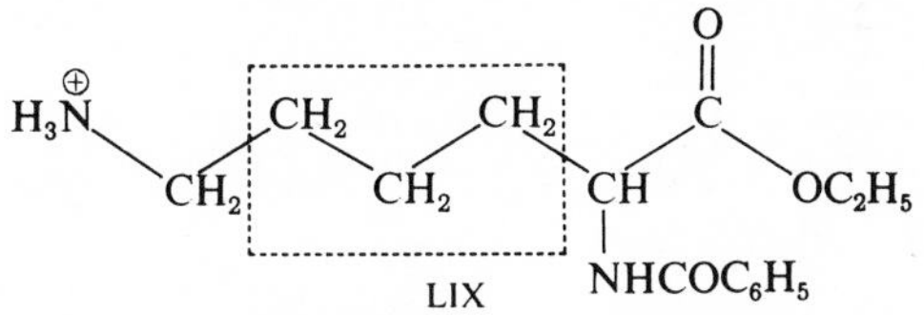

$$H_3\overset{\oplus}{N} \quad CH_2 \quad CH_2 \quad \overset{O}{\overset{\|}{C}}$$

$$CH_2 \quad CH_2 \quad CH \quad OC_2H_5$$

LIX $\quad NHCOC_6H_5$

$$H_3\overset{\oplus}{N} \quad CH_2 \quad H \quad \overset{O}{\overset{\|}{C}}$$

$$CH_2 \quad CH_2 \quad CH_2 \quad OC_2H_5$$

LX $\quad NHCOCH_3$

Note that in proceeding from methylammonium to butylammonium (Table 3–6) that each methylene group affords 0.9–1.2 kcal/mole of binding energy; because an alkyl group can only bind by a combination of hydrophobic bonding and van der Waals forces, such a binding is clearly opererative here and is within the 1.4 kcal/mole/CH_2 of maximum energy obtainable (See Chapter 2, pp. 39–40). It is unfortunate that ammonium ion was not measured as an inhibitor in order to determine the hydrophobic contribution of the methyl group of methylammonium; however, it is unlikely that the first methyl group would contribute to binding, for it would be positioned inside the NH region of the guanidino group of LVIII. The 0.7 kcal/mole of binding energy seen with the methylammonium group is well within the range of 1.5 kcal/mole previously seen with the $N^{\oplus}$ group.[39]

Since the phenyl group can have a hydrophobic bonding energy[40] of 4.3 kcal/mole and van der Waals forces could also contribute a nearly equal amount, this hydrophobic site also complexes benzylammonium ion

[39] D. Pressman, A. L. Grossberg, L. H. Pence, and L. Pauling, *J. Am. Chem. Soc.*, **68**, 250 (1946).

[40] G. Nemethy and H. A. Scheraga, *J. Chem. Phys.*, **36**, 3401 (1962).

with a 3.0 kcal/mole contribution by the phenyl ring; this is quite close to the increment of 3.1 kcal/mole in binding between methylammonium and *n*-butylammonium. Since the phenyl group is actually capable of giving twice the energy in hydrophobic bonding and van der Waals forces than a propyl group, it is clear that not all the benzene ring of benzylammonium is bonded in this way.

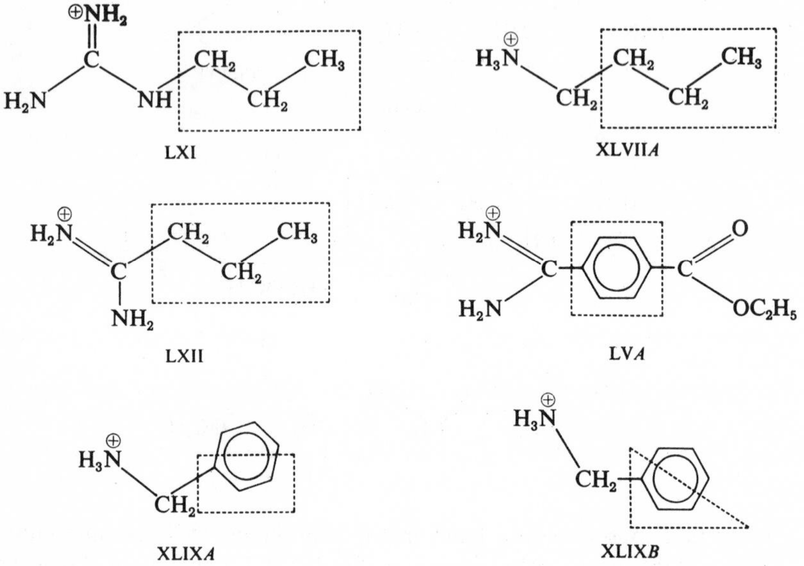

Fig. 3–2. Dotted lines indicate carbons that could be involved in hydrophobic bonding to trypsin.

Since the butylammonium ion, XLVII, (Fig. 3–2) should complex to trypsin in the same conformation as an *N*-benzoyl lysine ester (LIX), it is assigned configuration XLVII*A*; it follows that propylguanidine should have configuration LXI, for both propylguanidine and butylamine inhibit the hydrolysis of *N*-acetyl glycine ester, but ethylguanidine and propylamine accelerate the hydrolysis. Because acetamidine (L) binds slightly better than ethylammonium ion (XLV), it is clear that the terminal methyl group of each is involved in similar hydrophobic bonding; therefore acetamidine and its higher homolog, butryamidine are assigned configuration LXII. The carbon–carbon bond from the amidine to the benzene ring of benzamidine (LI) and *p*-carbethoxybenzamidine (LV) is shifted slightly to configuration LV*A* in order that the carbethoxy group can be properly positioned for substrate properties. Little can be said with any certainty about the stereochemistry of the enzyme with respect to the hydrophobic propyl group of LXI or XLVII*A*; from the energy involved in these complexes, the propyl group could well be surrounded on two sides by a crevice in the enzyme, as suggested by Shaw et al.,[41] but such an explanation is far from being unequivocal.

With the configuration assignments in Fig. 3–2 it is now possible to rationalize some of the data in Table 3–6 which at first glance seems inconsistent:

1. Benzylamine (XLIX) is a 25-fold better inhibitor than benzylcarboxamidine (LII). Note that if the configuration of the aminomethyl of benzylamine must be exactly the same as that of butylamine (LXI), it would position the benzyl group as in XLIX*A*; this configuration would require that the enzyme hydrophobic crevice approaches the bottom of structure XLIX*A*. If the crevice must approach from the top, then the benzylamine could be rotated to configuration XLIXb for good binding. In contrast, the benzylcarboxamidine (LII) must start with configuration LXII, and there is no way to place the benzene group to get appreciable hydrophobic contact with the enzyme; thus, LXII inhibits only slightly better than acetamidine.

2. Cyclohexylcarboxamidine (LIII) is an 84-fold better inhibitor of trypsin than acetamidine, but LIII is only one twenty-fourth effective as benzamidine. The cyclohexyl group contributes almost as much hydrophobic bonding as the terminal ethyl group of propylamine; these results indicate that the chair form of the cyclohexyl group cannot give as good binding as the flat phenyl group and that presumably only two carbons of the cyclohexyl are involved in hydrophobic bonding.

3. Cyclohexylcarboxamidine (LIII) is a 3.5-fold better inhibitor than cyclohexylguanidine (LVII); similarly; benzamidine (LI) is a four-fold better inhibitor than phenylguanidine (LVI). Apparently the guanidines cannot quite approach the maximum hydrophobic bonding that can be achieved by amidines in the LV*A* conformation.

4. The fact that *p*-carbethoxybenzamidine (LV) is a substrate further confirms that a hydrophobic bonding region is present between the binding point for the terminal cationic group and the catalytic site for the ester grouping of lysine or arginine derivatives.

The best inhibitor of trypsin known at the present time is *p*-aminobenzamidine (LIV), which is about twice as effective as benzamidine; it would be worthwhile investigating simple amide derivatives of LIV or *p*-acetobenzamidine to determine whether the C$=$O binding point of the substrate can be simulated to give even better inhibitors.

[41] M. Mares-Guia and E. Shaw, *J. Biol. Chem.*, **240**, 1579 (1965).

4 | Specific Mode of Binding to Enzymes: II. Pyrimidine Area

A myriad of enzymes utilize pyrimidines at the base, nucleoside, or nucleotide level, but few have been studied from the standpoint of the mode of binding. In addition to the two enzymes using thymidine, discussed in this chapter, the mode of binding to thymidylate synthetase can be found in Chapter 11.

THYMIDINE KINASE

Thymidylate (III) is the only precursor to thymidine triphosphate which, in turn, is one of the essential components for DNA synthesis. Thymidylate (III) can be synthesized intracellularly by two distinct metabolic routes, namely, thymidylate synthetase (I → III) and thymidine kinase (II → III). Some cell lines can use only one of the two routes to thymidylate and others can use both. Therefore, blockade of both thymidine kinase and thymidylate synthetase would be necessary to achieve "thymine-less death" of cells[1] in a host system if the target cell can utilize both enzymes. Thymidylate synthetase could be blocked either directly[1] or indirectly by blocking dihydrofolic reductase,[2] the enzyme regenerating tetrahydrofolate from dihydrofolate (Fig. 4–1); these two enzyme systems will be discussed in Chapters 10 and 11.

The presence of thymidine kinase in a variety of species and mammalian

[1] S. S. Cohen, J. G. Flaks, H. D. Barner, M. R. Loeb, and J. Lichtenstein, *Proc. Natl. Acad. Sci. (U.S.)*, **44**, 1004 (1958).
[2] T. H. Jukes and H. P. Broquist in *Metabolic Inhibitors*, R. M. Hochster and J. H. Quastel, eds., Academic Press, New York, 1963, pp. 481–534.

tissues has been demonstrated (*E. coli* B is a particularly good source for this kinase). Its isolation and assay with radioactive substrates has been described[3]; also, 2'-deoxyuridine and its 5-halogen derivatives have been used as effective substrates to detect thymidine kinase. An indirect spectrophotometric assay with high sensitivity has also been developed[4]; the

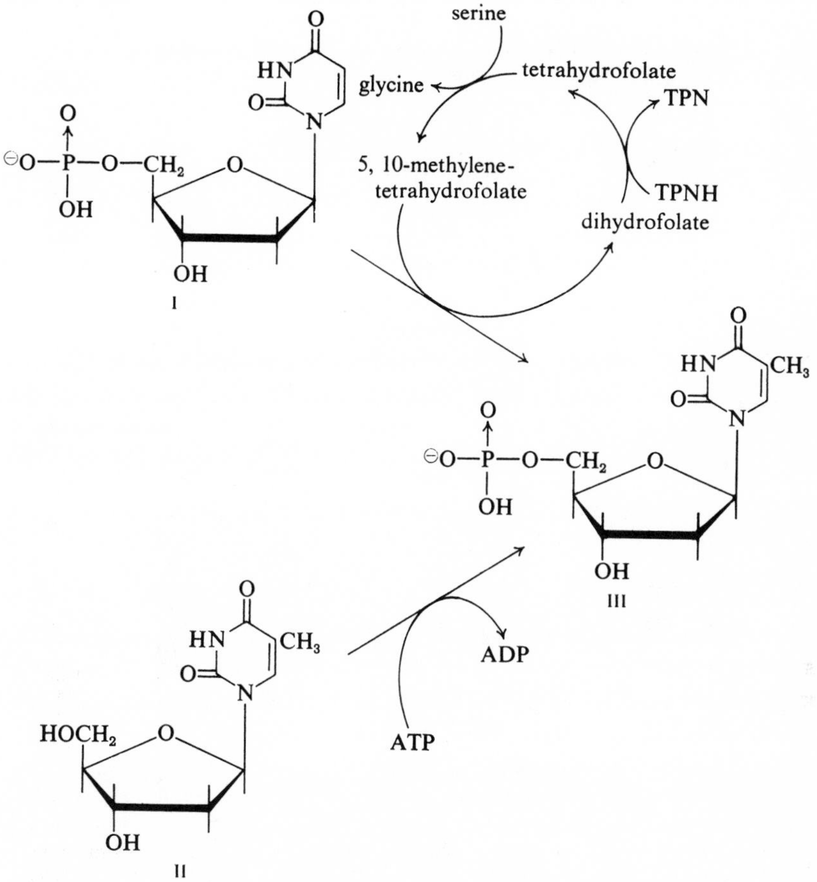

Fig. 4–1. Metabolic routes to thymidylate (III).

conversion of 5-fluoro-2'-deoxyuridine (FUDR) to its 5'-phosphate (FUDRP), was measured by relying on the ability of the generated FUDRP to inhibit thymidylate synthetase (I → III). FUDRP has been observed to bind to thymidylate synthetase 1000 times stronger than the

[3] R. Okazaki and A. Kornberg, *J. Biol. Chem.*, **239**, 269, 275 (1964).
[4] B. R. Baker, T. J. Schwan, and D. V. Santi, *J. Med. Chem.*, **9**, 66 (1966).

substrate, 2'-deoxyuridylate (I)[5]; therefore, the assay has a built-in magnification of 1000-fold, giving a sensitivity approaching that of the radioactive assay; it has the further advantage in that it is not necessary to separate the product from the radioactive substrate before assay.

Because both thymidine and FUDR are substrates for the thymidine kinase, thymidine should act as a competitive substrate of FUDR. When

Table 4–1. FUDR Conversion to FUDRP by Thymidine Kinase

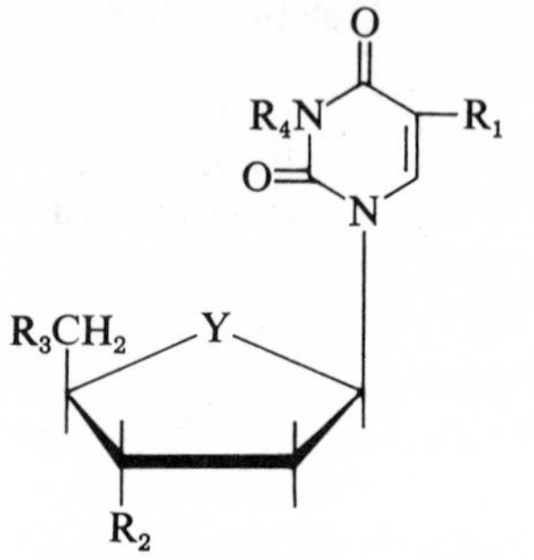

No.	R₁	R₂	R₃	R₄	Y	mM concentration	Per cent inhibition[a]	Relative inhibition concentration[b]
II	CH₃	OH	OH	H	O	0.1 / 0.04	85 / 68	1
IV	H	OH	OH	H	O	0.2	53	9
V	CH₃	H	OH	H	O	3	64	80
VI	CH₃	OH	H	H	O	3 / 1	84 / 16	30
VII	CH₃	OH	OH	H	CH₂	2	44	120
VIII	CH₃	OH	C₂H₅OOCO—	H	O	3	0	> 500
IX	CH₃	OH	CH₃NHCO—	H	O	3	0	> 500
X	CH₃	OH	OH	n-C₅H₁₁	O	3	70	50
XI	4-Thiothymidine					3	74	70
XII	5,6-Dihydrothymidine					1	0	180

[a] The thymidine kinase assay was performed with 0.1 mM 5-fluoro-2'-deoxyuridine; data from B. R. Baker, T. J. Schwan, and D. V. Santi, *J. Med. Chem.*, **9**, 66 (1966).
[b] Estimated ratio of concentrations of compound to thymidine giving 50 per cent inhibition.

equal concentrations of thymidine and FUDR were incubated with thymidine kinase, only about one fifth as much FUDRP was formed (Table 4–1). Because thymidylate (III) is bound to the thymidylate synthetase about as effectively as I[2] and because FUDRP binds 1000-fold better than I, the III generated by the thymidine kinase does not interfere

[5] See Reference 1, p. 70.

with the determination of the FUDRP concentration; therefore thymidine has the overall effect in the assay of inhibiting the formation of FUDRP from FUDR catalyzed by thymidine kinase.

2'-Deoxyuridine (IV), a known substrate for thymidine kinase,[6] also was a competitive substrate, showing a 53 per cent inhibition of FUDRP formation at a concentration of 0.2 mM; in contrast, thymidine (II) showed a 68 per cent inhibition at 0.04 mM. Thus, the order of binding to thymidine kinase is thymidine > FUDR > 2'-deoxyuridine, for FUDR is used at a concentration of 0.1 mM in the assay system.

Ribofuranose Binding

Several studies have been performed on the mode of binding thymidine and related nucleosides to thymidine kinase. The first study was on the relative contribution of the three oxygen functions of the 2'-deoxyribosyl moiety. 3'-Deoxythymidine (V) at 3 mM showed a 64 per cent inhibition of FUDRP formation (Table 4–1); thus about an 80-fold loss in binding occurred when the 3'-hydroxyl of thymidine (II) was replaced by hydrogen (V). 5'-Deoxythymidine (VI) at 3 mM showed an 84 per cent inhibition of FUDRP formation; the loss in binding when the 5'-hydroxyl of thymidine (II) was replaced by hydrogen was thus about 30-fold. The cyclopentane analog (VII) of thymidine (II) at 2 mM showed a 44 per cent inhibition of FUDRP formation; thus replacing the furanose oxygen of thymidine (II) by a methylene group (VII) led to an estimated 120-fold loss in binding.

It is clear that both the 3'- and 5'-hydroxyls of thymidine contribute to binding the thymidine kinase; because a hydrogen atom is smaller than a hydroxyl group, there could not have been any steric effects on binding. The situation with the cyclopentane analog (VII) is less clear, for the methylene group is larger than the furanose oxygen; therefore such a structural change leading to a 120-fold decrease in binding could be due either (a) to steric interaction of the methylene group with the enzyme that decreases binding, (b) the furanose oxygen might be serving as one of the binding points of thymidine to the enzyme, or (c), to different ground-state conformations between cyclopentane and furanose.

The fact that the 5'-hydroxyl of thymidine (II) contributes to binding to thymidine kinase is somewhat surprising. The 5'-hydroxyl is the position on the substrate where transfer of phosphate from ATP occurs. Usually a transfer point is not involved in binding to an enzyme using a cofactor,[7-9]

[6] R. L. Blakely, *J. Biol. Chem.*, **238**, 2113 (1963).

[7] B. R. Baker, *Cancer Chemotherapy Reports*, **4**, 1 (1959).

[8] B. R. Baker and H. S. Shapiro, *J. Med. Chem.*, **6**, 664 (1963).

[9] B. R. Baker, D. V. Santi, P. I. Alamaula, and W. C. Werkheiser, *J. Med. Chem.*, **7**, 24 (1964).

but an exception can occur when the enzyme aids in breaking an O—H bond. For example, the H of the O—H in lactate presumably complexes with an imidazole of lactic dehydrogenase, thus aiding in the breaking of the O—H bond.[10–12] It could therefore be considered a possibility that the 5'-hydroxyl of thymidine (II) is complexed with thymidine kinase in order to aid bond breaking of the O—H group as phosphorylation by ATP takes place. Such a suggestion would call for the hydrogen of the 5'-hydroxyl to complex with the enzyme rather than the oxygen atom.

It is difficult to devise an unequivocal experiment that can distinguish between H or O binding of the 5'-hydroxyl to thymidine; replacing the hydroxyl hydrogen with a carbon might lead to a bulk intolerance to complexing with the enzyme, which could also be mistakenly interpreted to mean that a binding point (the hydroxyl hydrogen) had been lost. For example, two compounds (VIII–IX), with a group in place of the 5'-hydrogen, failed to inhibit thymidine kinase at a concentration of 3mM. In contrast, 5'-deoxythymidine (VI) gives an 84 per cent inhibition at 3 mM, thus showing that the enzyme does not have a bulk tolerance for the relatively large carbamate and carbonate groups of VIII and IX. Otherwise these compounds should have been at least as effective as 5'-deoxythymidine (VI). Therefore, these experiments cannot be used as evidence either to support or to refute the concept that the hydrogen of the 5'-hydroxyl of thymidine is a binding point to the enzyme.

Pyrimidine Binding

Not much information is available on the mode of pyrimidine binding of thymidine to the enzyme. It is not too essential that the pyrimidine moiety be modified in order to construct an active-site-directed irreversible inhibitor, other than answering the question of bulk tolerance that is discussed in Chapter 7. 5,6-Dihydrothymidine failed to show any inhibition at 1 mM. In 5,6-dihydrothymidine, not only has the 5,6- double bond been reduced, but the resultant 5-methyl group is out of plane with the pyrimidine, which might be little tolerated sterically by the enzyme; of course, it is also possible that the pseudoaromatic pyrimidine system of thymidine is necessary for good binding. If the pseudoaromatic system with a 5,6-double bond were the main mode of binding of the pyrimidine ring system, such as in a charge-transfer complex, then "4-thiothymidine" (XI) should inhibit thymidine kinase conversion of FUDR to FUDRP to the same order as thymidine does; XI at a concentration of 3 mM showed

[10] B. R. Baker, W. W. Lee, W. A. Skinner, A. P. Martinez, and E. Tong, *J. Med. Pharm. Chem.*, **2**, 633 (1960).

[11] D. Dennis and N. O. Kaplan, *J. Biol. Chem.*, **235**, 810 (1960).

[12] A. D. Winer and G. W. Schwert, *J. Biol. Chem.*, **234**, 1155 (1959).

74 per cent inhibition of the enzyme, thus being complexed to the enzyme about one seventieth as well as thymidine. This result would indicate that the 4-oxo group of thymidine is bonded to the enzyme as an electron donor, for the thione group donates less effectively. Furthermore, this result with XI could also indicate that the 3-hydrogen contributes weakly— if at all—to binding to the enzyme because the thione at the 4 position makes the 3-hydrogen more acidic and therefore more capable of bonding as an acceptor to some donor site on the enzyme; however, it is also possible that the 3-NH does contribute to binding but that the loss of 4-oxo binding is more deleterious than the increased 3-NH binding.

Further evidence that the 3-NH most probably does not complex with a cationic site on the enzyme can be gleaned by comparing the binding of FUDR and 2′-deoxyuridine again, but considering the relative pK_a's of the 3-NH group. The 3-NH for FUDR has pK_a 7.66 and 2′-deoxyuridine has pK_a 9.31[13]; thus FUDR is 35 per cent ionized at the pH 7.4 used in the assays, whereas 2′-deoxyuridine is only 1.2 per cent ionized. Therefore, the 3-NH group does not appear to bond with a donor site on the enzyme, otherwise FUDR should have been complexed far more strongly than the twofold observed over 2′-deoxyuridine—similar to the previously observed 1000-fold greater binding of FUDRP over dUMP to thymidylate synthetase.[14,15] That either the 3-NH or the 4-oxo group is necessary for substrate properties is indicated by the fact that cytidine is not a substrate.[16]

Because it appeared possible that the 3-hydrogen may not have been binding to the enzyme, thymidine was converted to its 3-*n*-amyl derivative, X. At a concentration of 3 mM, X showed a 74 per cent inhibition of thymidine kinase (Table 4–1), about a 50-fold loss in binding compared to thymidine. Whether this loss in binding is due to steric interaction of the *n*-amyl group with the enzyme in the enzyme-inhibitor complex (low bulk tolerance) or is due to the loss of the possible 3-NH binding point or both will require further study.

Hydrophobic Bonding

No hydrophobic bonding with 1-substituted uracils has been detected.[17] 1-*n*-Butyluracil (XIII) showed no inhibition at 5 mM, which is 25 times stronger a concentration than that used when 2′-deoxyuridine (IV) (Table 4–1) showed a 50 per cent inhibition. At their maximum solubility,

[13] I. Wempen, R. Duschinsky, L. Kaplan, and J. J. Fox, *J. Am. Chem. Soc.*, **83**, 4755 (1961).
[14] See Reference 1, p. 70.
[15] See Reference 7, p. 73.
[16] See Reference 3, p. 71.
[17] B. R. Baker and T. J. Schwan, *J. Med. Chem.*, **9**, 73 (1966).

XVII (1.5 mM), XIV (1.5 mM) and XV (0.75 mM) showed no inhibition; similarly, XVI was ineffective at 3 mM.

No hydrophobic bonding could be detected at the 5- position with 5-ethoxymethyl-2'-deoxyuridine (XVIII), for XVIII showed 21 per cent

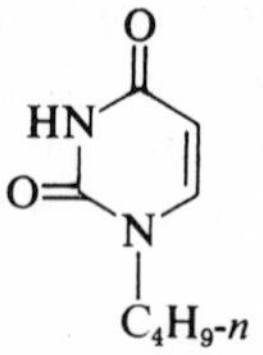

XIII	XIV, R = H XV, R = —COOC$_2$H$_5$ XVI, R = —COOH

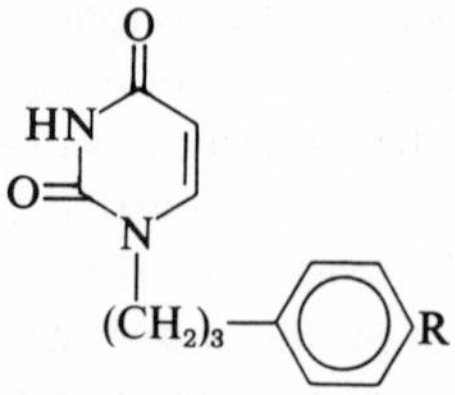

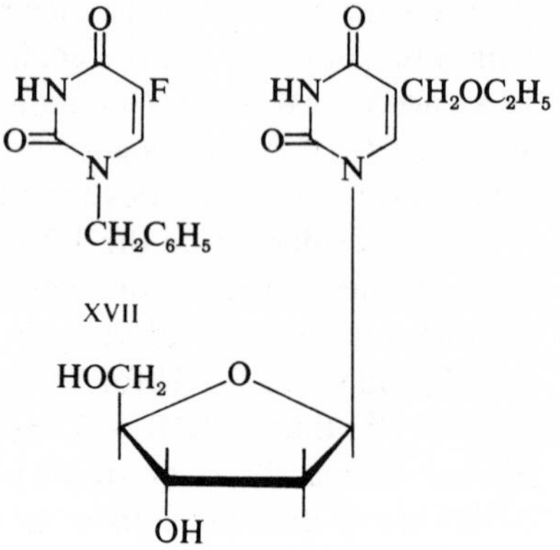

XVII

XVIII

inhibition at 3 mM, an estimated 600-fold loss in binding compared to thymidine (II).[18]

Ribofuranose Simulation

A series of ω-hydroxyalkyl uracils (XIX) were investigated to see if one hydroxyl group would impart sufficient binding to the 1-alkyuracils to be useful[19]; only one of these compounds showed measurable inhibition at 5 mM, which is 25 times the concentration necessary for 2'-deoxyuridine to show a 50 per cent inhibition, namely the 1-(4'-hydroxybutyl)-uracil (XIX, $n = 4$); the possible mode of binding of this compoond will be discussed later. Similarly, 1-(4'-methoxybutyl)-uracil (XX) showed no inhibition at 5 mM.

In order to determine whether two hydroxyl groups would give better binding, XXI was investigated, which has hydroxyl groups positioned corresponding to the 3'- and 5'-hydroxyl groups of 2'-deoxyuridine (IV). Unfortunately, XXI also showed no inhibition at 5 mM, even though the cyclopentane analog (VII) of thymidine at 2 mM showed a 44 per cent inhibition of thymidine kinase (Table 4–1).

The pyrimidine ring of thymidine and VII must have some given conformation when complexed to the enzyme (arbitrarily depicted in VII). The semienvelope of the cyclopentane can place either the hydroxymethyl

[18] See Reference 4, p. 71.
[19] Reference 17, p. 75.

or the pyrimidine ring in an equatorial conformation; the second of the two groups will change little in proton interaction at the base of the envelope when the conformation of the first group is shifted from equatorial (VII*A*) to axial (VII*B*). Because the uracil ring is planar, there is little difference in proton interaction between the 6-hydrogen of the uracil

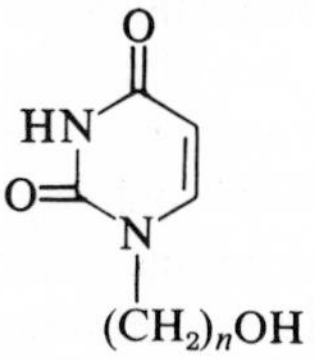

| XIX | XX | XXI |

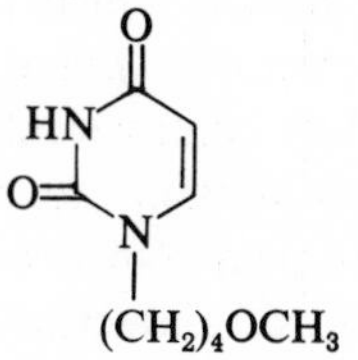

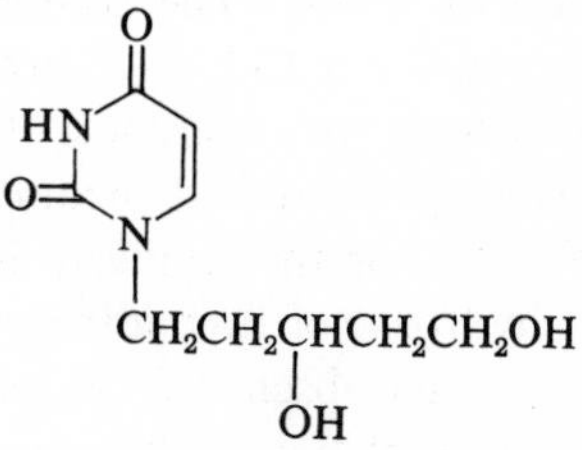

and the cyclopentane protons between the two conformations, VII*A* and VII*B*. However, there is slightly less proton interaction of the hydroxymethyl group of VII*C* compared to VII*A* or VII*B*; therefore conformation VII*C* would appear to be the most stable one. The cyclopentane ring of VII*C* still has considerable interaction between the ring protons that is less

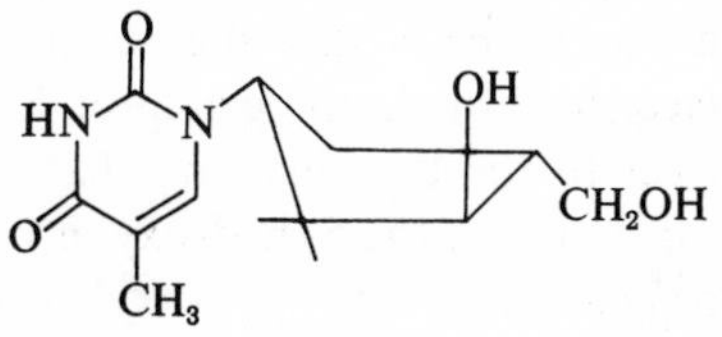

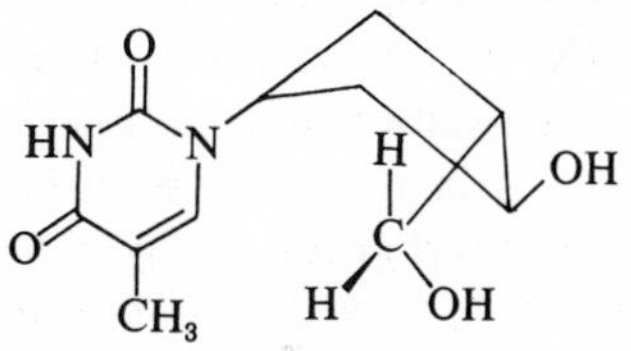

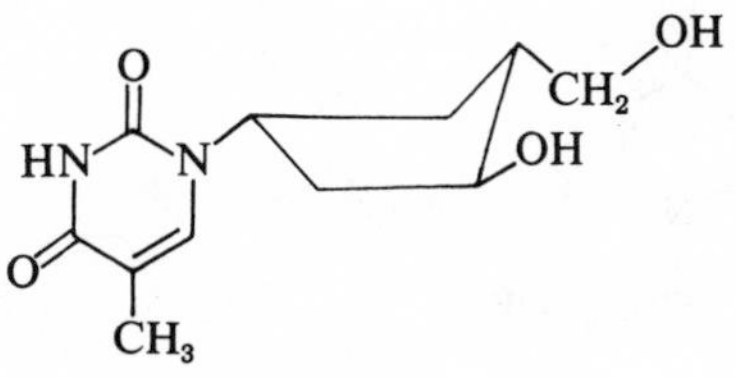

than an eclipsed butyl group but more than a skewed butyl group; thus, for XXI to assume the conformation of VII*A*–VII*C*, 2–4 kcal/mole of energy would probably be required that must be obtained from the energy released as the inhibitor complexes to the enzyme,[20] for about 0.8 kcal is needed for a skewed, and 5.3 kcal for an eclipsed, conformation. A 50–1000-fold loss in binding will occur, unless the enzyme can change in

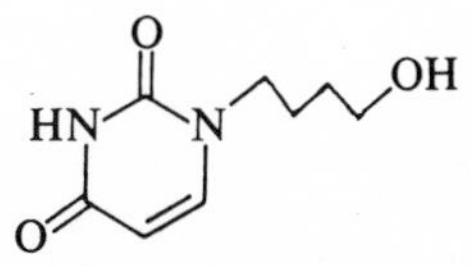

[20] B. R. Baker, B.-T. Ho, and D. V. Santi, *J. Pharm. Sci.*, **54**, 1415 (1965).

conformation, so that less energy is required. Thus, the inability of XXI to bind as well as VII*C* is most probably due to the energetically unfavorable conformation that XXI must assume for enzyme binding.

It is now possible to try to rationalize the binding of 1-(4'-hydroxybutyl)-uracil (XIX, $n = 4$) which showed a 38 per cent inhibition at a concentration of 5 mM. The conformation XIX*A*, which is essentially staggered except for a C-1'-C-2' proton interaction, should require less than 0.5 kcal/mole to overcome this slightly unfavorable conformation. The hydroxyl group is then almost exactly juxtapositioned with the 5'-hydroxyl of VII*C* or the similarly juxtapositioned 5'-hydroxyl of thymidine. The 5'-hydroxyl of thymidine was previously shown to contribute to binding, for in its absence a 30-fold loss in binding occurred (Table 4–1). The absence of the 3'-hydroxyl on thymidine caused an 80-fold reduction in binding; in contrast, the cyclopentane analog (VII) of thymidine was 120-fold less effective than thymidine. It can be estimated that the 1-(4'-hydroxybutyl)-uracil (XIX, $n = 4$) was complexed one fiftieth as well as 2'-deoxyuridine, which showed a 50 per cent inhibition at 0.18 mM. Thus the 4-hydroxybutyl group on uracil would appear to bind equally to what could be expected for 2',3'-dideoxyuridine.

Conversely, the lack of inhibition by 1-(3'-hydroxypropyl)-uracil (XIX, $n = 3$) can also be rationalized on the basis that the staggered ground-state conformation does not place the 3'-hydroxyl group of XIX ($n = 3$) in the same position with respect to the thymine ring that the 3'-hydroxyl group of thymidine occupies; similarly, the 5'-hydroxyl group of XIX ($n = 5$) does not occupy the same position as the 5'-hydroxyl group of thymidine when both are in their ground state.

XXII, R = H
XXIII, R = OH

XXIV, R = OH
XXV, R = NH$_2$

XXVI, R = COOH
XXVII, R = CONH$_2$
XXVIII, R = NO$_2$
XXIX, R = NHCOCH$_3$

A number of 1-alkyluracils bearing functional groups on the alkyl group were available from a previous study on the inhibition of thymidylate synthetase.[21] Of these compounds (XXII–XXVII) only XXVII showed inhibition of thymidine kinase at a concentration of 3 mM; XXVII showed

[21] B. R. Baker and G. B. Chheda, *J. Pharm. Sci.*, **54**, 25 (1965).

39 per cent inhibition, thus estimated to be about 24-fold less effective than 2'-deoxyuridine (IV) or about equivalent to what might be expected for 2',3'-dideoxyuridine.[22] The related amide, XXIX, which would be more suitable for construction of active-site-directed irreversible inhibitors, was then investigated[22]; neither XXIX nor its precursor XXVIII at their maximum solubility of 0.75 mM, showed any inhibition of thymidine kinase.

Molecular models show that the NH group of both XXVII and XXIX approach closely the position of the 5'-hydroxyl of 2'-deoxyuridine; if the binding of XXVII is due to the amide NH simulating the 5'-hydroxyl of 2'-deoxyuridine, then it is possible that there is no bulk tolerance for the methyl group of the acetamido moiety of XXIX.

Further studies on the mode of binding of compounds related to XXVII would be of interest. Also of interest would be further studies on the mode of binding of 1-(4'-hydroxybutyl)-uracil (XIX, $n = 4$), particularly its 2'-hydroxymethyl derivative (XXX), which in the ground state conformation has its two hydroxyl groups in the same position as the 3'- and 5'-hydroxyl groups of thymidine (II) (see structure VIIC).

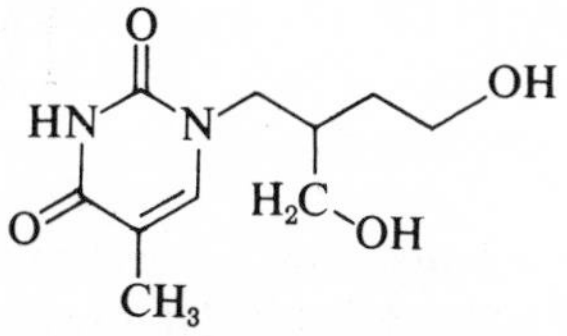

XXX

THYMIDINE PHOSPHORYLASE

Thymidine phosphorylase is an enzyme that catalyzes phosphorolysis of the nucleosidic linkage of pyrimidine 2'-deoxynucleosides with the formation of the pyrimidine and 2-deoxy-α,D-ribofuranose-1-phosphate (XXXII); the enzyme has been isolated from a variety of plant, animal, and bacterial sources. Its main metabolic function appears to be catabolic, although some bacteria and tumors utilize the reverse reaction anabolically under stress of certain genetic or dietary deficiencies. *E. coli* B is a particularly good source for the enzyme because its 2'deoxynucleoside phosphorylase is readily separable from pyrimidine ribonucleoside phosphorylase.[23] In contrast, these two enzymes from some mammalian source are not

[22] See Reference 17, p. 75.
[23] W. E. Razzell and H. G. Khorana, *Biochim. Biophys. Acta*, **28**, 562 (1958).

separable and may be one and the same enzyme[24,25]; however, separation of the two enzymes from other mammalian sources has been achieved.[26]

The main chemotherapeutic interests in thymidine phosphorylase reside in (a) its ability to convert 5-fluorouracil (FU) to its 2′-deoxynucleoside (FUDR), the first step in the intracellular activation of FU to FUDRP via thymidine phosphorylase and thymidine kinase,[27] and (b) the detoxification of preformed FUDR by cleavage to FU,[28] then further catabolism by other enzymes to α-fluoro-β-alanine.[29] Some tumors fail to detoxify FU or FUDR due to the genetic deletion[30] of these catabolic enzymes[28,29];

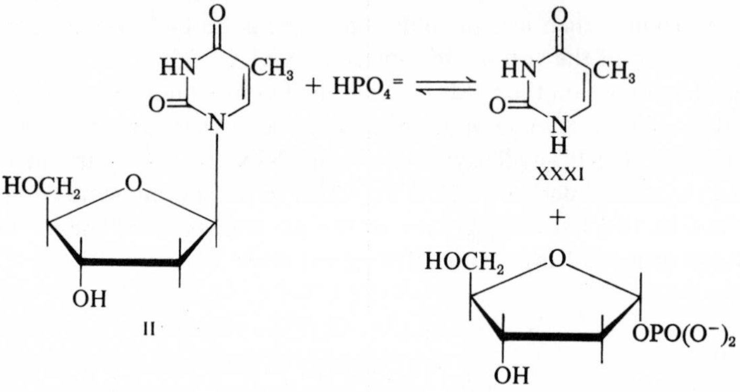

failure to detoxify the agents could serve as the basis for specificity against certain tumors, leaving tissues that do detoxify the agents relatively unharmed.[31]

Because the enzyme reaction is reversible, it can be assayed in either direction. For the anabolic direction either the rate of liberation of inorganic phosphate[32] or the rate of disappearance[33] of the pyrimidine base —as measured spectrophotometrically at pH 13 at 290–300 mμ—can be utilized. For the catabolic direction, the rate of formation of pyrimidine base,[34] as measured spectrophotometrically at 290–300 mμ, or the rate of

[24] T. A. Krenitsky, J. W. Mellors, and R. K. Barclay, *J. Biol. Chem.*, **240**, 1281 (1965).

[25] H. Pontis, G. Degerstedt, and P. Reichard, *Biochim. Biophys. Acta*, **51**, 138 (1961).

[26] M. Friedkin and D. Roberts, *J. Biol. Chem.*, **207**, 245 (1954).

[27] See Reference 1, p. 70.

[28] G. D. Birnie, H. Kroeger, and C. Heidelberger, *Biochemistry*, **2**, 566 (1963).

[29] E. Harbers, N. K. Chaudhuri, and C. Heidelberger, *J. Biol. Chem.*, **234**, 1255 (1959).

[30] V. P. Potter, *Univ. Michigan M. Bull.*, **23**, 401 (1957).

[31] See Reference 7, p. 73.

[32] See Reference 23, p. 79.

[33] M. Friedkin and D. Roberts, *J. Biol. Chem.*, **207**, 257 (1954).

[34] See Reference 26.

liberation of the sugar with thiobarbituric acid[35] can be determined. Since the reaction is reversible, an equilibrium is reached that decreases the per cent reaction linear with time. This difficulty has been neatly evaded by using arsenolysis of thymidine rather than phosphorolysis[36] since the resultant 2-deoxy-D-ribose-1-arsenate hydrolyzes rapidly in water—far more rapidly than it is condensed with the released thymine to re-form thymidine; the reaction can therefore go to completion, but thymine does show product inhibition.

The effect of inhibitors on this enzyme varies much more with the source of the enzyme than is normally observed[37]; therefore, the bulk of the data to be presented, which is with *E. coli* B enzyme, probably would not carry over completely to inhibition of this same enzyme from other sources. For example, 1-(2'-deoxy-β,D-glucopyranosyl)-thymine inhibits the phosphorylase from mouse tissue, whereas the horse liver enzyme is not inhibited.[38]

Ribofuranose Binding

With the *E. coli* B. enzyme 2-deoxy-α,D-ribofuranose-1-phosphate could act as a substrate,[39,40] but α,D-arabinofuranose-1-phosphate,[40] 1-(β,D-xylofuranosyl)-thymine,[40] uridine,[39] 1-(β-D-arabinofuranosyl)-uracil,[41] and 3'-deoxythymidine did not; thus the enzyme will not tolerate a 2'-hydroxyl group of either configuration and still allow substrate properties. Furthermore, the β- configuration is necessary for binding because the α anomer of thymidine was neither a substrate nor an inhibitor at a concentration equal to that of thymidine.[40]

In Table 4–2 a group of compounds is listed that give an estimate of the relative contribution of the oxygen functions of the 2-deoxy-D-ribofuranose moiety to binding. Note first that FUDR and thymidine bind about equally differing by a factor of only about 1.5 in their apparent K_m's.

5'-Deoxythymidine (VI) (Table 4–2) is as good a substrate as thymidine (II); furthermore, the apparent K_m's of II and VI are about equal. These results indicate that the 5'-hydroxyl is needed neither for binding to the enzyme nor for substrate properties.

The 3'-hydroxyl group is definitely needed for binding and for substrate properties, for 3'-deoxythymidine (V) is not a substrate and requires about a 30-fold greater concentration than the substrate, FUDR, for 50 per cent inhibition. Replacing the furanose oxygen of thymidine with methylene

[35] See Reference 25, p. 80.

[36] See Reference 26, p. 80.

[37] For a summary see Reference 24, p. 80.

[38] See Reference 24, p. 80.

[39] See Reference 23, p. 79.

[40] W. E. Razzell and P. Casshyap, *J. Biol. Chem.*, **239**, 1789 (1964).

[41] H. Tono and S. S. Cohen, *J. Biol. Chem.*, **237**, 1271 (1962).

results in a compound (VII) that shows no inhibition at relatively high concentration; that is, a greater than 15-fold loss in binding has occurred. This result is similar to that observed with VII during the inhibition of thymidine kinase, and it can be interpreted as either (a) the furanose oxygen is necessary for binding (b) that the enzyme cannot tolerate the larger —CH_2— group in place of —O— because it is so close to the

**Table 4–2. Mode of Ribofuranose Binding to Thymidine
Phosphorylase by**

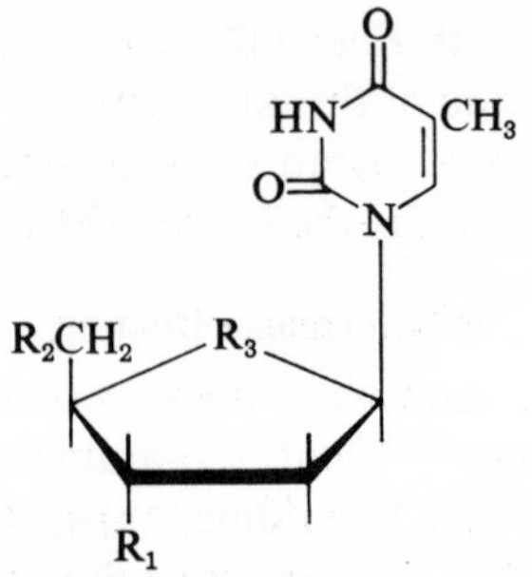

No.	R_1	R_2	R_3	mM concentration	Per cent inhibition	Estimated $[I/S]_{0.5}$[a]	Substrate velocity[b]	$K_m \times 10^4 M$[c]
II	OH	OH	O	0.4		1.5[d]	0.6	13
V	H	OH	O	6	33	30	0	
VI	OH	H	O	0.4		2.0[d]	0.4	17
VII	OH	OH	CH_2	1.5	0	>15	0	

The enzyme preparation was a 45–90 per cent saturated ammonium sulfate fraction from *E. coli* B; it was assayed with 0.4 mM FUDR in 0.1 *M* arsenate-succinate buffer (pH 5.9) in the presence of 10 per cent dimethylsulfoxide, essentially according to M. Friedkin and D. Roberts, *J. Biol. Chem.*, **207**, 257 (1954). FUDR[c] had $K_m = 8 \times 10^{-4}$ *M*. Unpublished data by B. R. Baker.

[a] Ratio of concentration of inhibitor to 0.4 mM FUDR giving 50 per cent inhibition.
[b] Relative to FUDR.
[c] Determined by the reciprocal plot method.
[d] Ratio of K_m to K_m of FUDR.

reaction site on the substrate, or (c) that the ground-state conformations of the five-membered rings of II and VII are not the same.

A series of 1-(ω-hydroxyalkyl)-uracils (XIX) were investigated as inhibitors to the phosphorylase in order to determine possible simulation of the ribofuranose group (Table 4–3). All four ω-hydroxyalkyl uracils showed about the same amount of poor inhibition; a loss in binding of

60–80-fold occurred, compared to FUDR. These compounds should be compared to 1-methyluracil (XXXIII) as a base line, the latter binding 200-fold more poorly than FUDR; thus, the hydroxyalkyl derivatives (XIX) were about two- to three-fold better than 1-methyluracil (XXXIII). Because it is unlikely that all four hydroxyalkyl derivatives could complex through their ω-hydroxyl group to the same point on the enzyme—due to

Table 4–3. Inhibition of Thymidine Phosphorylase by

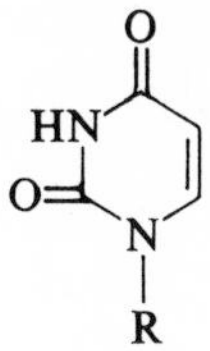

No.	R	mM concentration	Per cent inhibition	Estimated $[I/S]_{0.5}{}^{a}$
XIXa	—(CH$_2$)$_2$OH	12	30	70
XIXb	—(CH$_2$)$_3$OH	12	24	80
XIXc	—(CH$_2$)$_4$OH	12	33	60
XIXd	—(CH$_2$)$_5$OH	12	30	70
XX	—(CH$_2$)$_4$OCH$_3$	6	0	> 60
XXI	—(CH$_2$)$_2$CHOHCH$_2$CH$_2$OH	5.4	0	> 54
XXXIII	CH$_3$	50	50	200
XIII	—C$_4$H$_9$-n	7.5	50	22
XXXIV	—C$_6$H$_{13}$-i	6.0	50	15
XXXV	—C$_5$H$_{11}$-n	6.2	50	14

The enzyme from *E. coli* was assayed with 0.4 mM FUDR as described in Table 4–2. Unpublished data by B. R. Baker, and M. Kawazu.
[a] The ratio of concentration of the inhibitor to 0.4 mM FUDR, giving 50 per cent inhibition.

conformational restrictions from the ground state—another explanation is necessary. As will be discussed later, hydrophobic bonding with this enzyme was encountered; note that 1-*n*-butyluracil (XIII) is a nine-fold better inhibitor than 1-methyluracil (XXIII) and that hydrophobic bonding is not appreciably increased in the *n*-amyl- (XXXV) or *i*-hexyluracils (XXXIV). It is therefore plausible that the binding of the 1- substituent in the hydroxyalkyluracils (XIX) may be due to hydrophobic bonding by just the first two carbons of the 1- chain.[42]

[42] For a more detailed discussion of hydrophobic bonding to this enzyme see p. 85.

No pronounced inhibition was observed with the methoxybutyl (XX) or 3,5-dihydroxypentyl (XXI) side chains; apparently neither compound can shift its conformation sufficiently from the ground state to afford net binding, as was previously postulated with thymidine kinase.

The inhibition results with some nucleoside analogs (XXXVI–XXXVIII) of thymidine (II) are pertinent to the binding of the 2-deoxy-D-ribofuranosyl moiety of thymidine; of these three analogs, only the 2′-deoxy-D-glucopyranosyl analog (XXXVI) showed inhibition of the thymidine

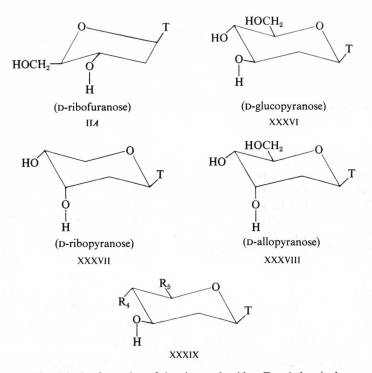

Fig. 4–2. Conformation of thymine nucleosides; T = 1-thyminyl.

phosphorylase from Dunning hepatoma.[43] As was pointed out on p. 77, the most stable conformation of thymidine would appear to be II*A* (Fig. 4–2). The most stable conformation for the glucosyl derivative would be XXXVI; this conformation allows the 3′-hydroxyl group of XXXVI to approach the same position as the 3′-hydroxyl group of thymidine (II*A*) with respect to the thymine moiety, which could allow similar binding. That XXXVI is not a substrate could be due to the fact that a furanosyl

[43] W. W. Zorbach, H. R. Munson, and K. V. Bhat, *J. Org. Chem.*, **30**, 3955 (1965); M. Zimmerman, *Biochem. Biophys. Res. Commun.*, **16**, 600 (1964).

derivative hydrolyzes about 50 to 200 times faster than the corresponding pyranosyl derivative[44] or that the conformation of XXXVI when complexed to the enzyme does not line up with the catalytic site properly for cleavage.

That the 3′-hydroxyl of the 2-deoxy-D-*gluco* isomer (XXXVI) is involved in binding is substantiated by the lack of inhibition by the 3′-epimer (XXXVIII) of D-*allo* configuration; similarly, the 2-deoxy-D-ribopyranosyl analog (XXXVII), which has its 3′-hydroxyl in the axial configuration rather than the required equatorial configuration of II*A* and XXXVI, does not inhibit at a concentration equal to that of substrate. Therefore, for pyranosides, the general structure XXXIX can be written for inhibitors where the 3′-hydroxyl and pyrimidine are equatorial. R_4 and R_5 are probably not involved in binding and could be H, CH_3, or $HOCH_2$; the species difference noted in the inhibition of horse liver thymidine phosphorylase and the mouse enzyme may well be a difference in bulk tolerance to the R_5 group.[45] Such comparative studies on phosphorylases from different tissues or species would be of considerable interest with thymine nucleosides derived from 2,6-dideoxy-D-glucopyranose, 2-deoxy-D-xylopyranose, and 6′-derivatives of XXXVI.

Hydrophobic Bonding

When the sugar moiety is completely removed from 2′-deoxyuridine to give uracil (XL), the resultant uracil is an inhibitor of FUDR cleavage that binds 3.9-fold less effectively than FUDR; because uracil is a substrate in the back reaction,[46] its ability to inhibit nucleoside cleavage would be expected. The 1- position of uracil was then checked for possible hydrophobic bonding (Table 4–4). Note that 1-methyluracil (XXXIII) was complexed about 50-fold less effectively than uracil; the possibility that the 1-NH group of uracil (XL) is complexed to the enzyme will be discussed in the section concerned with the mode of pyrimidine binding.

When the 1-methyl (XXXIII) was increased to 1-*n*-butyl (XIII), a ninefold increase in binding was observed; this increase in effectiveness by a hydrocarbon chain can only be due to a combination of hydrophobic bonding and van der Waals forces.[47] About the same binding was obtained with higher alkyl groups, such as *n*-amyl (XXXV), *i*-amyl (XLI), cyclopentyl (XLII), and *i*-hexyl (XXXIV) (Table 4–4) as was obtained with

---

[44] W. N. Haworth, *Ber.*, **65A**, 43 (1932).

[45] That differences in bulk tolerance between two enzymes or isoenzymes can occur has been previously noted. See B. R. Baker, W. W. Lee, W. A. Skinner, A. P. Martinez, and E. Tong, *J. Med. Pharm. Chem.*, **2**, 633 (1960); B. R. Baker and B.-T. Ho, *J. Pharm. Sci.*, **55**, 470 (1966).

[46] See Reference 26, p. 80.

[47] See Chapter 2, p. 39.

n-butyl. Because the increment in binding between methyl and butyl is about 1.3 kcal/mole, at least one methylene of the *n*-butyl past the 1'-methyl group is complexed to the enzyme.

Hydrophobic bonding with 1-aralkyluracils was also observed (Table 4–4). 1-Benzyluracil (XLIII) was a four-fold better inhibitor than *n*-butyluracil (XIII). The higher homologs were then investigated as inhibitors; phenethyl (XLIV) and phenylbutyl (XLV) were complexed to about

Table 4–4. **Hydrophobic Bonding to Thymidine Phosphorylase by**

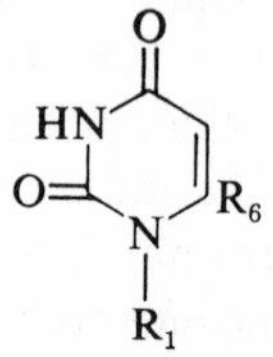

No.	R_1	R_6	$[I/S]_{0.5}$ [a]
XL	H	H	3.9
XXXIII	CH_3	H	200
XIII	$n\text{-}C_4H_9$—	H	22
XXXV	$n\text{-}C_5H_{11}$—	H	14
XLI	$i\text{-}C_5H_{11}$—	H	20
XLII	cyclopentyl	H	19
XXXIV	$i\text{-}C_6H_{13}$—	H	15
XLIII	$C_6H_5CH_2$—	H	5.7
XLIV	$C_6H_5(CH_2)_2$—	H	6.3
XIV	$C_6H_5(CH_2)_3$—	H	13
XLV	$C_6H_5(CH_2)_4$—	H	4.0
XLVI	$C_6H_5(CH_2)_5$—	H	2.1
XLVII	$C_6H_5CH_2$—	CH_3	6.0

The enzyme from *E. coli* B was assayed, as described in Table 4–2, with 0.4 mM FUDR. Unpublished data by B. R. Baker and M. Kawazu.
[a] The ratio of concentration of inhibitor to 0.4 mM FUDR giving 50 per cent inhibition.

the same extent as benzyl; phenylpropyl (XIV) was only half as good as benzyl (XLIII), but phenylamyl (XLVI) was about three times as effective, being the best inhibitor so far tested in this series.

In order to determine if additional hydrophobic bonding above that seen with the 1- substituent on uracil could be found at the 5- and 6- positions, the series of compounds in Table 4–5 were investigated; 1-phenylpropyluracil (XIV) was arbitrarily selected for the 1-substituent and was kept constant. That a hydrophobic region on the enzyme was near the 5- position of 1-phenylpropyluracil (XIV) when it was complexed to the enzyme was indicated by the results with the 5-hydroxymethyl group (XLIX) and its ethers, L and LI. A slight loss in binding was observed with the polar 5-hydroxymethyl group (XLIX); this loss was regained by the less polar ethyl ether (L). Unfortunately, no additional hydrophobic bonding occurred with the 5-(*i*-amyloxymethyl)-uracil (LI).

Table 4–5. Hydrophobic Bonding to Thymidine Phosphorylase by

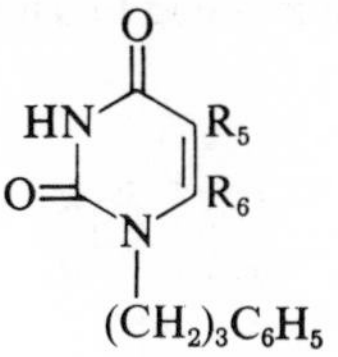

(CH$_2$)$_3$C$_6$H$_5$

No.	R$_5$	R$_6$	mM concentration	Per cent inhibition	Estimated $[I/S]_{0.5}$ [a]
XIV	H	H	5.4	50	13
XLVIII	CH$_2$=CHCH$_2$—	H	2.4	50	6.0
XLIX	HOCH$_2$—	H	8.5	50	21
L	C$_2$H$_5$OCH$_2$—	H	4.1	50	10
LI	*i*-C$_5$H$_{11}$OCH$_2$—	H	5.8	50	16
LII	C$_6$H$_5$	H	0.50[b]	20	~5
LIII	H	*n*-C$_3$H$_7$—	1.2	50	3.0
LIV	H	C$_6$H$_5$CH$_2$	1.2	50	3.0
LV	H	C$_6$H$_5$	0.83	50	2.1

The enzyme from *E. coli* B was assayed with 0.4 mM FUDR, as described in Table 4–2; unpublished data by B. R. Baker, T. J. Schwan, D. V. Santi, and M. Kawazu.
[a] The ratio of concentration of inhibitor to 0.4 mM FUDR giving 50 per cent inhibition.
[b] Maximum concentration allowing full light transmission.

About a twofold increment in binding was observed by substituting XIV with a 5-allyl (XLVIII) or 5-phenyl group. Similarly, an additional four-fold increment in hydrophobic bonding was observed with a 6-propyl (LIII) or 6-benzyl group (LIV), but a sixfold increment was observed with a 6-phenyl group (LV).

Since the loss of 1-H binding of uracil (XL) when the 1-NH was substituted by methyl (XXXIII) could just about be regained by some of the arakyl groups listed in Table 4–4, and because it appeared that hydrophobic bonding might be attainable by C^5 or C^6 substituents on uracil, the C^5 and C^6 substituted uracils in Table 4–6 were investigated. Only a small increment in hydrophobic bonding was noted with 6-(n-propyl)-uracil (LVI) which was doubled with 6-(n-amyl)-uracil (LVII); 5-(n-amyl)-6-(n-propyl)-uracil (LXI) showed a further twofold increment in binding over LVI. Good hydrophobic bonding was noted with 6-benzyluracil (LVIII) which gave a 17-fold increment in binding over uracil (XL). Neither 5-phenyl (LX) nor 6-phenyl groups (LIX) gave an increment in binding over uracil (XL); note that the phenyl group in each case is

Table 4–6. Hydrophobic Bonding to Thymidine Phosphorylase by

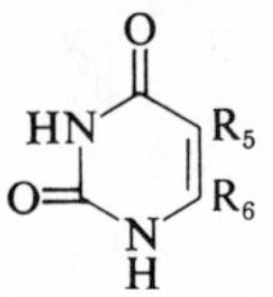

No.	R_5	R_6	mM concentration	Per cent inhibition	Estimated $[I/S]_{0.5}$ [a]
XL	H	H	1.5	50	3.9
LVI	H	n-C_3H_7—	1.0	50	2.5
LVII	H	n-C_5H_{11}—	0.46	50	1.1
LVIII	H	$C_6H_5CH_2$—	0.090	50	0.22
LIX	H	C_6H_5—	0.5[b]	0	>5
LX	C_6H_5—	H	0.40[b]	16	~2
LXI	n-C_5H_{11}	n-C_3H_7	0.24	50	0.60

The enzyme from *E. coli* B was assayed with 0.4 mM FUDR, as described in Table 4–2; unpublished data by B. R. Baker and M. Kawazu.

[a] The ratio of concentration of inhibitor to 0.4 mM FUDR giving 50 per cent inhibition.

[b] Maximum concentration allowing full light transmission.

coplanar with the pyrimidine ring, but 6-benzyluracil has the two aromatic systems out of plane. An interesting contrast is the appreciable increment in binding by the 5- (LII) or 6-phenyl (LV) group in the 1-phenylpropyluracil (XIV) series (Table 4–5); the ultraviolet spectrum of LV shows that the 6-phenyl group is out of plane with the uracil ring, which could account for this increment in the 1-phenylpropyluracil series that is not present in the uracil series without a 1- substituent.

Pyrimidine Binding

That the 3-NH group of the pyrimidine is most probably complexed to the enzyme can be gleaned by comparison of the nucleosides II, X, and

XI. Replacement of the 3-hydrogen of thymidine (II) by *n*-amyl (X) leads to a loss of substrate properties and a 40-fold loss in binding[48,49]; this result could also be explained by a lack of bulk tolerance at the 3- position. 4-Thiothymidine (XI) had no substrate properties but was an inhibitor that complexed one half as well as thymidine.[48] It therefore seems unlikely that the 4-oxo group is complexed to the enzyme, for the thione is a considerably poorer donor than oxo. The 5-fluoro of FUDR, which enhances the acidity of the 3-NH by 2 pK_a units, gives little increment in binding over II. Thus a compensating effect of increased binding by 3-NH

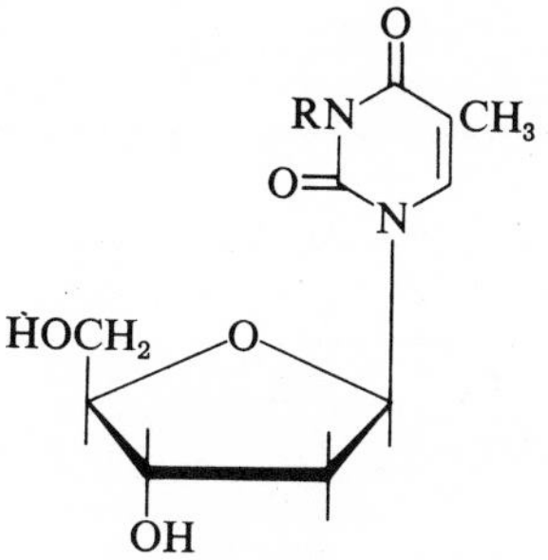

II, R = H
X, R = *n*-C$_5$H$_{11}$

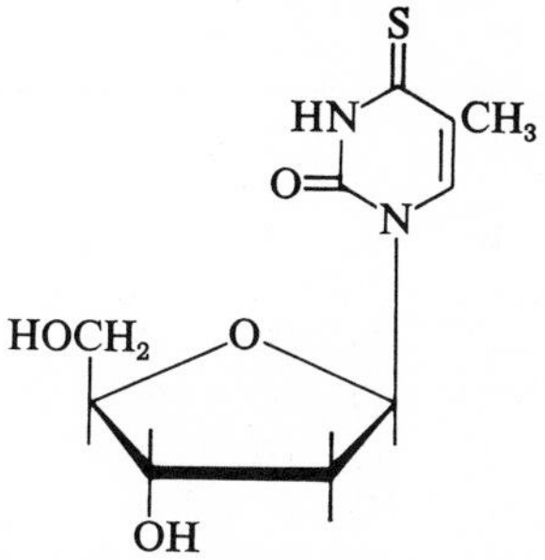

XI

and decreased binding by the thione is unlikely; note that 4-thiothymidine was 70-fold less effectively complexed to thymidine kinase than thymidine, showing a definite loss of 4-oxo binding.[50]

That the 1-H of uracil (XL) could complex to the enzyme was strongly indicated by the 50-fold loss in binding when the 1-H was substituted by methyl (XXXIII) (Table 4–7). Although binding by the 3-NH of 2'-deoxyuridine was not influenced by increased acidity, the binding by the 1-NH of uracil was strongly influenced by its acidity. 5-Nitrouracil (LXV) (Table 4–7) with pK_a 5.3 is 80 per cent ionized at the pH 5.9 of the assay and is the strongest inhibitor observed that does not have hydrophobic bonding; LXV is bound to the enzyme 18-fold more than uracil (XL), which is only 0.03 per cent ionized at the pH of the assay. 5-Fluorouracil (LXIII) is 1.5 pK_a units stronger as an acid than uracil (XL), and LXIII complexes to the enzyme about threefold better than uracil. 5-Fluoro-uracil (LXIII) is only 0.8 per cent ionized at pH 5.9, which is an ionization about 25 times more than that of uracil; it would therefore appear that

---

[48] Unpublished data by B. R. Baker and T. J. Schwan.

[49] Razzell and Casshyap noted that 3-methylthymidine had no substrate properties and that at an *I/S* ratio of 0.08, it showed no inhibitory properties. See Reference 40, p. 81.

[50] See Chapter 4, p. 75.

either an anion at N_1 can complex to the enzyme, as in the case of 5-nitrouracil (LXV) or the 1-H can complex, the ability of the latter to be an acceptor being dependent upon its acidity.

Table 4–7. Pyrimidine Binding to Thymidine Phosphorylase by

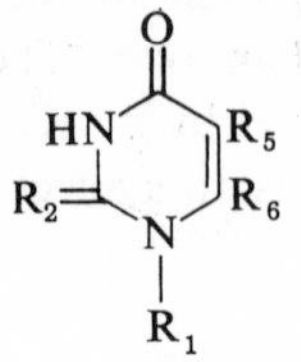

No.	R_1	R_2	R_5	R_6	$[I/S]_{0.5}$ [a]	Acidic pK_a [b]	R_5-π constant [c]	Per cent ionized [d]
XL	H	O	H	H	3.9	9.5	0	0.03
XXXIII	CH_3	O	H	H	200	9.9[e]	0	0.01
LXII	H	O	CH_3	H	1.9[f]	9.9	0.56	0.01
LXIII	H	O	F	H	1.3[f]	8.0[e]	0.15	0.78
LXIV	H	O	Br	H	0.45[f]	8.0[e]	0.86	0.78
LXV	H	O	NO_2	H	0.22[f]	5.3	−0.28	80
LVIII	H	O	H	$C_6H_5CH_2$	0.22		0	
LXVI	H	S	H	$C_6H_5CH_2$	0.16		0	
LXVII	H	O	Br	$C_6H_5CH_2$	0.025		0.86	

The enzyme from *E. coli* B was assayed with 0.4 mM FUDR at pH 5.9, as described in Table 4–2; unpublished data by B. R. Baker and M. Kawazu.

[a] The ratio of concentration of inhibitor to 0.4 mM FUDR giving 50 per cent inhibition.

[b] Data from D. J. Brown, *The Pyrimidines*, Interscience Publishers, New York, 1962, pp. 472–476 unless otherwise indicated.

[c] Relative hydrophobic character on log scale; from T. Fujita, J. Iwasa, and C. Hansch, *J. Am. Chem. Soc.*, **86**, 5175 (1964).

[d] At pH 5.9 of the assay.

[e] I. Wempen and J. J. Fox, *J. Am. Chem. Soc.*, **86**, 2474 (1964).

[f] Also observed to be an inhibitor under different assay conditions by W. E. Razzell and P. Casshyap, *J. Biol. Chem.*, **239**, 1789 (1964).

A complication arises with these 5- substituents, pointed up by the fact that thymine (LXII) is about twice as good an inhibitor as uracil (XL); this difference is probably due to hydrophobic bonding of the 5-methyl group of thymine to the enzyme, for larger hydrocarbon groups at the 5- position can give hydrophobic bonding (Tables 4–5 and 4–6). Conversely, the enzyme probably has a hydrophobic region near that where the 5- position of uracil resides in the enzyme complex. Therefore any interpretation of the effect on acidity by an electron-withdrawing group at the 5- position must also take into consideration the hydrophobic or hydrophilic character of the 5- substituent. For example, 5-bromuracil (LXIV) has the same pK_a as 5-fluorouracil (LXIII), but the bromine atom is more hydrophobic than methyl (Table 4–7) and considerably more hydrophobic than fluoro. Since the 5-methyl group of thymine gives a twofold increment in binding over that of uracil—presumably by hydrophobic bonding—it follows the 5-bromouracil (XIV) should be a better inhibitor than 5-fluorouracil; in fact, 5-bromouracil is a threefold better inhibitor than 5-fluorouracil.

Conversely, if a strong electron-withdrawing group is also polar, some repulsion of this polar group from the hydrophobic area on the enzyme could occur. Note that the nitro group of 5-nitrouracil is quite polar with a Hantsch π constant[51] of -0.28, compared to bromo with $+0.86$. It follows that nitro gives nearly maximum anion formation, but probably some repulsion of this hydrophilic group occurs. Therefore what is needed at the 5- position for optimum electron-withdrawing effect is a hydrophobic electron-withdrawing group. Unfortunately, the better electron-withdrawing groups such as NO_2, SO_2NH_2, SO_2CH_3, and CN with Hammett σ-constants[52] in the $+0.7$ range also are quite polar with Hantsch π constants[53] of -0.28, -1.82, -1.3, and -0.57, respectively; conversely, the hydrophobic CF_3 group with a π constant of $+1.2$ is not a sufficiently good electron-withdrawing group, for it has a σ-constant of $+0.32$ compared to bromo with $+0.23$ or NO_2 with $+0.7$. Therefore 5-(trifluoromethyl)-uracil would only be about as good as 5-bromouracil as an inhibitor. An interesting group to try at the 5- position would be the hydrophobic SO_2CF_3 group which has a π constant[53] of $+0.93$; it should be as good or better electron-withdrawing group than SO_2CH_3. Other interesting groups to try might be SO_2F or SO_2Cl.

Another possible approach emerges if we consider that 6-(trifluoromethyl)-uracil has a pK_a of 5.7[54]; apparently, an electron-withdrawing group at the 6- position of uracil has a greater influence on the acidity of the uracil than the same electron-withdrawing group at the 5- position. Because 6-(trifluoromethyl)-uracil would be as ionized as 5-nitrouracil at pH 5.9, but the trifluoromethyl group is hydrophobic (π constant $= +1.3$), whereas the nitro group is hydrophilic ($\pi = -0.28$), it follows that

[51] T. Fujita, J. Iwasa, and C. Hantsch, *J. Am. Chem. Soc.*, **86**, 5175 (1964).
[52] M. Charton, *J. Org. Chem.*, **28**, 3121 (1963).
[53] See Reference 51.
[54] D. J. Brown, *The Pyrimidines*, Interscience Publishers, New York, 1962, pp. 472–476.

6-(trifluoromethyl) uracil might be a better inhibitor than 5-nitrouracil due to enzymic hydrophobic repulsion of the 5-nitro group. Studies on 6-trifluoromethyluracil with and without 5- substituents are continuing.

That the 2-oxo group of uracil (XL) was not complexed to the enzyme has been indicated by comparison of 6-benzyuracil (LVIII) and 6-benzyl-2-thiouracil (LXVI); the latter was complexed about twice as effectively as LVIII. This difference is probably due to the increased acidity of the thiouracil, which increases binding by the 1-NH as can be seen with 5-fluorouracil (LXIII); note that uracil has pK_a 9.5 and 2-thiouracil has pK_a 7.7. If the 2-oxo group as a donor were complexed to the enzyme, then the 2-thione should have been a poorer inhibitor, as has been noted in comparison of thymidine (II) with 4-thiothymidine (XI) on binding to thymidine kinase.[55]

Because an 18-fold increment in binding over that of uracil (XL) could be obtained by the bonding of a benzyl group of LVIII, and because an increase in acidity by the 5-bromo group of LXIV could give a ninefold increment in binding, it was of interest to see if both increments could be achieved in one molecule. If these increments were additive, then 5-bromo-6-benzyluracil (LXVII) could be expected to bind 160-fold better than uracil (XL); it was noted that LXVII (Table 4–7) did bind 150-fold better than uracil (XL), thus binding 16-fold better than FUDR to thymidine phosphorylase.

It would be of interest to determine if a molecule such as 5-nitro-6-benzyluracil (LXVIII) could show the 18-fold benzyl increment and the

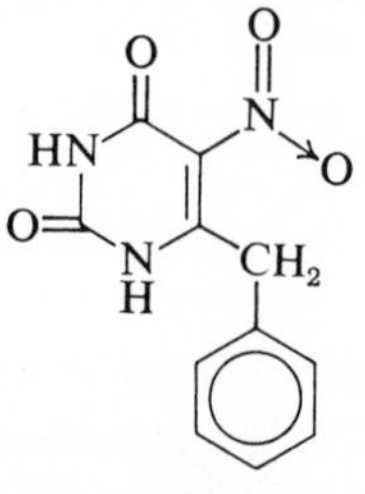

LXVIII

18-fold nitro increment—a total of 320-fold if additive. In order for the 5-nitro group to exert full influence on the acidity of uracil by π-orbital overlap, the nitro group must be coplanar to the uracil ring. An *ortho* substituent might force the nitro group out of coplanarity, thus reducing the acidity of the 1-NH group; therefore the total predicted additive increment for LXVIII might not be observed.

Whether other aralkyl or alkyl groups at the 6- position of 5-bromo-

[55] See Chapter 4, p. 75.

uracil and 5-nitrouracil could give better overall binding to thymidine phosphorylase remains to be determined. Even if compounds better than 5-bromo-6-benzyluracil (LXVII) cannot be found, it is quite obvious that proper utilization of an available hydrophobic bonding area on thymidine phosphorylase or other enzymes can have considerable utility for obtaining potent inhibitors.[56]

CONTRAST IN THYMIDINE BINDING TO ITS KINASE AND PHOSPHORYLASE

The contrast in binding of the identical substrate—thymidine—to its phosphorylase and kinase is informative from both theoretical and practical viewpoints. Both enzymes can use 2'-deoxyuridine (IV), its 5-methyl derivative (II), or its 5-fluoro derivative (LXIX) as substrates. Therefore

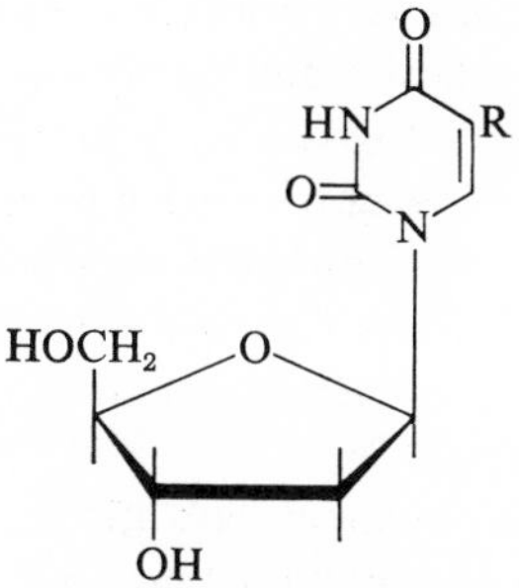

II, R = CH$_3$
IV, R = H
LXIX, R = F (FUDR)
LXX, R = —CH$_2$—CH=CH$_2$

one of the practical questions for chemotherapy is "How can the phosphorylase which detoxifies FUDR be blocked without blocking the kinase that converts FUDR to its active form, the cytoxic nucleotide, FUDRP?" Classical antimetabolites that are close analogs of these deoxynucleosides are likely to block both enzyme reactions; in contrast, nonclassical antimetabolites with larger structural changes are more likely to give the desired enzyme specificity.

Because the 5'-hydroxyl of thymidine (II) is necessary for good binding to the kinase, but does not bind to the phosphorylase, it is clear that 5'-deoxythymidine could slow the phosphorylysis of FUDR by being a competitive substrate but would not slow the kinase catalyzed conversion of FUDR to FUDRP. For similar reasons, 1-(β-D-glucofuranosyl) thymine

---

[56] See Chapter 10, Hydrophobic Bonding, for a discussion of the potent hydrophobic bonding to dihydrofolic reductase.

(XXXVI) could complex to some phosphorylases but does not have the proper conformation for good binding to the kinase. Both of these nucleosides suffer from the same drawback; there is no obvious way in which they could be modified further to give tissue or species specificity; that is, for chemotherapeutic use in cancer, the tumor phosphorylase will probably not have sufficient difference from the phosphorylase in normal cells to gain any appreciable chemotherapeutic advantage.

Another nucleoside that can block the phosphorylase and not the kinase is 5-allyl-2'-deoxyuridine (LXX).[57] This nucleoside binds to an ascites cell phosphorylase seven times better than FUDR (LXIX) but probably would not bind to the kinase, for there is little bulk tolerance at the 5-position[58]; from the studies presented in this chapter it is highly probable that the allyl group gives additional binding to the enzyme by hydrophobic bonding, and therefore it might be worthwhile knowing if other 5-alkyl, aryl, or aralkyl groups on 2'-deoxyuridine would give better binding. Such a study has a severe drawback; nucleosides such as LXX are gruellingly difficult to synthesize and purify starting with the appropriate pyrimidine. This type of analog (LXX) is more likely to show species or tissue specificity when the 5- group is varied because the allyl group is most probably complexed in a hydrophobic region of the phosphorylase not used by normal substrates; it is the area outside the active-site where the biggest changes in enzyme structure are likely to occur that can be exploited[59] for chemotherapy.[59,60]

Both the kinase and the phosphorylase appear to complex the 3-H group of thymidine (II). The 4-oxo group of II is apparently necessary for binding to the kinase, but not the phosphorylase; the 2-oxo group is not directly bonded to the phosphorylase, but no information on this point is known with the kinase.

One of the two biggest differences in binding between the kinase and the phosphorylase is that uracil and its natural analogs are complexed to the phosphorylase since the phosphorylase is a reversible reaction and must be able to complex uracil or thymine to reverse the reaction; in contrast, the kinase has no measurable affinity for a free pyrimidine "base" such as uracil.

The second biggest difference is the hydrophobic bonding by aryl, aralkyl, and alkyl groups substituted at the 1-, 5-, and 6- positions of uracils; these hydrophobic groups give a useful increment in binding to the

---

[57] C. Heidelberger and J. Boohar, *Biochim. Biophys. Acta*, **91**, 639 (1964).
[58] See Chapter 7.
[59] See Chapter 10 on species differences in hydrophobic bonding to dihydrofolic reductase.
[60] See Chapter 9 on enzyme evolution.

phosphorylase, but no hydrophobic bonding occurs in this area with the kinase. Furthermore, the kinase does not even have bulk tolerance for groups at the 5- position of thymidine (II) any larger than the methyl or iodo group.[61]

When these two major differences are combined, some relatively simply synthesized molecules, compared to nucleosides—emerge, such as LXXI, which is an effective inhibitor that can complex 16 times better than FUDR to the *E. coli* B phosphorylase but would have no affinity for the kinase. Inhibitors such as LXXI are clearly of the nonclassical type[62,63] and can be

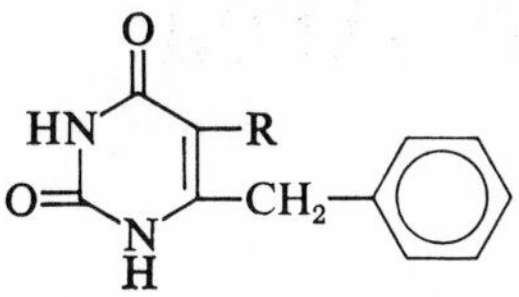

LXXI

A, R = Br
B, R = NO$_2$

utilized in two ways, (a) due to the fact that species and tissue differences in an enzyme are likely to exist in a nonfunctional hydrophobic region and (b) that species and tissue differences can be further magnified by further conversion to active-site-directed irreversible inhibitors.[64]

---

[61] See Chapter 7.

[62] B. R. Baker, *Cancer Chemotherapy Reports*, **4**, 1 (1959).

[63] B. R. Baker, W. W. Lee, W. A. Skinner, A. P. Martinez, and E. Tong, *J. Med. Pharm. Chem.*, **2**, 633 (1960).

[64] See Chapter 10, p. 258 for a discussion on utilization of the hydrophobic bonding locus of dihydrofolic reductase for the design of species and tissue specific active-site-directed irreversible inhibitors.

5 | Specific Mode of Binding to Enzymes: III. Purine Area

The large number of enzymes involved in purine anabolism and catabolism[1] can be divided into the following classes: (a) *de novo* synthesis of purine nucleotides from 5-phospho-*a*,D-ribofuranose-1-pyrophosphate, (b) utilization of preformed purines by conversion to the nucleotides, (c) interconversion of purine bases, nucleosides, and nucleotides, and (d) catabolic degradation of purine bases, nucleosides, and nucleotides. Few of these enzymes have been studied in detail to determine the mode of binding of substrates or inhibitors, although two have been subjected to at least some preliminary study: (a) succinoadenylate kinosynthetase, an anabolic nucleotide interconverting enzyme and (b), guanine deaminase, a catabolic enzyme.

SUCCINOADENYLATE KINOSYNTHETASE

Succinoadenylate kinosynthetase was first isolated by Lieberman[2] from *E. coli* B; the enzyme condenses inosinate (I) with L-aspartate to give succinoadenylate (II). The reaction requires guanosine triphosphate (GTP) as a cofactor, appears to proceed via the O^6-phosphate of I,[2,3] and is believed to be reversible.[3] The rate of enzymatic reaction is readily followed spectrophotometrically[2,3] by the increase in optical density at 280 mμ, the wavelength of the greatest optical density difference between I and II.

[1] A. G. Moat and H. Friedman, *Bact. Rev.*, **24**, 309 (1960).
[2] I. Lieberman, *J. Biol. Chem.*, **223**, 327 (1956).
[3] H. J. Fromm, *Biochim. Biophys. Acta.* **29**, 255 (1958).

6-Mercaptopurine ribonucleotide[4] and adenylic acid[5] are known inhibitors of the reaction.

Purine Binding

Little study has been carried out on the problem of purine binding. However, from what has been determined, AMP (III, Table 5-1)[4] and 6-mercaptopurine ribonucleotide[5] can bind almost as well as the substrate, IMP (I); these results indicate that the HN—C=O moiety of I is

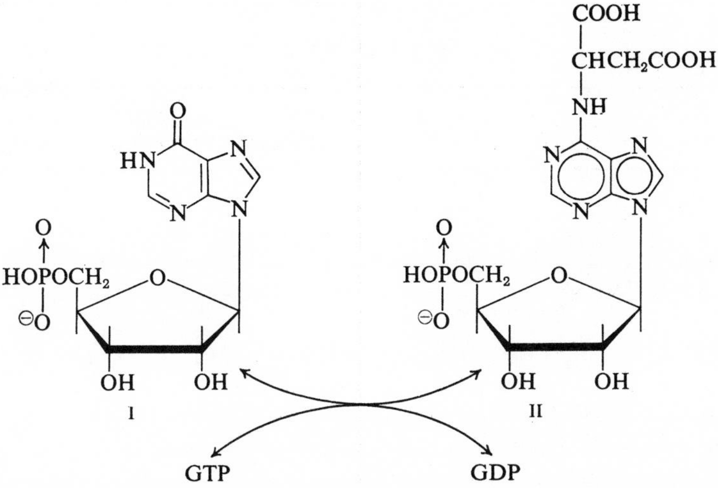

not involved directly in binding to the enzyme because this moiety is acidic and the NH=CNH$_2$ moiety of AMP is basic. Whether or not N^3, N^7, or N^9 are involved directly in binding, or the general ring system is complexed as a donor or an acceptor, remains to be determined.

Ribofuranose-5'-phosphate Binding

The enzyme binding of the ribofuranose-5'-phosphate moiety of AMP can be due to a combination of binding of the phosphate group, the two alcohol functions, the ring oxygen, and less likely, hydrophobic bonding by the CH groups. An estimate of the relative binding of these functions can be gleaned by comparison of the compounds in Table 5-1. Removal of the phosphate group caused a 46-fold loss in binding, as shown by the comparison of AMP (III) and adenosine (VI). Removal of all of the oxygen functions except the phosphate moiety, as in V, gave only a 14-fold loss in binding; unless there is hydrophobic bonding by the pentyl group

[4] J. B. Wyngaarden and R. A. Greenland, *J. Biol. Chem.*, **238**, 1054 (1963).
[5] B. R. Baker and P. M. Tanna, *J. Pharm. Sci.*, **54**, 845 (1965).

of V, these data indicate that the phosphate moiety contributes more to binding than the other three oxygen functions of the ribofuranose moiety.

Comparison of III, IV, and V indicates that most of the 14-fold loss in

Table 5–1. Inhibition of Succinoadenylate Kinosynthetase by

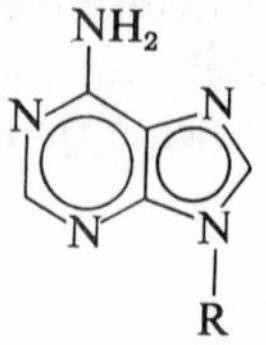

No.	R	mM concentration	Per cent inhibition	$[I/S]_{0.5}$ [a]
III	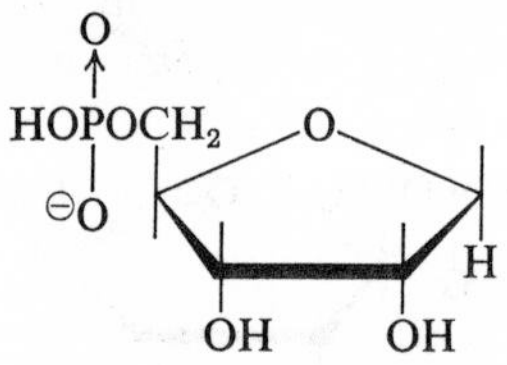	0.068	50	2.3
IV	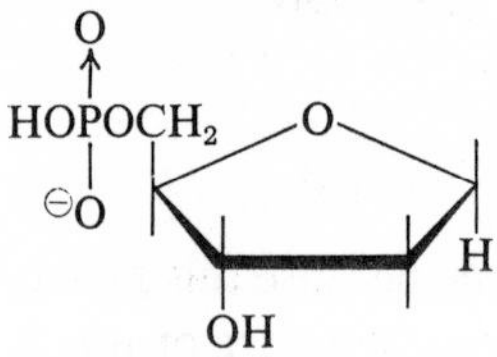	0.39	50	13
V	$-(CH_2)_5OPO(OH)_2$	0.97	50	32
VI	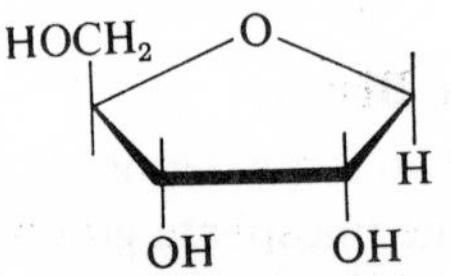	3.2	50	105

The enzyme was isolated by a modification of the procedure of I. Lieberman as described in *J. Biol. Chem.*, **223**, 327 (1956) and assayed with 30.6 μM IMP(I), 100 μM GTP, 3.75 mM L-aspartate as described by B. R. Baker and P. M. Tanna, *J. Pharm. Sci.*, **54**, 845 (1965); data also from the latter.

[a] Ratio of concentrations of inhibitor to substrate giving 50 per cent inhibition.

binding with V is due to the loss of the 2′-hydroxyl, for III binds about sixfold better than IV. In fact, it is somewhat surprising that V is actually as good an inhibitor as it has been observed to be, for V has a staggered conformation in the ground state, whereas III has a ground state conformation more folded than skewed, but less than eclipsed, in its semi-envelope conformation. It would therefore be expected that the difference in binding between IV and V should be on the order of at least 1 kcal/mole rather than the 0.4 kcal/mole observed—unless the enzyme should be capable of changing conformation slightly with little energy loss.

Similar results to those found with III–VI were obtained with corresponding 6-mercaptopurine derivatives, except for the nucleoside; 6-mercaptopurine ribonucleoside had an $[I/S]_{0.5}$ of greater than 140, and the pentanol phosphate corresponding to V had an $[I/S]_{0.5}$ of 27.[6]

The purine-9-pentanol phosphates substituted by 6-amino (V) or 6-mercapto groups are sufficiently good inhibitors of succinoadenylate kinosynthetase that substitution of other groups for the phosphate moiety of V or its 6-mercapto could then be studied to simulate phosphate binding. As pointed out in Chapter 1, nucleotides cannot penetrate a cell wall either by active transport or passive diffusion; therefore, simulation of phosphate binding by one or more relatively unionized functional groups could allow penetration of the cell wall by passive diffusion, then a complex with the requisite receptor site could be formed in vivo.[7]

Twenty-two different ways were previously envisioned for the mode of binding of the phosphate moiety of a nucleotide to an enzyme, depending upon whether one, two, or three phosphate oxygens are involved in the complex.[8] From the generalized donor-acceptor complex theory presented in Chapter 2, this number can be reduced to 13 if we do not define the complementary donor or acceptor group in the enzyme; these modes of binding are shown in Fig. 5–1. In some cases it is even questionable that there are 13 discrete binding forms; for example, C–1, in Fig. 5–1, is a protonated species of C–2, E–4 is a protonated species of E–3, and an unprotonated species of C–4 can be written. Whether this extra proton is significant in these species is questionable, for the second hydroxyl group of a phosphate ester has a pK_a of about 6.

There is no a priori reason to believe that all phosphate mono esters would bind to different enzymes in an identical fashion. If there are indeed different modes of phosphate binding to enzymes, then moieties designed to simulate one mode of phosphate binding might not bind to a different enzyme using the same substrate or to the same enzyme from a different species.[9]

[6] B. R. Baker and P. M. Tanna, *J. Pharm. Sci.*, **54**, 845 (1965).

[7] B. R. Baker and H. S. Sachdev, *J. Pharm. Sci.*, **52**, 933 (1963).

[8] B. R. Baker, P. M. Tanna, and G. D. F. Jackson, *J. Pharm. Sci.*, **54**, 988 (1965).

[9] See Reference 8.

A. Single Donor Bond

$$
\begin{array}{ccc}
\underset{\underset{\text{OH}}{|}}{\overset{\overset{\displaystyle O}{\uparrow}}{\text{ROP}}} \!-\! O^{\ominus} \rightarrow A\!-\!E
&
\underset{\underset{\underset{H}{|}}{O \rightarrow A-E}}{\overset{\overset{\displaystyle O}{\uparrow}}{\text{ROP}}} \!-\! O^{\ominus}
&
\underset{\underset{\underset{A-E}{|}}{\text{OH}}}{\text{RO}\!-\!\overset{\overset{\displaystyle O}{\uparrow}}{P}\!-\!O^{\ominus}}
\\
\text{A–1} & \text{A–2} & \text{A–3}
\end{array}
$$

B. Single Acceptor Bond

$$
\underset{\underset{\text{B–1}}{O\!-\!H \leftarrow D\!-\!E}}{\overset{\overset{\displaystyle O}{\uparrow}}{\text{ROP}}}\!-\!O^{\ominus}
$$

C. Two Donor Bonds

R—O—P—O⁻ → A   ROP—O⁻ → A   R—O—P—OH   R—O—P—O⁻

C–1   C–2   C–3   C–4

D. One Acceptor Bond, One Donor Bond

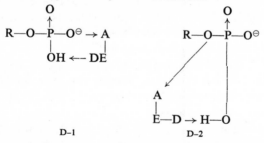

R—O—P—O⁻ → A

OH ←- DE

D–1

R—O—P—O⁻

E—D → H—O

D–2

E. Three Bonds

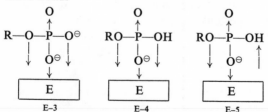

R—O—P—O⁻ | E

E–3

RO—P—OH | E

E–4

RO—P—OH | E

E–5

Fig. 5–1. Possible modes of binding of a phosphate ester to an enzyme E; A is the electron-acceptor group; D is the electron-donor group.

Bonding forms involving a polarized $P \rightarrow O$ group (F-1, F-2) can

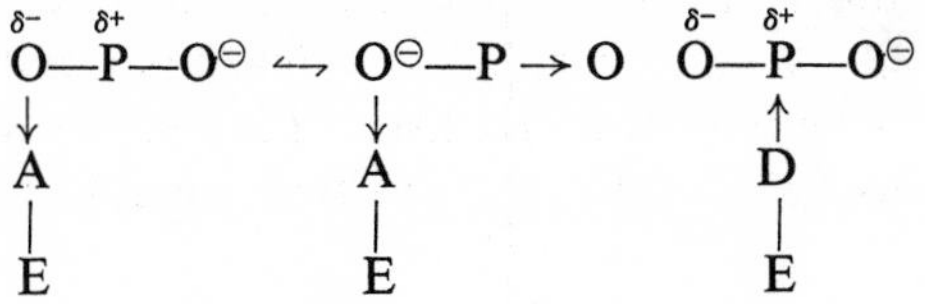

$$\overset{\delta-}{O}-\overset{\delta+}{P}-O^{\ominus} \;\rightharpoonup\; O^{\ominus}-P \rightarrow O \qquad \overset{\delta-}{O}-\overset{\delta+}{P}-O^{\ominus}$$

theoretically exist with phosphate triesters or diester phosphofluoridates.[9]
The shift of electrons shows that F-1 is equivalent to A-1.

The carbamate analog (VII) of 6-mercaptopurine ribonucleotide should be able to simulate all the phosphate binding forms but those involving an

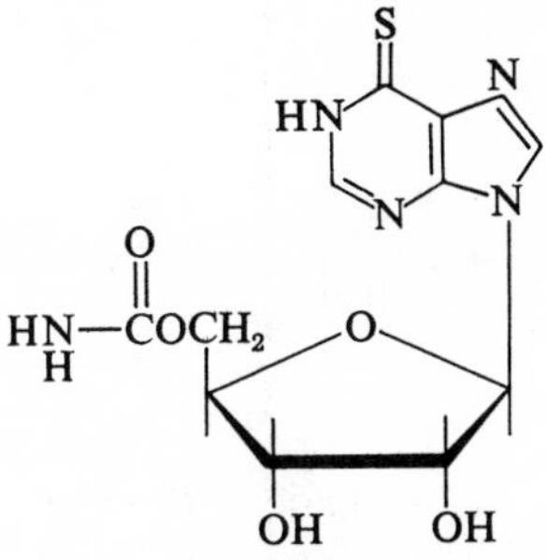

VII

electron-donor group on the enzyme; the fact that VII is a poor inhibitor of succinoadenylate kinosynthetase indicates that the phosphate could bind to this enzyme in forms C-1, C-2, E-3, or E-4.[10]

Additional studies[11,12] on simulation of phosphate binding have given some interesting leads, but unfortunately they are not yet sufficiently definitive to warrant full discussion at this time.

GUANINE DEAMINASE

Guanine deaminase is a catabolic enzyme that converts guanine (VIII) to xanthine (IX) irreversibly.[13] 8-Azaguanine (X)[13] and thioguanine (XI)[14] are known substrates and 5-aminoimidazole-4-carboxamide (XII) is a

[10] See Reference 8, p. 99.
[11] B. R. Baker and P. M. Tanna, *J. Pharm. Sci.*, **54**, 1609 (1965).
[12] B. R. Baker and P. M. Tanna, *J. Pharm. Sci.*, **54**, 1774 (1965).
[13] A. Roush and E. R. Norris, *Arch. Biochem.*, **29**, 124 (1950).
[14] E. C. Moore and G. A. LePage, *Cancer Res.*, **18**, 1075 (1958).

known inhibitor.[15] The partially purified enzyme from rabbit liver is commercially available and is easily assayed[13] by the rate of decrease of optical density at 245 mμ where guanine has a maximum and xanthine has a minimum. With the enzyme from rat liver[13] guanine has $K_m = 5 \times 10^{-6}$ and 8-azaguanine has $K_m = 70 \times 10^{-6}$; neither guanosine nor guanylic acid are attacked.

It has been proposed that the selective action of thioguanine (XI) on certain tumors may be due to the lack of guanine deaminase in these cell

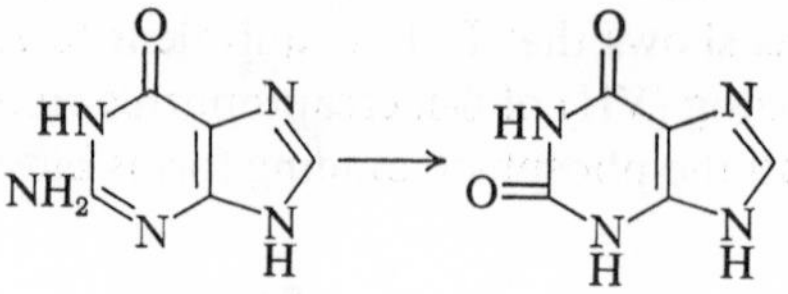

lines;[16] thus a tissue-specific blockade of this enzyme could be useful as an adjunct to therapy with thioguanine (XI).

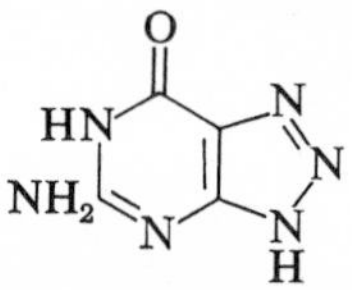

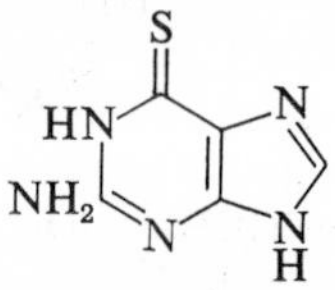

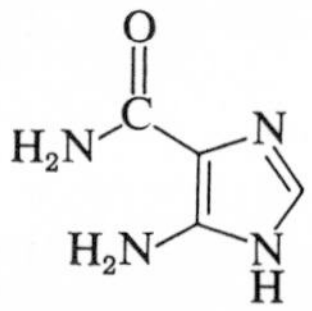

A systematic study on the mode of binding of guanine has been carried out[17] and the results are recorded in Tables 5–2 and 5–3. The inhibitory properties of 5-aminoimidazole-4-carboxamide (XII)[18] were checked; XII was complexed about one half as well as the substrate (VIII), indicating that the NH_2—C group at the 2- position is not necessary for binding. That the 7-nitrogen complexes to the enzyme as an electron donor is indicated by the lack of inhibition by the corresponding pyrazole, XIII; because the pyrazole is a weaker base than the imidazole XII, it is possible that this weakening of base strength could decrease binding if the π cloud of the ring system were a donor; the latter interpretation is eliminated by the following results:

1. 7-Methylguanine (XVII) is not an inhibitor. If the imidazole π cloud were a donor to the enzyme, then XVII should have been a good substrate or inhibitor; in contrast, if the lone electron pair on the 7-nitrogen is a donor, N-methylation to XVII could hinder complexing to the enzyme.

[15] H. G. Mandel, *Biochim. Biophs. Acta,* **25,** 402 (1957).

[16] B. R. Baker, *Cancer Chemotherapy Reports,* **4,** 1 (1959).

[17] B. R. Baker, *J. Med. Chem.,* **10,** 59 (1967).

[18] See Reference 15.

Table 5–2. Inhibition of Guanine Deaminase by Some Purines and Monocyclic Analogs

No.	Structure	μM concentration	Per cent inhibition[a]	$[I/S]_{0.5}$[b]
XII	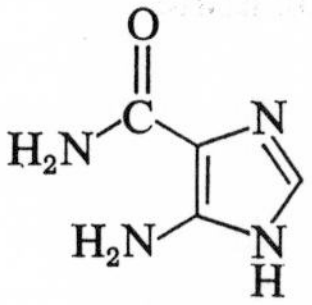	28	50	2.1
XIII	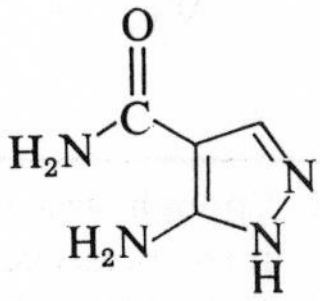	500	0	> 150
IX	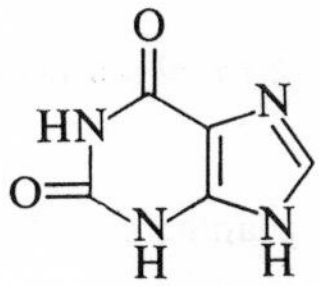	500	0	> 150
XIV	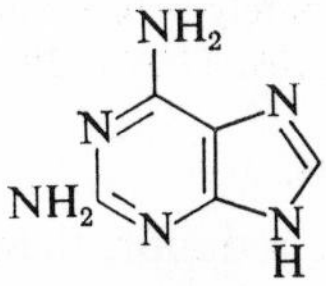	300	0[c]	> 90
XV	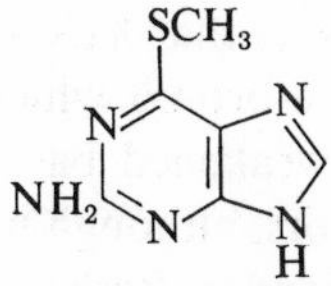	250	0	> 75
XI	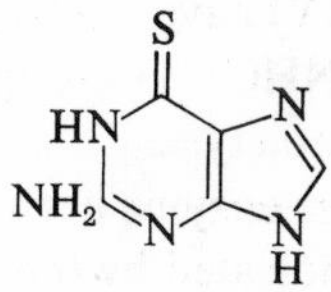	100	slow substrate[d]	
X	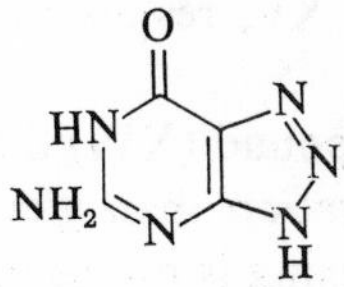	200	substrate[e]	

Table 5–2. (*continued*)

No.	Structure	μM concentration	Per cent inhibition[a]	$[I/S]_{0.5}$[b]
XVI	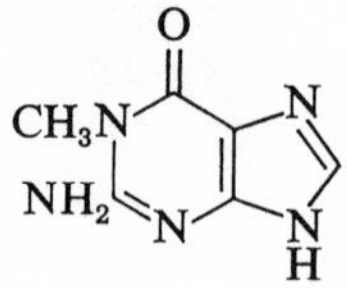	125	substrate[f]	
XVII	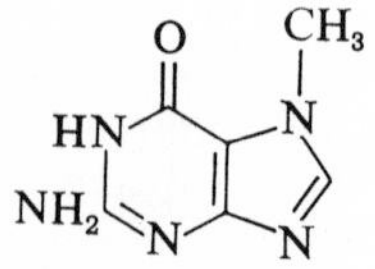	250	0[g]	> 75

[a] Commercial enzyme from rabbit liver was employed. Enough was used to give about 0.005 optical density units/min change at 245 mμ in the presence of 13.3 μM guanine in 0.05 *M tris* buffer, pH 7.4; $K_m = 3.2 \times 10^{-6}$ *M*. From B. R. Baker, *J. Med. Chem.*, 10, 59 (1957).

[b] The ratio of concentrations of inhibitor to substrate to give 50 per cent inhibition.

[c] No substrate properties were observed at 300 μM.

[d] Measured by optical density changes at 335 mμ

[e] This is about one half the rate observed with 13.3 μM guanine and the compound showed no inhibitor properties at 200 μM.

[f] This is one half the rate of 13.3 μM guanine, but it is barely perceptible at 25 μM; G. H. Hitchings and E. A. Falco, *Proc. Natl. Acad. Sci.* (*U.S.*), 30, 294 (1944) reported this compound was a substrate.

[g] No substrate properties were observed at 25 or 500 μM.

2. If the lone-electron pair on the 7-nitrogen is a donor, then the more basic is the 7-nitrogen, the better should be complexing, but the less basic is the 7-nitrogen, the poorer binding should be. Note that XIX actually has an acidic 7-NH group, XVIII has an adjacent 8-bromo which weakens basicity of the 7-nitrogen and xanthine has a weakened basicity of the 7-nitrogen; all three compounds are poor inhibitors, although in each case the results could be interpreted in an alternate manner. Both 2,6-diamino-purine (XIV) and 2-amino-6-methylthiopurine (XV) have 7-nitrogens more basic than guanine, but in these two cases the NHC=O grouping at 1,6 has been replaced which is a probable binding moiety.

That the HNC=O 1,6- linkage complexes to the enzyme in two places—the H as an acceptor and the O as a donor—is indicated by the following:

1. Removal of this grouping, as in XIV or XV, results in decreased binding.

2. Methylation of the 1-nitrogen gives a compound (XVI) that is still a substrate but requires a much higher concentration than guanine for a similar rate of reaction—indicating that complexing is not as effective.

3. Conversion of the 6-oxo group of guanine to a 6-thione (XI) still allows substrate properties. That such a structural change leads to a ninefold loss in binding can be seen by comparing the corresponding 9-phenyl derivatives, XXI and XXIV; this result indicates that the 6-oxo group complexes as an electron donor, for the 6-thione is a poorer electron donor. Actually a larger difference between XXI and XXIV could have been anticipated if only the 6-oxo group were complexed; the 1-hydrogen of XXIV, being a stronger acid, should complex better as an acceptor than

Table 5–3. Inhibition of Guanine Deaminase by

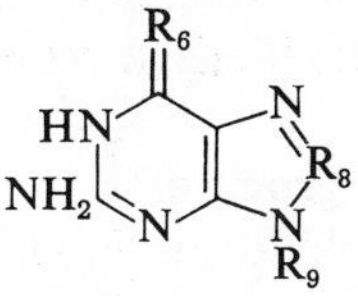

No.	R_6	R_8	R_9	μM concentration	Per cent inhibition[a]	$[I/S]_{0.5}$[b]
XVIII	O	C—Br	H	250	0	> 75
XIX	O	C—OH	H	250	0	> 75
XX	O	CH	CH_3	275	50	21
XXI	O	CH	C_6H_5	9.8	50	0.73
XXII	O	CH	$p\text{-}ClC_6H_4$	3.8	50	0.29
XXIII	O	N	$p\text{-}ClC_6H_4$	18	50	1.4
XXIV	S	CH	C_6H_5	83	50	6.2

[a] From B. R. Baker and D. V. Santi, *J. Med. Chem.*, **10**, 62 (1967). Assayed according to footnote a, Table 5–2, except 10 per cent dimethylsulfoxide was present.

[b] The ratio of concentration of inhibitor to 13.3 μM guanine giving 50 per cent inhibition.

the 1-hydrogen of guanine, thus partially compensating for the decrease in binding with the 6-thione group.

Whether or not 3-nitrogen of guanine is involved in binding cannot be certain, for removal of this amino group from 5-aminoimidazole-4-carboxamide (XII) would decrease the basicity of the ring system and hence decrease binding by the nitrogen corresponding to N^7 of guanine; whether other compounds could answer this question more unequivocally remains to be determined.

Whether or not the acidic 9-NH of guanine is needed for binding also cannot be answered with certainty considering only the compounds in Table 5–3. Replacement of the 9-hydrogen by methyl (XX), leads to a

21-fold loss in binding; this result indicates that either the 9-hydrogen is necessary for binding or that the enzyme cannot tolerate the bulk of a methyl group at this position. Replacement of the 9-hydrogen by 9-phenyl (XXI) gives an excellent inhibitor, and inhibition is even stronger with the 9-(*p*-chlorophenyl) group (XXII); because XXII binds to the enzyme 3.5-fold better than substrate, this result could be interpreted to mean that the loss in binding of a 9-hydrogen is actually overcompensated by strong binding of the in-plane 9-phenyl group. Whether the 9-phenyl group does actually bind as a donor or acceptor or by hydrophobic bonding remains to be determined; regardless of mechanism, the 9-(substituted-phenyl)-guanines are excellent inhibitors and will be studied further for ultimate construction of an active-site-directed irreversible inhibitor of guanine deaminase.

Replacement of the 8-CH group of 9-(*p*-chlorophenyl) guanine (XXII) by 8-N (XXIII) gives a fivefold loss in binding; although this result could be interpreted to indicate that the 8-CH is involved in binding, a more logical explanation is the base weakening effect of the 8-nitrogen of XXIII on the 7-nitrogen because v-triazole is a weaker base than imidazole.

6 | Substrate or Inhibitor?

In Chapters 3 through 5, the mode of binding of substrates and inhibitors to a number of enzymes was discussed. In some of the cases described a structural change in the substrate led to a modified substrate and in other cases to an inhibitor. For example, replacement of the 6-oxo group of inosinic acid by a 6-thione gave an inhibitor of succinoadenylate kinosynthetase,[1] whereas the identical structural change on guanine gave a modified substrate for guanine deaminase.[2] Are there any ways in which one can predict in advance whether the structural change will lead to an inhibitor or to a modified substrate?

STRUCTURAL CHANGE AT REACTION SITE

If the functional group of the substrate that is undergoing enzymic-catalyzed reaction is modified so that the functional group can no longer undergo the chemical reaction, it is clear that such a molecule can no longer be a substrate; if this structural change does not lead to a severe loss in binding to the enzyme, then this structural modification leads to an inhibitor.

Some years ago it was proposed[3] that an enzyme catalyzing the transfer of a group from one substrate to a second substrate is unlikely to complex with the transfer position on either substrate—else the two groups involved in the transfer reaction may not juxtapose properly.[4] Since that time further observations with about half of the enzymes investigated have supported this concept. The most noticeable exceptions are encountered when an O—H bond must be broken; in many of these cases, it appears

[1] J. B. Wyngaarden and R. A. Greenland, *J. Biol. Chem.*, **238**, 1054 (1963).
[2] E. C. Moore and G. A. Le Page *Cancer Res.*, **18**, 1075 (1958).
[3] B. R. Baker, *Cancer Chemotherapy Reports*, **4**, 1 (1959).
[4] See pages 21–22 for a diagram and discussion of the transferase type of enzyme reaction.

that complexing to the hydroxylic hydrogen also aids in the bond-breaking process.

Chymotrypsin and Trypsin

The mode of binding to the enzymes chymotrypsin and trypsin was discussed in detail in Chapter 3. The chemical reaction catalyzed by these

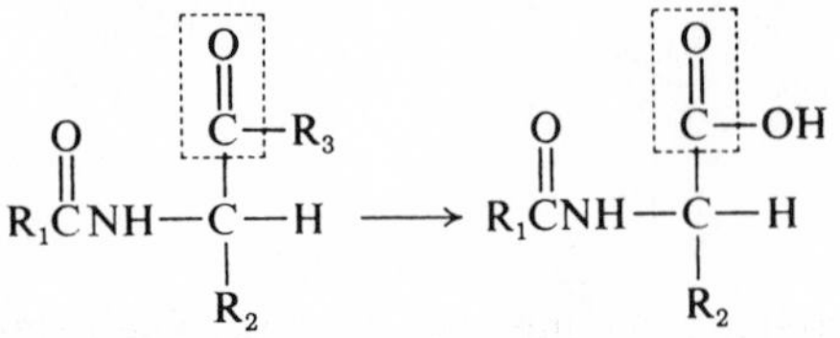

two enzymes, and proteolytic enzymes in general, can be summarized in the transformation I → II, where the encircled carbonyl group represents the reaction site. The carbonyl group of I is most probably complexed to both trypsin and chymotrypsin, presumably through a polarized form of the carbonyl group.[5] Thus any molecule related to I that has a carbonyl group unable to undergo the chemical transformation should be an inhibitor and therefore the product, II, is an inhibitor. Similarly, when the carbonyl group is part of a ketone, it cannot undergo hydrolysis and is therefore an

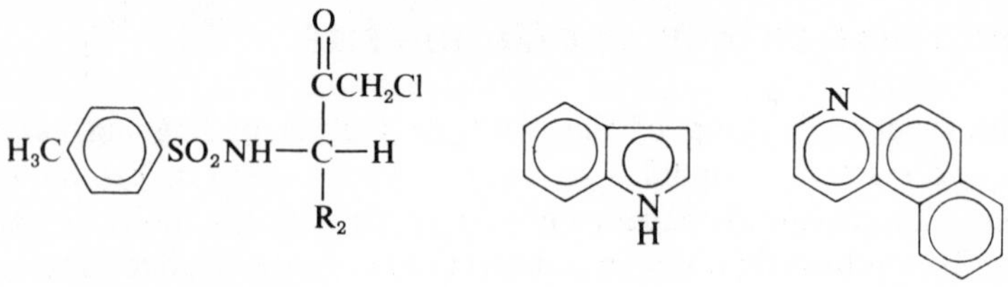

III, $R_2 = C_6H_5CH_2^-$
IV, $R_2 = \overset{\oplus}{N}H_3(CH_2)_4^-$

inhibitor; thus III is an inhibitor of chymotrypsin[6] and IV is an inhibitor of trypsin.[7]

Another approach is to remove the functional group completely; loss of a binding point may occur, but it is frequently possible to increase binding in another area to compensate for this loss. For example, indole (V) is a reasonably good inhibitor ($K_i = 8 \times 10^{-4}$ M) of chymotrypsin and presumably complexes only in the ρ_2 area; the affinity for the enzyme can be increased by further modifying V to VI ($K_i = 6 \times 10^{-5}$ M), which

---

[5] For a detailed discussion of this point see Chapter 3, pp. 50–51.
[6] G. Schoellman and E. Shaw, *Biochemistry*, **2**, 252 (1963).
[7] E. Shaw, M. Mares-Guia, and W. Cohen, *Biochemistry*, **4**, 2219 (1965).

complexes considerably more tightly than a typical substrate, *N*-benzoyl-
DL-tryptophane ethyl ester ($K_m = 5 \times 10^{-3}$ M).[8]

Similar results have been observed with trypsin; the ρ_2 moiety of lysine,
propylamine (VII), is a weak inhibitor of trypsin ($K_i = 9 \times 10^{-3}$ M);

$$n\text{-}C_3H_7\overset{\oplus}{N}H_3 \qquad CH_3C\overset{NH_2}{\underset{NH_2}{\diagup}}\overset{\oplus}{} \qquad \langle\!\langle\,\rangle\!\rangle\!-\!C\overset{NH_2}{\underset{NH_2}{\diagup}}\overset{\oplus}{}$$

VII   VIII   IX

similarly the partial ρ_2 moiety of arginine, acetamidine (VIII), is a weak
inhibitor ($K_i = 36 \times 10^{-3}$ M). Affinity to the ρ_2 area is considerably
increased—presumably due to hydrophobic bonding—with benzamidine
(IX) ($K_i = 2 \times 10^{-5}$ M), which is bound considerably tighter than the
substrate, *N*-benzoyl-L-arginineamide ($K_m = 2 \times 10^{-3}$ M).[9]

The normal substrate for chymotrypsin is a protein where the amide
of an aromatic amino acid is hydrolyzed; for trypsin the amide link of the
basic amino acids, lysine and arginine, is hydrolyzed. It follows that any
structural change in the carbonyl of the polyamide that still gives a
hydrolyzable molecule could be a substrate; thus esters of these acylated
amino acids are substrates, and, in fact, the more reactive is the ester, the
faster is the maximum rate of hydrolysis.

Thymidine Kinase

The chemical transformation catalyzed by thymidine kinase is represented by IX → X, and the reactive functional group is encircled. It is
relatively simple to predict that 5'-deoxythymidine (XI) cannot be a
substrate, for it has no hydroxyl group at the 5'- position; how good an
inhibitor XI would be would depend upon whether or not the transfer
position, namely the 5'-hydroxyl, is also a binding point to the enzyme.
Evaluation of XI as an inhibitor showed that it was indeed an inhibitor,
but considerable loss in binding occurred, for XI was completed only
one thirtieth as well as thymidine (IX).[10]

When the 5'-hydroxyl group of thymidine (IX) was blocked by carbethoxy (XII) no inhibition was observed at 70 times the concentration of
thymidine; because XII is less effective than XI, it follows that the enzyme
does not have the tolerance within the enzyme-inhibitor complex for the
bulk of the carbethoxy group—a result that could be anticipated because it
was established that the 5'-hydroxyl was a binding point to the enzyme.

---

[8] For a more detailed discussion see p. 53.
[9] For a more detailed discussion see p. 65.
[10] See Chapter 4 for a more detailed discussion.

3'-Deoxythymidine (XIII) is one example of a structural change that is totally unpredictable with the current state of knowledge; XIII certainly has the 5'-hydroxyl group for substrate properties and might be anticipated to be at least a poor substrate even though the 3'-hydroxyl may be a binding point. In fact, XIII was not a substrate but an inhibitor that complexed to the enzyme only one eightieth as well as thymidine (IX); it is

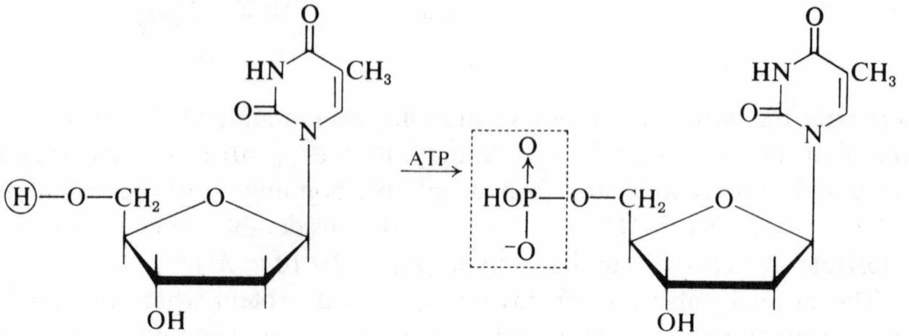

IX

X

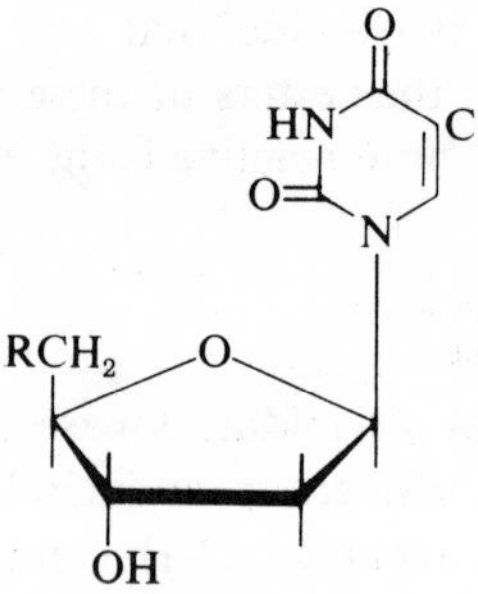

XI, R = H

XII, R = C$_2$H$_5$OC—

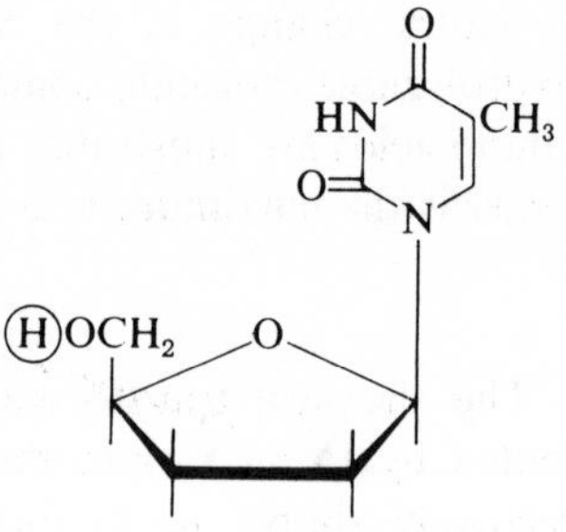

XIII

therefore obvious that the 3'-hydroxyl group is a binding point, but it is less obvious why XIII is an inhibitor and not a substrate. This result can be rationalized by the induced-fit theory of Koshland.[11,12]

Koshland proposed and obtained experimental support for the proposition that an enzyme is not rigid but may undergo spontaneous conformational changes to give maximum bonding between substrate (or inhibitor) and enzyme; "this rearrangement will be limited by both kinetic and thermodynamic considerations."[11] Such conformational changes could align the catalytic site of the enzyme with the reaction site on the substrate,

---

[11] D. E. Koshland, Jr., J. A. Yankeelov, Jr., and J. A. Thoma, *Fed. Proc.*, **21**, 1031 (1962).

[12] D. E. Koshland, Jr., *Proc. Natl. Acad. Sci. (U.S.)*, **44**, 98 (1958).

such a realignment leading to an accelerated reaction rate. The "thermo-dynamic considerations" were not further elaborated upon. However, it is clear that some conformational changes in the enzyme necessary to attack the substrate may be thermodynamically unfavorable; such an energetically unfavorable conformational change could take place when the energy is supplied by part of the energy released when the substrate and the enzyme form a complex. Thus the fact that XIII is a weak inhibitor, but not a substrate, can now be rationalized as follows:

In order for the 3'-hydroxyl group to bond to the enzyme, the enzyme might have to undergo an energetically unfavorable conformational change, the energy for which is more than provided for by the bonding of the 3'-hydroxyl to the enzyme; this energetically unfavorable conforma-tional change, that is, energetically unfavorable in the absence of substrate, may then align the catalytic site properly to the reaction site. Other exam-ples were observed with chymotrypsin. Methyl hydrocinnamate apparently complexes as well to the enzyme as its α-acetamido derivate, yet the latter is a much faster substrate; the α-acetamido group is probably involved in complexing to the enzyme, but the net complexing energy from this group may be used to cause an energetically unfavorable conformation change in the enzyme which better aligns the catalytic site.[13]

Thus the result of structural changes other than at the reaction site cannot as yet be predicted, but must be measured.

Thymidine Phosphorylase

The chemical transformation catalyzed by thymidine phosphorylase is

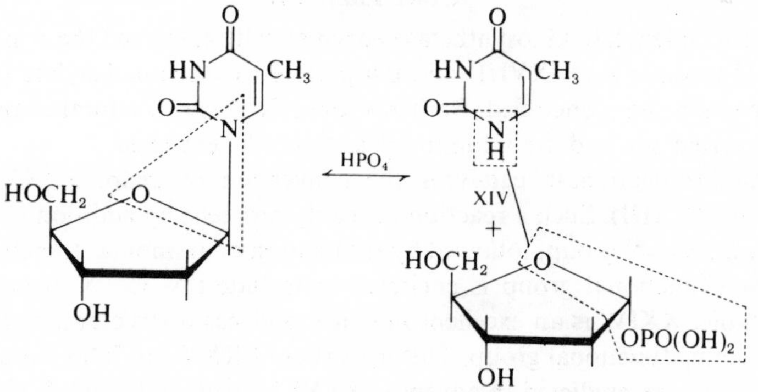

represented by IX ⇌ XIV + XV; the reaction sites are encircled. Because the reaction is reversible, it can be anticipated that the product thymine (XIV) would be an inhibitor. What could not be anticipated is that thymine

[13] See p. 51 for a more detailed discussion.

actually complexes to the enzyme more tightly than thymidine; apparently the 1-NH group of XIV complexes strongly to the enzyme.[14]

It can be predicted with certainty that the cyclopentane analog (XVI) of thymidine would not be a substrate, for exchange of the furanose oxygen by methylene gives an unhydrolyzable C_1'- linkage, a modification of the reacting functional group; however, XVI was a poor inhibitor due either to loss of a binding point or hindrance to complex formation by the methylene group. With 3'-deoxythymidine (XVIIA) and 5'-deoxythymidine

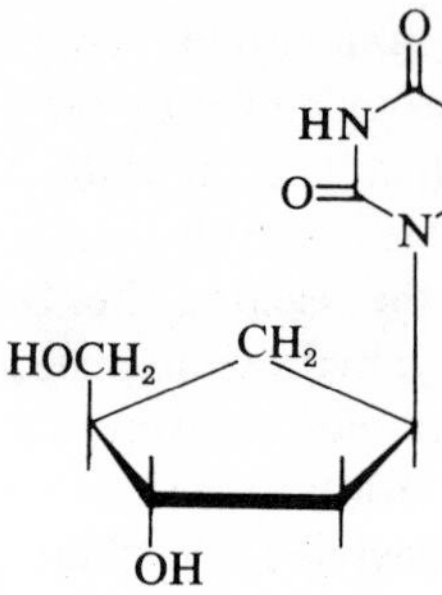

XVI

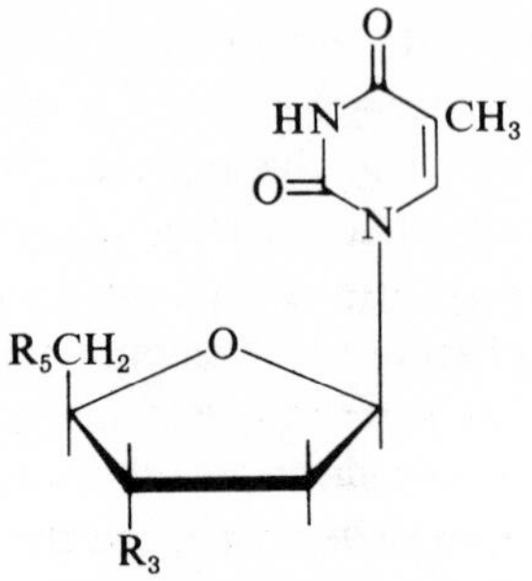

XVIIA, R_3 = H, R_5 = OH
XVIIB, R_3 = OH, R_5 = H

(XVIIB), it is not possible to predict whether either compound should be a substrate or an inhibitor, for neither structural change is at the reaction site; in fact, XVIIA is a poor inhibitor, but XVIIB is a good substrate.

Other Enzymes

Succinoadenylate kinosynthetase enzymatically catalyzed the condensation of inosinic acid (XVIII) and L-aspartate to succinoadenylate (XIX); the reaction site is encircled. Both XX and XXI have structural changes at the reaction site and are inhibitors[15] as might be expected.

Guanine deaminase catalyzes the conversion of guanine (XXII) to xanthine (XXIII). Such a reaction probably proceeds by addition of water to the 2,3-C=N group, followed by elimination of ammonia; therefore the reacting functional group is encircled to include this C=N group. The imidazole, XXIV, is an excellent inhibitor and has a structural change at the reacting functional group. The properties of XXV and XXVI could not at this time be predicted in advance; XXVI is a substrate, but XXV is an inhibitor even though it contains the proper groups for transformation. That XXV is an inhibitor most probably involves a conformational change in the enzyme which unaligns the catalytic site; such a conformational

[14] For more detail see Chapter 5, p. 97.
[15] See Chapter 5 for a more detailed discussion.

change may be due to a relatively strong net binding obtained by complexing of the 9-phenyl group to the enzyme.

Thymidylate synthetase is an enzyme that reductively transfers a formaldehyde group from 5,10-methylene-*l*-tetrahydrofolate to the 5-

XVIII XIX

XX XXI

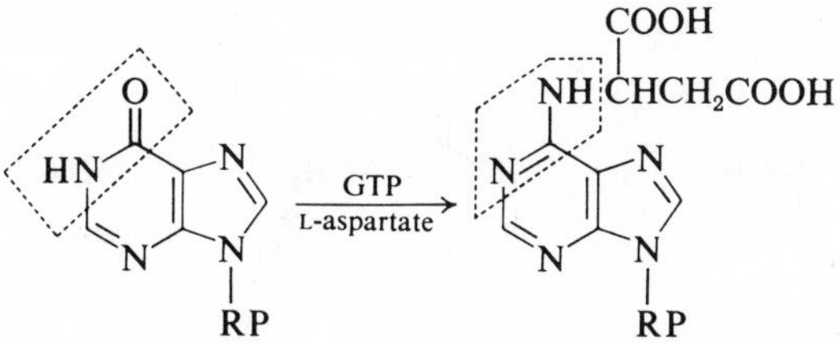

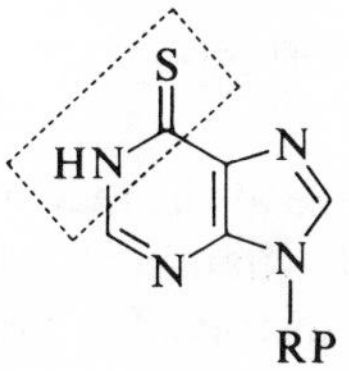

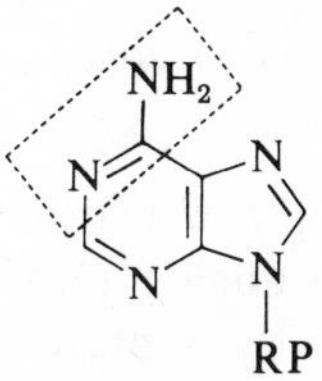

RP = β-D-ribofuranose-5′-phosphate

XXII XXIII

XXIV

XXV XXVI

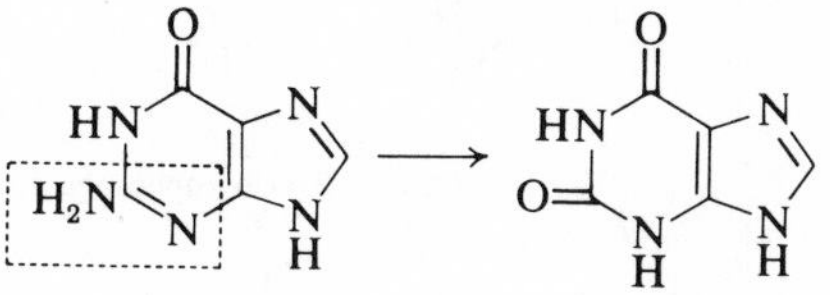

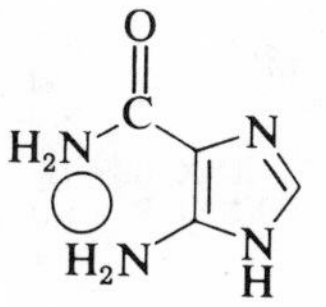

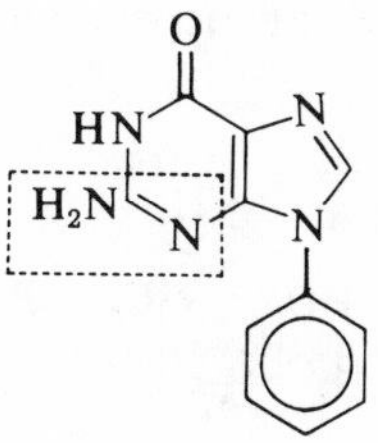

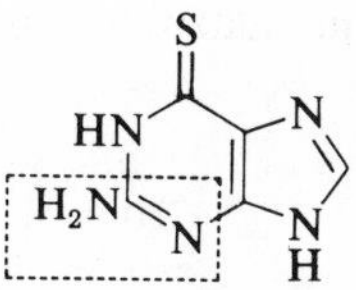

position of 2′-deoxyuridylate (XXVII) with formation of thymidylate (XXVIII). Any structural change removing the 5-hydrogen should result in an inhibitor if the enzyme has sufficient bulk tolerance for the structural change in question. Thus, the product, thymidylate (XXVIII), is a good inhibitor of the reaction.[16] Similarly the 5-fluoronucleotide (XXIX) is an inhibitor of the enzyme; what could not be predicted with any certainty was the observation that XXIX binds 1000-fold better than the substrate,[17] presumably because of the stronger bonding of the more acidic 3-NH group of XXIX to the enzyme.

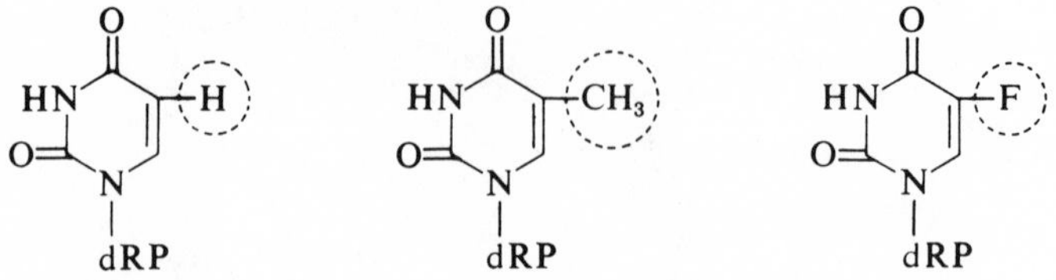

$$dRP = 2'\text{-deoxy-}\beta\text{-D-ribofuranose-5'-phosphate}$$

An interesting example of a structural change at the reacting functional group is the pyridine analog (XXXII)[18] of vitamin B_1 (XXX). The pyridine analog (XXXII) is presumably a substrate for the kinase that

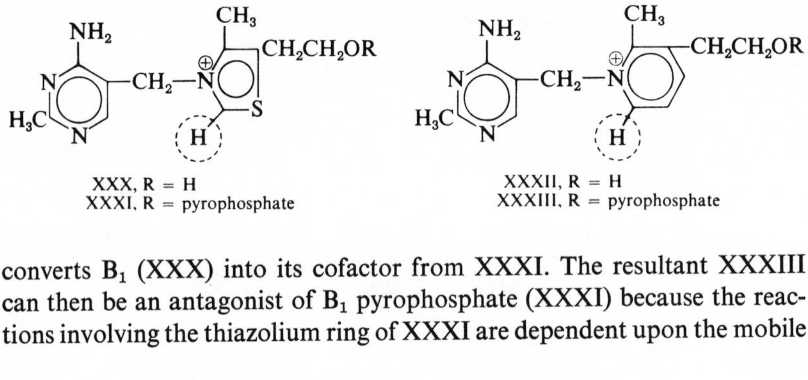

XXX, R = H
XXXI, R = pyrophosphate

XXXII, R = H
XXXIII, R = pyrophosphate

converts B_1 (XXX) into its cofactor from XXXI. The resultant XXXIII can then be an antagonist of B_1 pyrophosphate (XXXI) because the reactions involving the thiazolium ring of XXXI are dependent upon the mobile

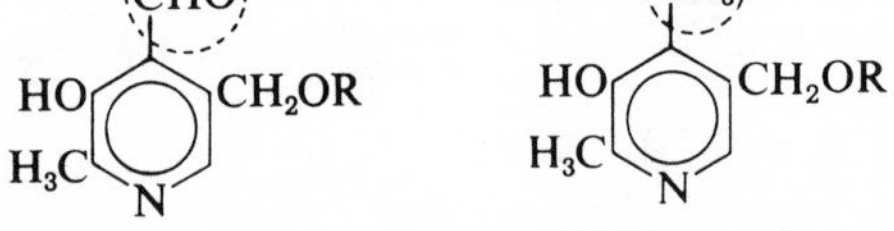

XXXIV, R = H
XXXV, R = phosphate

XXXVI, R = H
XXXVII, R = phosphate

[16] R. L. Blakely, *J. Biol. Chem.*, **238**, 2113 (1963).
[17] S. S. Cohen, J. A. Flaks, H. D. Barner, M. R. Loeb, and J. Lichtenstein, *Proc. Natl. Acad. Sci. (U.S.)*, **44**, 1004 (1958).
[18] A. H. Tracy and R. C. Elderfield, *J. Org. Chem.*, **6**, 54 (1941).

proton (encircled)[19] of XXXI; the corresponding proton of XXXIII is not mobile, and therefore XXXIII is an antagonist rather than a substrate.

Similarly, deoxypyridoxine (XXXVI) is a substrate for the kinase that converts pyridoxal (XXXIV) to its phosphate, XXXV[20]; the resultant XXXVII is then an inhibitor of certain enzymatic reactions of XXXV, for XXXVII now has a change in the reacting functional group.

[19] R. Breslow and E. McNelis, *J. Am. Chem. Soc.*, **81**, 3080 (1959).
[20] D. B. McCormick and E. E. Snell, *J. Biol. Chem.* **236**, 2085 (1961).

7 | Bulk Tolerance in Enzyme-inhibitor Complexes

The concept of active-site-directed irreversible enzyme inhibitors was presented in Chapter 1. There are presumably two types of irreversible inhibitors operating by this mechanism; the *endo* type covalently bonds *within* the complexing region and the *exo* type covalently bonds *adjacent* to the complexing region of the enzyme. The endo type, by definition, can have little tolerance for bulky groups within the complexing region; in contrast, the exo type, by definition, should have tolerance for bulky groups outside of the complexing region. Is there evidence among the enzymes discussed in previous chapters that there are bulk tolerance areas in enzyme-inhibitor complexes; that is, is there an area on the inhibitor that is not in contact with the enzyme where large groups can be placed?

CHYMOTRYPSIN AND TRYPSIN

The ρ concept of binding to trypsin and chymotrypsin can be generalized in structure I.[1] From the data presented in Chapter 3 it is clear that there is considerable bulk tolerance in all four ρ areas. It would appear that the interaction between inhibitors and trypsin or chymotrypsin is a fairly flat one, although little study has been made with substrates or inhibitors having three-dimensional bulk.

Of these four ρ areas of chymotrypsin, the ρ_1 area has been investigated the most extensively for active-site-directed irreversible inhibitors of the exo type. The ρ_3 area has been investigated only for endo type irreversible inhibitors; the ρ_2 and ρ_H areas have not as yet been investigated for irreversible inhibitors of either type.[2]

[1] See Chapter 3 for a detailed discussion.
[2] See Chapter 8 for more detailed suggestions on such studies.

116

Of the four ρ areas of trypsin, only the ρ_3 area has been investigated for endo inhibitors[2]; all other areas are good candidates for further exploration.

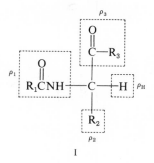

I

THYMIDINE KINASE

The mode of binding thymidine and inhibitors to thymidine kinase, the enzyme that converts thymidine to thymidylate, was discussed in Chapter 4. Studies on the bulk tolerance of this enzyme have so far been disappointing in that no area of bulk tolerance has been uncovered.

Substitution on the 5-methyl group of thymidine (II) (Table 7–1) with an ethoxymethyl group (III) led to a 550-fold loss in binding. Similarly, substitution at the 3- position by *n*-amyl (IV), benzyl (V), or phenylpropyl (VI) led to a 50–90-fold loss in binding; part or all of this loss may be due to the loss of the 3-NH group as a binding point to the enzyme. The 2-, 4-, and 6- positions remain to be studied, but the 4- position is probably a binding point and might therefore not be replaceable without a loss in binding.[3]

Neither uridine nor 1-(β,D-arabinofuranosyl)-thymine are substrates for the enzyme[4]; therefore there is no bulk tolerance for a group of either D or L configuration at 2′ that allows retention of substrate properties. However, whether uridine or 1-(β,D-arabinofuranosyl)-thymine are inhibitors has not been determined; thus, it cannot be stated whether or not there is bulk tolerance at the 2′- position.

Four 5′-carbonate derivatives (VII–X) of thymidine were ineffective as inhibitors at high concentration; there is therefore no bulk tolerance for carbonate-type groups, Whether or not 5′-ethers would be tolerated remains to be determined; if the hydrogen of the 5′-hydroxyl group is a

---

[3] See Chapter 4 for a more detailed discussion.
[4] R. Okazaki and A. Kornberg, *J. Biol. Chem.*, **239**, 269 (1964).

Table 7-1. Inhibition of Thymidine Kinase by

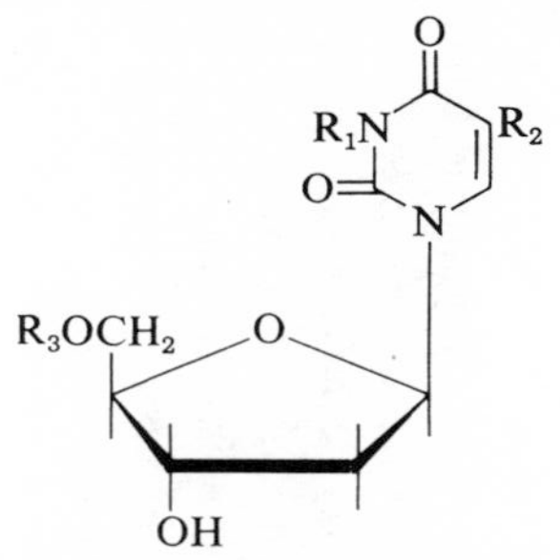

No.	R_1	R_2	R_3	μM concentration	Per cent inhibition[a]	$[I/S]_{0.5}$[b]
II	H	CH_3—	H	0.04	68	1
III	H	$C_2H_5OCH_2$—	H	3	21	550
IV	$n\text{-}C_5H_{11}$	CH_3	H	3	70	75
V	$C_6H_5CH_2$	CH_3	H	3	62[c]	90
VI	$C_6H_5(CH_2)_3$	CH_3	H	2	68[c]	50
VII	H	CH_3	C_2H_5OCO—	3	0	> 600
VIII	H	CH_3	C_6H_5OCO—	3	0	> 600
IX	H	CH_3	$C_6H_5(CH_2)_2NHCO$—	3	0	> 600
X	H	CH_3	CH_3NHCO—	3	0	> 600

[a] Data found on thymidine kinase, isolated from *E. coli* B and assayed with 0.1 mM FUDR; data from B. R. Baker, T. J. Schwan, and D. V. Santi, *J. Med. Chem.*, **9** 66 (1966), unless otherwise indicated.

[b] The estimated ratio of concentration of inhibitor to concentration of thymidine giving 50 per cent inhibition of formation of FUDRP.

[c] Unpublished data by B. R. Baker and T. J. Schwan.

binding point to the enzyme, then loss in binding will occur whether or not there is tolerance for the ether group. Substitution on the carbon atoms at 1'-5'- may allow emergence of one or more areas of bulk tolerance, but such compounds can be synthetized only with tremendous difficulty and may not be worth the effort.

With the present knowledge, thymidine kinase does not appear to be a good candidate for inhibition by active-site-directed irreversible inhibitors of the exo type; further studies on bulk tolerance or on ways to increase binding by one group so that another group may be removed might reveal a useful approach, but the odds are discouraging.

GUANINE DEAMINASE

The mode of binding of guanine and inhibitors to guanine deaminase, the enzyme that converts guanine (XI) to xanthine (XII), was discussed in Chapter 5. There are theoretically seven positions on guanine that could

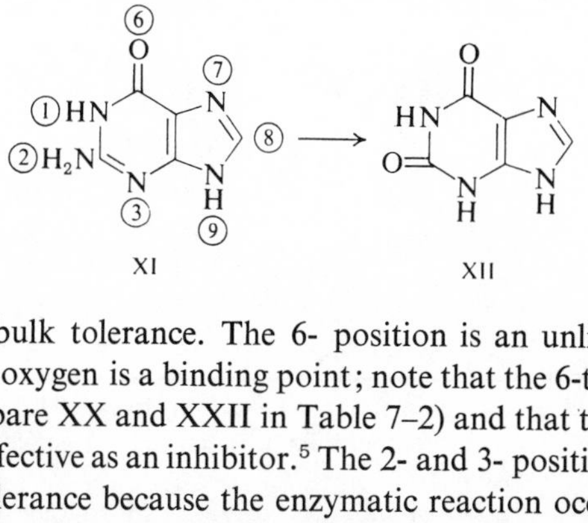

be studied for bulk tolerance. The 6- position is an unlikely candidate, for the cabonyl oxygen is a binding point; note that the 6-thione binds less effectively (compare XX and XXII in Table 7–2) and that the 6-methylthio derivative is ineffective as an inhibitor.[5] The 2- and 3- positions are unlikely to have bulk tolerance because the enzymatic reaction occurs here; however, it would be of interest to verify this guess by evaluation of some N_2- and N^3- alkyguanines.

Although 1-methylguanine is a substrate, it does not bind as well as guanine; qualitatively, 1-methylguanine is a barely perceptible substrate at twice the concentration of guanine and about one half as effective at 10 times the concentration of guanine. The loss in binding is probably due to the fact that the hydrogen of the NH group is a binding point to the enzyme.

7-Methylguanine shows no substrate or inhibitor properties at 20 times the level of guanine, even though 7-methylguanine still has an electron pair

[5] See Chapter 5, Table 5.

for binding; thus there is no bulk tolerance at the 7- position. This result might also be attributed to the loss of the 9-H binding point.

Study of the 8- and 9- positions for bulk tolerance (Table 7–2) were more rewarding. 8-Phenyguanine (XIII) was an inhibitor, but about a 20-fold loss in binding occurred. The 8-(phenylpropyl)-guanine (XIV) showed no inhibitory properties at about 20 times substrate concentration; thus the

Table 7–2. Inhibition of Guanine Deaminase by

No.	R_1	R_2	R_3	μM con-centration	Per cent inhibition[a]	$[I/S]_{0.5}$[b,c]
XIII	$=O$	C_6H_5C-	H	250	50	19
XIV	$=O$	$C_6H_5(CH_2)_3C-$	H	250	0	> 75
XV	$=O$	CH	CH_3	275	50	21
XVI	$=O$	CH	$n\text{-}C_5H_{11}-$	450	50	34
XVII	$=O$	CH	$i\text{-}C_5H_{11}-$	210	50	16
XVIII	$=O$	CH	cyclohexyl-	125	50	9.4
XIX	$=O$	CH	$C_6H_5CH_2$-	370	50	28
XX	$=O$	CH	C_6H_5-	10	50	0.75
XXI	$=O$	CH	$p\text{-}ClC_6H_4-$	3.8	50	0.29
XXII	$=S$	CH	C_6H_5-	83	50	6.2
XXIII	$=O$	N	$p\text{-}ClC_6H_4$	18	50	1.4

[a] The guanase used was a commercial preparation, isolated from rabbit liver, that was assayed with 13.3 μM guanine in 0.05 M tris pH 7.4 buffer, in the presence of 10 per cent dimethylsulfoxide.

[b] The ratio of concentration of inhibitor to 13.3 μM guanine giving 50 per cent inhibition; data from B. R. Baker and D. V. Santi, *J. Med. Chem.*, **10**, 62 (1967).

[c] No substrate properties were observable.

in-plane 8-phenyl group was better tolerated than the staggered propyl group of XIV with its terminal phenyl group.

9-Methylguanine (XV) showed no substrate properties but was complexed as an inhibitor with a 21-fold loss in binding; this result could be due to the need of a 9-NH for binding or a lack of bulk tolerance for the methyl group. Other alkyl groups (XVI–XVIII) or benzyl (XIX) showed little, if any, improvement in binding. In contrast, 9-phenylguanine (XX) was an excellent inhibitor that was complexed slightly better than the substrate; binding was further tightened by introduction of a *p*-chloro group (XXI).

The results with 9-methyl (XV), 9-phenyl (XX) and 9-(*p*-chlorophenyl) guanine (XXI) can be interpreted several ways: (a) the methyl group has more three-dimensional bulk, which is less tolerated, than the in-plane phenyl group; (b) the 9-NH is a binding point, which is lost by 9-substitution of an alkyl group, but the in-plane phenyl group gives additional direct binding to the enzyme. Studies underway should shed light on whether the 9-phenyl group is actually complexing with the enzyme and, if so, by what mode of binding. Furthermore, substitution of covalent forming groups on the 9-phenyl moiety of XX should make good candidates for active-site-directed irreversible inhibitors of this enzyme.

9-Phenyl-6-thioguanine (XXII) is also an inhibitor but complexes about eightfold less effectively than 9-phenylguanine; similarly, 9-(*p*-chloro-phenyl)-8-azaguanine (XXIII) is an inhibitor that complexes about one fifth as effectively as 9-(*p*-chlorophenyl)-guanine (XXI). These results with XXII and XXIII agree with the observed facts that 8-azaguanine and 6-thioguanine are substrates.[6]

The fact that guanosine and guanylic acid are not substrates[7] could be rationalized on the basis that neither can complex to the enzyme effectively, for the 9-NH group is substituted; furthermore, if the phenyl (XX) and cyclohexyl (XVIII) groups are complexed to the enzyme hydrophobically, this hydrophobic region could repulse the polar ribose moiety of guanosine and guanylic acid.

THYMIDINE PHOSPHORYLASE

In Chapter 4 we showed that uracils substituted by a variety of alkyl and aralkyl groups at 1-, 5-, and 6- positions (XXIV) were inhibitors. Thus

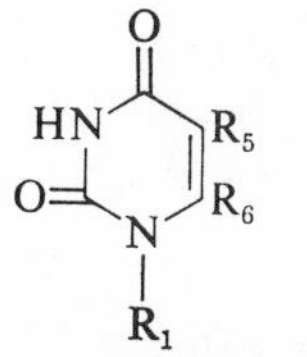

XXIV

there is considerable bulk tolerance in these three areas. Substitution of covalent forming groups such as bromoacetamido on one of the aralkyl groups at the 1-, 5-, or 6- positions would make likely candidates for active-site-directed irreversible inhibitors of this enzyme.

---

[6] See Chapter 5.
[7] A. Roush and E. R. Norris, *Arch. Biochem.*, **29**, 124 (1950).

8 | Active-Site-Directed Irreversible Inhibitors

KINETIC PARAMETERS

The concept of active-site-directed irreversible inhibitors was presented in Chapter 1. Of utmost importance to this concept is the fact that the inactivation reaction proceeds through an enzyme inhibitor complex, as indicated in (8–1); by means of this mechanism a neighboring group

$$E + A\text{—}B \underset{k_2}{\overset{k_1}{\rightleftharpoons}} \overset{\frown}{E\cdots A}\overset{\frown}{\text{—}B} \overset{k_3}{\longrightarrow} \overset{\frown}{E\cdots A} + B^- \qquad (8\text{–}1)$$

reaction occurs within the enzyme-inhibitor complex, which can be accelerated 1000–10,000-fold, compared to the equivalent bimolecular reaction indicated in (8–2). Specificity of reaction is obtained by the mechanism

$$E + A\text{—}B \overset{k_3}{\longrightarrow} \overset{\frown}{E\ A} + B^- \qquad (8\text{–}2)$$

shown in (8–1), for the reaction is dependent upon the concentration of enzyme-inhibitor complex. This in turn is dependent not only on the concentrations of the enzyme and the inhibitor but the affinity of the enzyme for the inhibitor—the so-called dissociation constant of the enzyme-inhibitor complex.

Active-Site-Directed Inactivation

In (8–1) k_1 and k_2 are extremely rapid diffusion processes, whereas k_3 is relatively slow; therefore the rate-limiting step is k_3, and the rate of inactivation of the enzyme is as follows[1]:

$$\frac{-dE}{dt} = \frac{d(\overset{\frown}{E\cdots A})}{dt} = k_3[E\cdots A\text{—}B] \qquad (8\text{–}3)$$

[1] B. R. Baker, W. W. Lee, and E. Tong, *J. Theoret Biol.*, **3**, 459 (1962).

The concentration of E····A—B is dependent upon the concentrations of E, A—B (equals I), and the dissociation constant K_i:

$$K_i = \frac{[E] \, [I]}{[EI]} \tag{8-4}$$

also,

$$E_t = [E] + [EI] \tag{8-5}$$

where E_t is the total enzyme concentration excluding that portion that has become inactivated.

Substitution of (8-5) in (8-4) gives (8-6)

$$K_i = \frac{(E_t - [EI])[I]}{[EI]}$$

$$[EI] = \frac{E_t}{(K_i/[I]) + 1} \tag{8-6}$$

This equation is the same form as that for the velocity of conversion of substrate to product.[2]

If $I = K_i$, then $[EI] = 0.5 \, E_t$; if $I = 2K_i$, then

$$[EI] = \frac{E_t}{(K_i/2K_i) + 1} = \frac{E_t}{1.5} = 0.67 \, E_t$$

Therefore increasing [I] from a concentration of K_i to a concentration of $2K_i$ increases the [EI] complex by $0.67 \, E_t/0.5 \, E_t = 1.3$, a so-called rate-saturation effect; if no equilibrium were involved, the rate of inactivation would be doubled when [I] is doubled.

Bimolecular Inactivation

There are two cases of bimolecular inactivation to consider, depending on whether a reversible complex is formed between inhibitor and enzyme. If a reversible complex is not formed, then the reaction is expressed simply as (8-2); in this reaction the rate of inactivation of the enzyme is as follows:

$$-\frac{dE}{dt} = [E] \, [I] \tag{8-7}$$

Therefore doubling the concentration of [I] will double the rate; this mechanism is therefore easily distinguished from the active-site-directed mechanism of Equation (8-1) as expressed by Equation (8-6).

However, if the inhibitor reacts bimolecularly as in Equation (8-2), but

[2] M. Dixon and E. C. Webb, *The Enzymes*, Academic Press, New York, 1958, p. 75.

also forms a reversible complex which does not inactivate, as in (8–8) the mechanism is kinetically indistinguishable from mechanism (8–1).[3]

$$E + A\!-\!B \xrightarrow{k_3} E \overparen{} A + B^- \qquad (8\text{–}2)$$

$$E + A\!-\!B \underset{k_2}{\overset{k_1}{\rightleftharpoons}} E\cdots A\!-\!B \qquad (8\text{–}8)$$

The rate of bimolecular inactivation of the enzyme is expressed by

$$\frac{-dE}{dt} = k_3'[\text{E}]\,[\text{I}] \qquad (8\text{–}9)$$

where [I] is equal to [AB] standing for the inhibitor concentration; the rate of reaction is dependent upon the free-enzyme concentration [E]. Because (8–8) is operational and is expressed by Equation (8–4), the latter can be substituted in Equation (8–9) to give

$$\frac{-dE}{dt} = k_3'K_i[\text{EI}] = k''[\text{EI}] = \text{rate of inactivation} \qquad (8\text{–}10)$$

as k_3'/K_i becomes a new constant k''.

Equation (8–10), which expresses a bimolecular inactivation with self-protection by formation of a complex (8–8), is kinetically indistinguishable from active-site-directed inactivation as expressed by Equation (8–3). When two concentrations of inhibitor are compared, the ratio of the rates cancels k_3 or k'' from the equation. Thus, the "rate-saturation" effect does not distinguish between the two mechanisms, but at best can only be used as evidence that a complex is involved in the inactivation. Fortunately, these two mechanisms can be resolved by structure-activity relationships; if a compound A′—B is employed that does not form a reversible complex with the enzyme in (8–8), it will still inactivate the enzyme if the bimolecular mechanism in (8–2) is operational. It will not inactivate the enzyme if the active-site-directed mechanism in (8–1) is operational.

It is conceivable that a third type of bimolecular reaction could occur. Suppose an inhibitor AB forms a reversible complex with the enzyme that causes a conformational change in the enzyme with concomitant exposure of a group that can now be attacked bimolecularly by a second molecule of AB; the following reactions are involved:

$$E + AB \rightleftharpoons E\cdots AB$$

$$\hspace{4cm} A$$
$$\hspace{3.7cm} \diagup$$
$$E\cdots AB + AB \xrightarrow{k_3} E\cdots AB + B^-$$

---

[3] B. R. Baker and R. P. Patel, *J. Pharm. Sci.*, **53**, 714 (1964).

Then,

$$r = \frac{-dE}{dt} = \frac{d[\text{E}\cdots\text{AB}]}{dt} = k_3[\text{E}\cdots\text{AB}]\,[\text{AB}] \qquad (8\text{--}11)$$

with the structure A over E····AB above the middle term.

where r is the rate of inactivation and $[\text{E}\cdots\text{AB}]$ is negligible compared to $[\text{AB}]$; that is, AB is in large excess over E.

Substitute Equation (8–6) in (8–11); then

$$r = k_3\left[\frac{E_t}{\dfrac{K_i}{[\text{AB}]} + 1}\right][\text{AB}] \qquad (8\text{--}12)$$

If $[\text{AB}] = K_i$, then

$$r_1 = k_3\left[\frac{E_t}{2}\right]K_1 = 0.5k_3[E_t]K_i$$

If $[\text{AB}]$ equals $2K_i$, then

$$r_2 = k_3\left[\frac{E_t}{1.5}\right][2K_i] = 1.33k_3[E_t]K_i$$

$$\frac{r_2}{r_1} = \frac{1.33k_3[E_t]K_i}{0.5k_3[E_t]K_i} = 2.66$$

Thus increasing $[\text{AB}]$ from a concentration equal to K_i to $2K_i$ will give a 2.6-fold increase in the rate of inactivation; in contrast, both the active-site-directed mechanism in (8–1) and the bimolecular inactivation with self-protection, given in (8–10), will give only a 1.3-fold increase in rate when $[\text{AB}]$ is increased from K_i to $2K_i$.

Both mechanisms in (8–6) and (8–12) would be useful for chemotherapy because a complex between enzyme and inhibitor is essential for inactivation; in contrast, the bimolecular mechanisms in (8–7) and (8–10) would not be useful, for a complex between enzyme and inhibitor is *not* necessary for inactivation.

If the mechanism in (8–12) is operating, it should be possible in most cases to verify it further in the following manner. If the leaving group B of AB is replaced by hydrogen, the resulting inhibitor AH should in most cases still cause a conformational change in the enzyme with exposure of the group that is subject to bimolecular attack; this group should also be subject to attack by a second molecule A′B, where A′ does not form a reversible complex with the enzyme and is preferably smaller than A to avoid steric complications. The mechanism involves the following equations:

$$E + AH \rightleftharpoons E\cdots AH$$

$$E\cdots AH + A'B \xrightarrow{k_3} \overset{A'}{\overset{\diagup}{E\cdots AH}} + B^-$$

Then

$$r = \frac{-dE}{dt} = \frac{d[\overset{A'}{\overset{\diagup}{E\cdots AH}}]}{dt} = k_3[E\cdots AH][A'B] \qquad (8\text{--}13)$$

where r is the rate of inactivation of the enzyme. Substitute Equation (8–6) in (8–13); then

$$r = k_3[(E_t/K_i)[E\cdots AH] + 1]\,[A'B] \qquad (8\text{--}14)$$

If AH equals K_i, then

$$r_1 = k_3\left[\frac{E_t}{2}\right][A'B] = 0.50k_3[E_t][A'B]$$

If AH $= 2K_i$, then

$$r_2 = k_3\left[\frac{E_t}{1.5}\right][A'B] = 0.67[E_t][A'B]$$

$$\frac{r_2}{r_1} = \frac{0.67[E_t][A'B]}{0.50[E_t][A'B]} = 1.3,$$

when A'B is held constant; that is, a rate saturation with respect to [AH] will be observed. If [AH] is held constant and [A'B] is doubled, then the rate of inactivation should double; hence by these two additional criteria, this mechanism is readily distinguished from the preceding two types of bimolecular inactivations. Presumably this mechanism has recently been observed with trypsin[4]; the rate of inactivation of trypsin by iodoacetamide is considerably increased in the presence of the reversible inhibitor, N-methylguanidine.

Protective Effects

Now consider the effect of a protecting agent on the kinetics of the four mechanisms of inactivation that have been discussed. When a reversible

---

[4] T. Inagami, *J. Biol. Chem.*, **240**, PC3453 (1965).

inhibitor complexes with the enzyme, less enzyme is available for attack by the inactivating agent, regardless of mechanism. Then

$$E + R \rightleftharpoons E \cdots R \qquad (8\text{--}15)$$

where R is a reversible inhibitor that can complex with the enzyme. The case of active-site-directed irreversible inhibition is expressed by Equation (8–1), where the rate of inactivation is dependent upon the concentration of reversible EI complex, as expressed by (8–6).

By visual inspection you can see that this is the kinetic situation that occurs when a reversible inhibitor R inhibits a normal substrate-enzyme conversion to a product; the rate of the latter is dependent upon the E$\cdots$S concentration, and the inactivation is also dependent upon the concentration of E$\cdots$I complex, except that enzyme is being used up in this process. It can be derived that—at any point on the time axis—the velocity of inactivating the remaining enzyme can be expressed as follows[5]:

$$V = \frac{kE_t}{1 + (K_i/I)[1 + (R/K_r)]} \qquad (8\text{--}16)$$

where E_t equals [E] + [ER] + [EI] and does not include inactivated enzyme.

When no reversible inhibitor (R = 0) is present then the second term in the denominator is equal to 1 and

$$V_1 = \frac{kE_t}{1 + (K_i/I)} \qquad (8\text{--}17)$$

which is the same expression as Equation (8–6).

If the reversible protecting agent were used at a concentration equal to K_r, then

$$V_2 = \frac{kE_t}{1 + (2K_i/I)} \qquad (8\text{--}18)$$

Therefore,

$$\frac{V_1}{V_2} = \frac{1 + (2K_i/I)}{1 + (K_i/I)} = \frac{I + 2K_i}{I + K_i}$$

for any given concentration of I.

If I equals K_i, then

$$\frac{V_1}{V_2} = \frac{3K_i}{2K_i} = \frac{3}{2}$$

The second class of inactivation is the bimolecular type where no reversible complex is formed between the inactivator (I) and the enzyme. The

[5] See Reference 1, p. 122.

rate of inactivation is expressed by (8–7) and is dependent upon the concentrations of I and free enzyme. When (8–15) is also operational in the presence of a reversible inhibitor R, then,

$$E_t = [ER] + [E]$$

$$[ER] = \frac{E_t}{(K_r/R) + 1} \tag{8–19}$$

When the two expressions are combined, then

$$[E] = [E_t]\left(1 - \frac{1}{(K_r/R) + 1}\right) \tag{8–20}$$

Substituting Equation (8–20) into (8–7) gives

$$V = k[I][E_t]\left(1 - \frac{1}{(K_r/R) + 1}\right) \tag{8–21}$$

If R equals 0, then Equation (8–21) reduces to

$$V_1 = k[I][E_t]$$

If R equals K_r, then (8–21) reduces to

$$V_2 = \tfrac{1}{2}k[I][E_t]$$

Therefore

$$V_1/V_2 = 2$$

Thus when R equals K_r, the protection is greater with the bimolecular process than with the active-site-directed process; furthermore, the amount of protection in the bimolecular process is independent of the inactivator (I) concentration, while in the active-site-directed inactivation, the amount of protection is dependent on the inactivator (I) concentration.

The third type of inactivation is bimolecular with self-protection when E is complexed with I; because this type is kinetically indistinguishable from active-site-directed inactivation, the protection from this type of bimolecular inactivation is also expressed by (8–16).

The fourth type of inactivation is a bimolecular reaction between I and E····I complex, the velocity of which is

$$V = k[EI][I] \tag{8–11}$$

By combining Equation (8–11) with (8–16),

$$V = \frac{k[E_t][I]}{1 + (K_i/I)[1 + (R/K_r)]}$$

If R equals 0, then

$$V_1 = \frac{k[E_t][I]}{1 + (K_i/I)}$$

If R equals K_r, then

$$V_2 = \frac{k[E_t][I]}{1 + (2K_i/I)}$$

Then $(V_1/V_2) = (I + 2K_i)/(I + K_i)$ and is therefore dependent upon the concentration of I.

If $I = K_i$, then $(V_1/V_2) = 3/2$, the same as the active-site-directed inactivation. This calculation is valid only when the reversible inhibitor, R, does not cause the same conformational change as the inhibitor, I.

CHYMOTRYPSIN

Acylation of Serine-195

As was pointed out in Chapter 1, the discovery that diisopropyl fluorophosphate (DFP) (I) was a specific reagent for the active-site of a number of esterases and proteolytic enzymes was a major milestone in the development of the concept of active-site-directed irreversible inhibitors. The fact that DFP reacted selectively with only one out of 20 or more serine residues evaded explanation for many years because no rate-saturation effect was observable.[6]

DFP inactivates enzymes such as cholinesterase and chymotrypsin with extreme rapidity; Equation (8–1) is operating and k_3 is rapid. A concentration of inhibitor equal to K_i would give such a fast reaction that the rate could not be measured by the usual techniques. Suppose the concentration of DFP $= [I] = K_i/100$ in one run and $K_i/50$ in a second run; furthermore because

$$[EI] = \frac{E_t}{(K_i/[I]) + 1} \tag{8–6}$$

then [EI] equals $0.01\, E_t$ in the first case and [EI] equals $0.02\, E_t$ in the second case. Then the ratio of the rates would be 2, the same as a bimolecular reaction; thus for years, the reaction was considered to be bimolecular, but one serine residue was "uniquely" active.[7]

By use of a phosphorylating agent that has a slower k_3, namely 0,0-dimethyl-S-(1,2-dicarbomethoxyethyl)-phosphorothiolate (malaoxon),

[6] W. N. Aldridge, *Biochem. J.*, **46**, 451 (1950).
[7] See Reference 6, p. 129.

Main[8] was able to demonstrate that a reversible complex was first formed between cholinesterase and the irreversible inhibitor; DFP still gave such a rapid reaction under his conditions that he could not demonstrate unequivocally that a complex was formed. It is highly probable that further refinements will demonstrate a reversible complex between DFP and these hydrolytic enzymes, as is shown in Equation (8–22).

$$
\begin{array}{cc}
\underset{\mid}{\text{CH}_2\text{OH}} & \underset{\mid}{\text{F}} \\
\text{E} & + \ \text{P}\text{—(OC}_3\text{H}_7\text{-}i)_2 \\
& \quad\downarrow \\
& \quad \text{O}
\end{array}
\ \rightleftharpoons \
\begin{array}{c}
\underset{\mid}{\text{CH}_2\text{OH}} \ \underset{\mid}{\text{F}} \\
\text{E} \ \cdots\cdots \ \text{P}\text{—(OC}_3\text{H}_7\text{-}i)_2 \\
\downarrow \\
\text{O}
\end{array}
$$

I

$$
\begin{array}{c}
\underset{\mid}{\text{CH}_2\text{—O}} \\
\text{E} \ \cdots \ \underset{\mid}{\text{P}}\text{—(OC}_3\text{H}_7\text{-}i)_2 \\
\downarrow \\
\text{O}
\end{array}
$$

(8–22)

Alkylation of Histidine-57

Schoellmann and Shaw[9] wished "to develop new, specific reagents for locating the active centers of enzymes by designing molecules which combine two kinds of structural features—namely, those which provide affinity to the active center and, in addition, a chemically reactive grouping which may anchor irreversibly to the enzyme . . .." Based on the observation that *N*-tosyl-L-phenylalanine ethyl ester (II) was a substrate for chymotrypsin,[10] they synthesized and evaluated the related chloromethyl ketone (III) as an irreversible inhibitor. In the discussion in Chapter 3 on the mode of binding of chymotrypsin it was pointed out that the carbonyl group of esters such as II were complexed in the ρ_3 area most probably as an acceptor in an $\text{E—D:} \rightarrow \overset{\delta^+}{\text{C}}\text{—}\overset{\delta^-}{\text{O}}$ bond where the donor group was most probably the hydroxylic oxygen of serine-195; therefore the carbonyl group of III should also be complexed in the ρ_3 area in the same fashion.

TPCK (III) gave 50 per cent inactivation of chymotrypsin in 50 minutes at 37° and at pH 6. After completion of the reaction, amino acid analysis showed that one of the two histidines had disappeared. Subsequent experiments on pretreatment with performic acid followed by hydrolysis gave one mole of N^3-carboxymethyl histidine (VII) per mole of enzyme; this alkylated histidine was then located at position 57 in the chymotrypsin

[8] A. R. Main, *Science*, **144**, 992 (1964).

[9] G. Schoellman and E. Shaw, *Biochem. Biophys. Res. Comm.*, **7**, 36 (1962); *Biochemistry*, **2**, 252 (1963).

[10] B. C. W. Hummel, *Can. J. Biochem. Physiol.*, **37**, 1393 (1959).

sequence.[11] The following evidence was presented that the inactivation reaction (step 2) proceeded through a reversible complex (V) (Step 1).

1. The inactivation was slowed in the presence of the reversible inhibitor, β-phenylpropionic acid; this would reduce the concentration of reversible

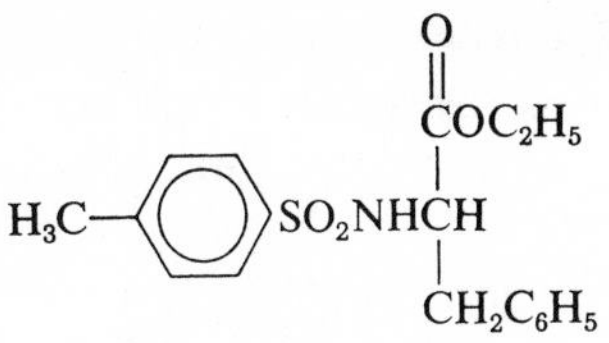

II

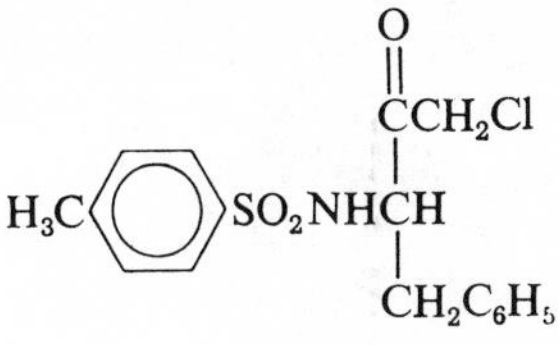

III (TPCK)

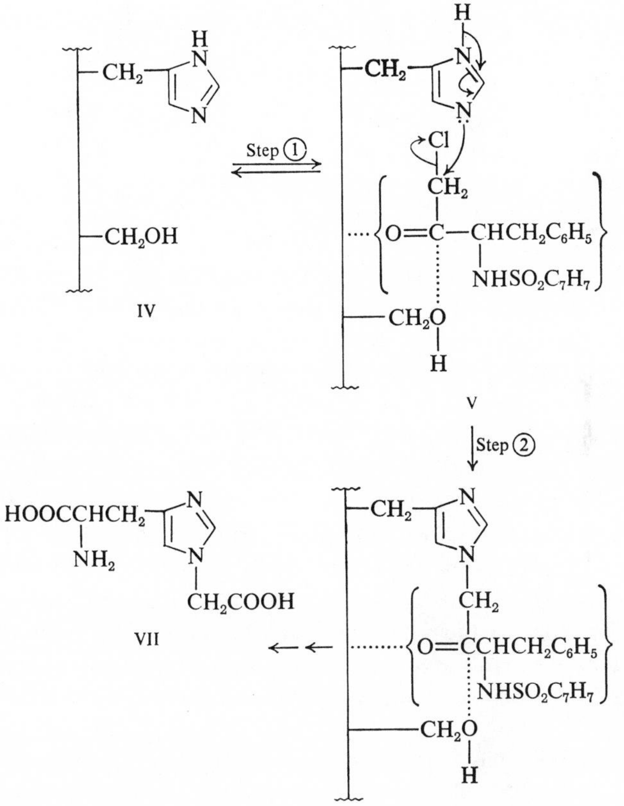

IV

Step ① ⇌

V

Step ②

VII

VI

enzyme-inhibitor complex (V), thus slowing the reaction, for the rate of Step 2 is dependent upon the concentration of V.

2. When C^{14}-TPCK (III) was employed, a 1:1 ratio of nondialyzable

[11] E. B. Ong, E. Shaw, and G. Schoellmann, *J. Am. Chem. Soc.*, **86**, 1271 (1964); *J. Biol. Chem.*, **240**, 694 (1965).

C^{14} to chymotrypsin was observed after inactivation was complete. In 8 M urea, which unfolds the enzyme to an inactive protein, no significant amount of reaction with C^{14}-TPCK (III) took place; these results indicate that a complex (V) must be able to form (Step 1) in order for the facile neighboring group reaction (Step 2) to take place.

3. N-Methylation of II greatly decreases the substrate ability of II; similarly, N-methylation of the bromoketone corresponding to III gave a greatly reduced rate in inactivation of the enzyme, thus implicating the complex V as an intermediate. This experiment would have been much cleaner if (a) the K_i's of III and of the N-methyl analog had been determined and (b), the rate of inactivation determined at a concentration of inhibitor forming 50 per cent E····I reversible complex; in this way, Steps 1 and 2 could be separated; that is, k_3 may be similar for both compounds, but the K_i's may be drastically different.

4. DFP-inactivated chymotrypsin failed to react with C^{14}-TPCK (III); because TPCK chemically reacts with histidine in Step 2, but DFP phosphorylates serine, this experiment indicated that Step 1—the formation of the complex (V)—fails to take place.

5. The inactivation of chymotrypsin showed the same bell-shaped pH profile with a maximum at pH 7.2, as was seen with the pH profile of a substrate. Schoellmann and Shaw cite this as evidence that the active-site is involved.

6. TPCK (III) had no effect on trypsin, a related proteolytic enzyme; III would not be expected to form a complex with trypsin (see Chapter 3) and therefore would not inactivate the enzyme by the active-site-directed mechanism.

The evidence therefore is strong that III inactivates chymotrypsin by active-site-direction, but by the endo mechanism.[12]

An important facet is missing in this work of Schoellmann and Shaw; it would have been even more convincing if the K_i's of III and the N-methyl analog were related to their own rates of inactivation. Furthermore, it would have been useful to relate the amount of protection given by β-phenylpropionic acid to the respective enzyme-inhibitor concentrations.[13]

Stevenson and Smillie[14] have noted that 1-phenoxy-3-chloroacetone (VIII) also alkylated histidine-57 and that the inactivation was slowed in the presence of β-phenylpropionate; VIII at a concentration of 5 mM required five hours for 50 per cent inactivation at 25° and pH 7.0. In contrast, TPCK at a concentration of 0.03 mM required only 50 minutes

---

[12] See Chapter 1, p. 17.
[13] See Reference 1, p. 122; see also p. 127.
[14] K. J. Stevenson and L. B. Smillie, *J. Mol. Biol.*, **12**, 937 (1965).

at 37° and pH 6.0. It is difficult to make a significant comparison of these two rates because in neither case was the K_i for Step 1 measured so that the relative amount of reversible EI concentrations could be compared.

It is highly probable that the carbonyl group of VIII is complexed within the ρ_3 area to serine-195, thus juxtaposing the chloro group to histine-57.

$$
\begin{array}{ll}
(\rho_3)\text{O} & (\rho_3)\text{O} \\
\parallel & \parallel \\
\text{CCH}_2\text{Cl} & \text{CCH}_2\text{Cl} \\
\mid & \mid \\
\text{CH}_2 & \text{C}_6\text{H}_5\text{O}-\text{CH}_2 \\
\mid & (\rho_1) \\
\text{OC}_6\text{H}_5(\rho_2) & \text{VIII}B \\
\text{VIII}A &
\end{array}
$$

Whether the phenoxy group is complexed to the ρ_2 area (VIIIA) or ρ_1 area (VIIIB) cannot be stated at this time; such an answer might be obtained by determining if the ρ_2 area inhibitor indole does or does not protect against irreversible inhibition.[15]

Alkylation of Methionine-192

In an elegant study Lawson and Schramm[16] selected p-nitrophenyl N-bromoacetyl-α-aminoisobutyrate (XI) as a bifunctional reagent for chymotrypsin (X) "so designed that it becomes covalently bound to an amino acid at the active site, and then, fixed in position, reacts with another amino acid in the vicinity." That the acyl group of XI first becomes bound to serine-195 (XII), then attacks methionine-192 to give XIV and finally XV is supported by the following evidence; such a sequence would be a further modification of active-site-directed irreversible inhibition, but by the exo mechanism.[17]

The effect of pH on temporary and permanent inactivation is shown in Fig. 8–1. The evidence for Step 2 is as follows: At pH 7 nitrophenol is released rapidly with formation of XII and about 50 per cent temporary inactivation occurs; then the enzyme slowly regenerates by Step 3a but does not return to 100 per cent activity as observed with pivaloyl chymotrypsin[18]; the latter will regenerate rapidly at pH 8 but extremely slowly at pH 5, which indicates an unprotonated imidazole is needed for Step 3a.

The evidence for Step 1 is that the reversible inhibitor β-phenylpropionate slows both the rate of liberation of p-nitrophenol and the subsequent rate

---

[15] See Chapter 3, p. 58 for a more detailed discussion of the mode of binding of indole as an inhibitor.

[16] W. B. Lawson and H. Schramm, *J. Am. Chem. Soc.*, **84**, 2017 (1962); *Biochemistry*, **4**, 377 (1965).

[17] See Chapter 1, p. 20 for a detailed definition.

[18] C. E. McDonald and A. K. Balls, *J. Biol. Chem.*, **227**, 727 (1957).

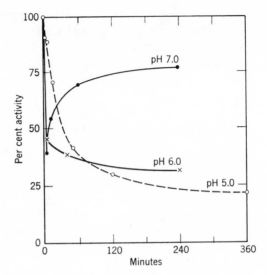

Fig. 8–1. Effect of pH on the inactivation of chymotrypsin by the nitrophenyl ester (XI). The molar ratio of inhibitor to chymotrypsin was 10 at pH 5, 22 at pH 6, and 44 at pH 7. The enzyme concentrations in these experiments were 1.3, 2.0, and 1.0 mg/ml, respectively. From W. B. Lawson and H. J. Schramm, *Biochemistry*, **2**, 377 (1965).

of permanent inactivation; confirmation by determination of the K_m of XI and its relation to the rate of inactivation would have been better evidence, even though the mechanism of acylation of serine-195 by other substrates proceeds through an intermediate reversible complex of type IX.[19]

The almost total lack of regeneration to native enzyme (X) at pH 5 and almost total regeneration at pH 7 is evidence for Step 3a; thus the lower pH gives more time for the intermediate XII to undergo internal alkylation by Step 3b because alkylation of methionine—sulfur is pH independent. Furthermore, XI without one of the α-methyl groups is rapidly hydrolyzed by Step 3a, thus negating Step 3b. Further evidence that the acyl intermediate (XII) is undergoing the neighboring group reaction by Step 3b is indicated by the fact that XIII at 20 times the concentration of XI fails to inactivate the enzyme, thus eliminating the possibility of a simple bimolecular reaction between the enzyme (X) and XI or XIII; also DFP-inactivated enzyme fails to react with XI. Bromoacetamide at 100 times the concentration of X will give 30 per cent inactivation in 17 days, presumably by a bimolecular reaction; in contrast XI gives 80 per cent inactivation in two hours under the same conditions, Finally, XI is slowly

[19] See Chapter 3, p. 49 for a more detailed discussion.

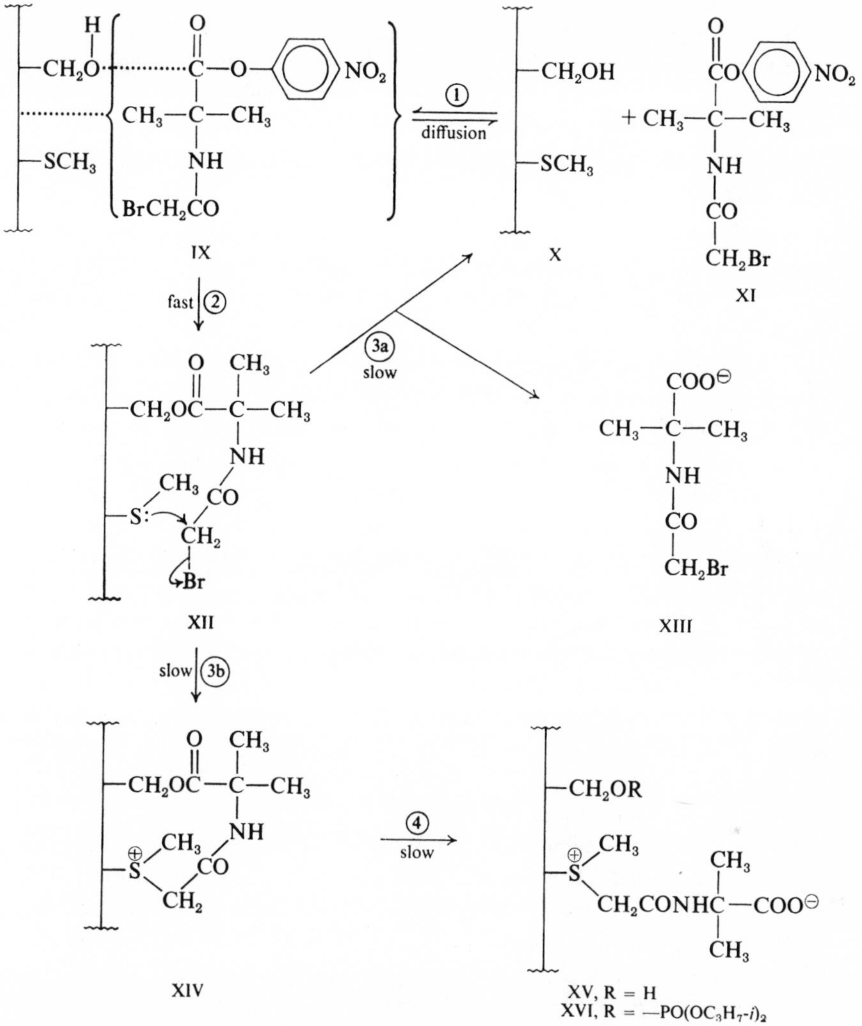

hydrolyzed by trypsin but no alkylation occurs, indicating that in the acylated trypsin, with a structure akin to XII, there is no nucleophilic group properly positioned to attack the bromoacetamido function; this lends further support to the neighboring group reaction in chymotrypsin represented by Step 3b.

The evidence that serine-195 is finally regenerated by Step 4 to give XV, which has 20 per cent of the activity of the native enzyme (X) is the following:

1. When inactivation of the enzyme at pH 5 ceases (about 300 minutes, Fig. 8–1), further treatment with XI fails to give additional inactivation.

2. Treatment of the presumed modified enzyme (XV) with DFP gives complete inactivation, and a 1:1 ratio of nondialyzable phosphorus to enzyme was noted, as was the case with the native enzyme X; this showed that all of serine-195 has been freed, as indicated in XVI.

Evidence that the modified enzyme has the structure shown in XV is the following:

1. The enzyme still has 20 per cent activity compared to the native enzyme (X) which cannot be decreased by further treatment with XI.

2. DFP still reacts with XV in a 1:1 ratio to give a totally inactive enzyme, XVI.

3. Acid hydrolysis of the modified enzyme followed by amino acid analysis showed that one of the two methionines had been attacked but no other amino acid; the attacked methionine appeared as 20 per cent S-carboxymethyl-L-homocysteine, 30 per cent homoserine lactone, and 10 per cent homoserine, the same splitting pattern that has been observed with S-carboxymethyl-L-methionine.[20] In addition, 1 mole of α-amino-isobutyric acid was recovered, indicating that it must have bound to XV.

4. With N-acetyl-L-tyrosine ester as a substrate, the modified chymotrypsin (XV) shows $K_m = 7 \times 10^{-3}$ M and $k_3 = 5.6$; unmodified chymotrypsin (X) under the same conditions shows $K_m = 0.7 \times 10^{-3}$ M and $k_3 = 3.9$. Thus the rate of reaction is accelerated by about 1.5-fold, but binding is poorer by a factor of about 10. It can be concluded that methionine-192 is probably not involved in the catalytic activity, but is either a binding point for the substrate or, when modified as in XV, sterically hinders effective binding of the substrate.

In another paper, Schramm and Lawson[21] observed that a variety of other N- substituted α-bromoacetamides could alkylate the methionine-192 of chymotrypsin at varying rates (Table 8–1); in these cases, the reaction could not proceed through an acylated intermediate of type XII but through the more classical type of reversible enzyme-inhibitor complex. The following general observations were pertinent:

1. The reversible inhibitor, β-phenylpropionate, slowed the rate of inactivation in all cases, indicating that the active-site was involved; the active-site was further implicated by the fact that DFP-inactivated chymotrypsin failed to react with the halogen compounds.

2. A phenyl ring was needed for a reasonable rate of inactivation, indicating that the phenyl ring complexed with the enzyme, presumably in the ρ_2 area.

3. Methionine-192 was alkylated in all cases.

[20] H. G. Gundlach, W. H. Stein, and S. Moore, *J. Biol. Chem.*, **234**, 1754, 1761 (1959).
[21] H. Schramm and W. B. Lawson, *Z. Physiol. Chem.*, **332**, 97 (1963).

Table 8–1. Inactivation of Chymotrypsin by some Active
Halogen Compounds[a]

No.	Compound	$t_{1/2}$(min)[b]	Per cent activity at completion	$K_m \times 10^{3c}$	k_3
X	Unmodified enzyme		100	0.7	3.9
XI	p-$NO_2C_6H_4O_2CC(CH_3)_2$-NHCOCH$_2$Br		20	7	5.6
XVII	$C_6H_5CH_2Br$	7	5–7	8	8
XVIII	$C_6H_5COCH_2Br$	15	1–2	8	0.5
XIX	$C_6H_5NHCOCH_2Br$	30	1–2	20	0.6
XX	$C_6H_5CH_2$-NHCOCH$_2$Br	3000	7	10	2
XXI	$C_6H_5(CH_2)_2$-NHCOCH$_2$Br	60	3	20	2
XXII	NH_2COCH_2Br	$\sim 2 \times 10^4$			

[a] Data from H. Schramm and W. B. Lawson, *Z. Physiol. Chem.*, **332**, 97 (1963).
[b] The half time for the inactivation of chymotrypsin with a 20-fold excess of inhibitor
at pH 5 and 25°; methionine-192 was alkylated in all cases.
[c] With *N*-acetyl-L-tyrosine ethyl ester as substrate.

4. K_m was increased in all cases; k_3 was slowed in some cases and accelerated in others.

The data in Table 8–1 cannot be directly correlated between the reaction half-life and the structure for the following reasons:

1. As we discussed earlier in this chapter on kinetic parameters, the $t_{1/2}$ values should take into consideration the relative amounts of reversible enzyme-inhibitor complex in each case, for the rate of reaction is dependent upon the concentration of complex and not on the absolute concentration of inhibitor; that is, for a given concentration of E····I complex—say 50 per cent—XXI may react faster than XVIII, but a higher absolute concentration of XXI than XVIII may be necessary for formation of 50 per cent E····I complex.

2. It would also have been useful to know the relative halogen reactivity of the compounds in Table 8–1 towards a thioether; for example, with 4-(*p*-nitrobenzyl)-pyridine as a nucleophile, XVII is about 4 times as reactive as XIX, and XIX, in turn, is about twice as reactive as XXII, where XVII, XIX, and XXII have an identical *p*- substituent.[22]

[22] Unpublished data of B. R. Baker and coworkers.

If the two parameters listed above were known, it would be possible to draw a firmer conclusion on the mode of reversible binding of the inhibitors in relationship to their alkylation of methionine-192. As a working hypothesis for future studies, conformation XI*A* is proposed for XI and conformation XXIII is proposed for XVII–XXI. From such conformations it can be proposed as a corollary that methionine-192 is in the ρ_1 binding area; furthermore such proposed conformations can rationalize some of the data that follow in this chapter.

Stevenson and Smillie[23] have made a comparison of the effects of XXIV, XXV, VIII*A*, and III on the inactivation of chymotrypsin; XXIV alkylated methionine-192, III and VIII*A* alkylated histidine-57, and XXV (the D isomer of III) failed to react.[24] They offered two possible explanations for the difference between the two phenoxy compounds, VIII*A* and XXIV, namely, (a) the epoxide of XXIV could not approach histidine-57 due to steric difficulties, or (b) the difference in the ability of an epoxide to alkylate the thioether of methionine-192 versus the imidazole of histidine-57.

A more attractive explanation follows from the ρ-area theory of binding to chymotrypsin[25] when it is combined with the concept of active-site-directed irreversible inhibition. The ketone of VIII*A*, as an electron acceptor, is most probably complexed in the ρ_3 area with serine-195, which juxtaposes the chloromethyl group next to histidine-57 for subsequent alkylation.[26] In contrast, there would be no affinity in the ρ_3 area for the epoxide group of XXIV, which can only be an electron donor; the resultant repulsion from the ρ_3 area plus a possible hydrophobic affinity of the ρ_1 area for the two carbons of the epoxide would juxtapose the epoxide into the ρ_1 area where the methionine-192 presumably resides.

That the D isomer (XXV) of TPCK (III) does not inactivate chymotrypsin follows from the mode of binding of D isomers to this enzyme.[27] The D isomer presumably positions the sulfonamide group in the ρ_H area, which could hinder the attack of the histidine-57; alternately the carbonyl group could be positioned in the ρ_H area.[27] The results of Stevenson and Smillie would have been much cleaner if the K_i's of the various inhibitors had been determined, so that a comparison of inactivation rates at the same E····I concentration could be made.

In contrast to the results with the D (XXV) and L isomers (III) of TPCK,

[23] See Reference 14, p. 132.
[24] J. R. Brown and B. S. Hartley, *Abstr. First Meeting Fed. European Biochem. Soc.*, Academic Press, London, 1964, p. 25.
[25] See Chapter 3 for a detailed discussion.
[26] See Chapter 8, p. 131.
[27] See Chapter 3, p. 55.

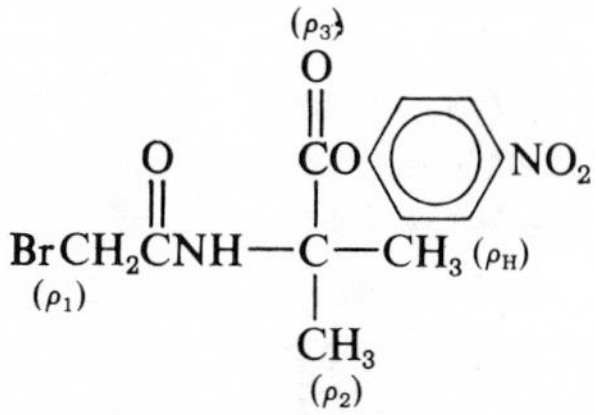

XI*A*

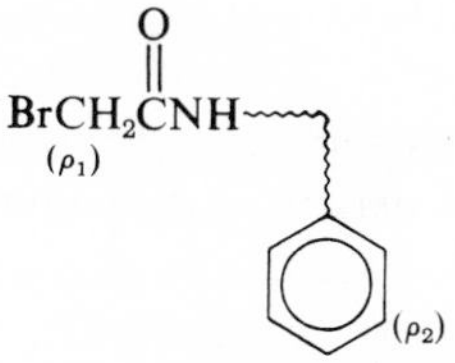

XXIII

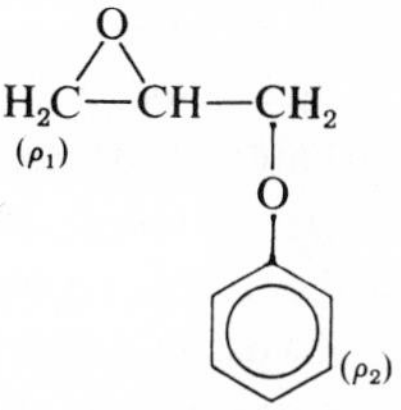

XXIV

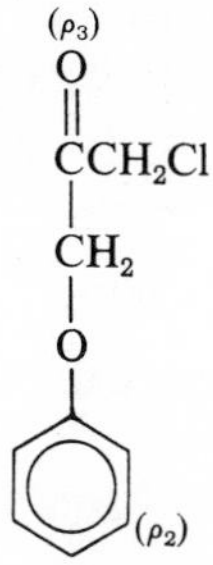

VIII*A*

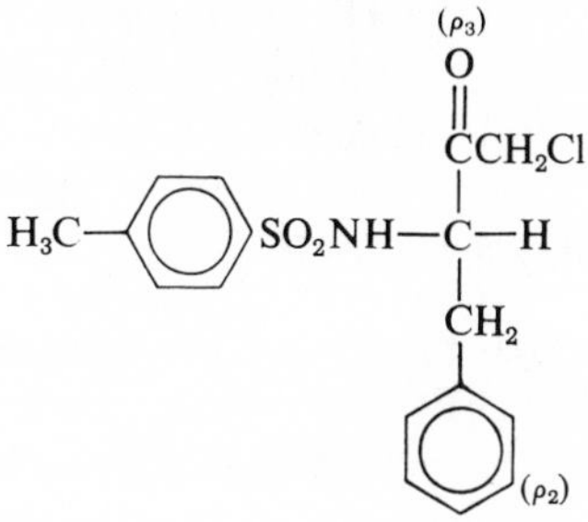

III

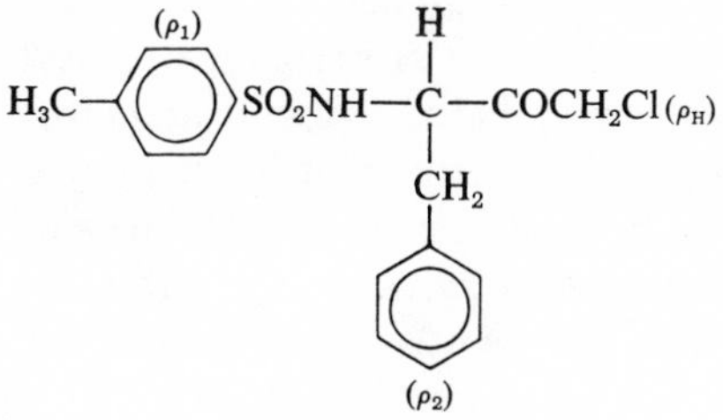

XXV

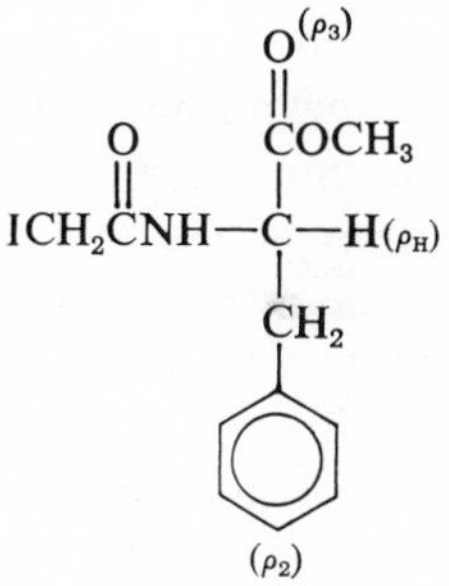

XXVI

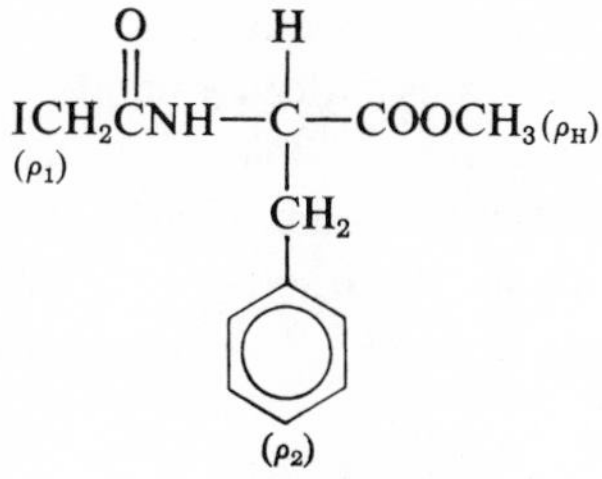

XXVII

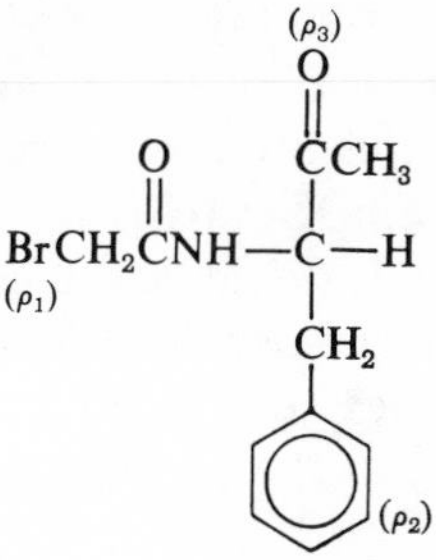

XXVIII

where the L isomer inactivated and the D isomer did not, an opposite stereochemistry was observed with the D (XXVII) and L isomers (XXVI) of methyl *N*-(iodoacetyl)-phenylalaninate; only the D isomer (XXVII) inactivated chymotrypsin.[28] Again it was a methionine, probably 192, that was alkylated; it was also noted that the hydrolysis product, *N*-(iodoacetyl)-L-phenylalanine did not inactivate the enzyme. These results can be rationalized nicely by the ρ-area concept of binding. The L isomer (XXVI) is probably hydrolyzed by the enzyme to the acid; because the acid is not an irreversible inhibitor and because the acyl enzyme from XXVI is short-lived, no alkylation occurs, as previously was observed with *p*-nitrophenyl ester derivative, XIa.[29] The D isomer can form a reversible complex with the carbomethoxy group in the ρ_H area, as is depicted in XXVII, but it will not undergo hydrolysis; such a complex would position the iodoacetamido group in the ρ_1 area with resultant alkylation of methionine-192. The following missing data would certainly aid interpretation:

1. How fast does the L isomer hydrolyze with respect to the alkylation rate of the D isomer?

2. What is the K_i of the D isomer (XXVII) and what was the concentration of the rate determining E····I complex?

3. What is the K_i of the L acid of XXVI, and at an E····I concentration equal to that between chymotrypsin and XXVII, does the L acid inactivate the enzyme under the same conditions? It is highly probable that the L acid does not complex in exactly the same manner as an L ester for the carboxyl group of the L acid is an anion that cannot be an electron acceptor; furthermore L acids are noncompetitive inhibitors[30]; thus, even though the L acid forms a complex, perhaps by carboxylate interaction with histidine-57, the fact stands that the iodoacetamide group within this complex is not juxtaposed with methionine-192 because the latter is not attacked.

To shed further light on the questions raised above it would be useful to evaluate the L-methyl ketone (XXVIII) as an irreversible inhibitor; binding to the ρ_1, ρ_2, and ρ_3 areas should occur as depicted in XXVIII, which would juxtapose the bromoacetamido group with methionine-192 within the chymotrypsin-XXVIII complex. If XXVIII does indeed operate as predicted, then it would be useful to determine if the D isomer (XXIX) would react with methionine-192 at the same rate with the same amount of E····I complex; this could give direct evidence on whether a D isomer is complexed to the ρ_H area, as is depicted in XXIX*B*—which could not

[28] G. Gundlach and F. Turba, *Biochem. Z.*, **335**, 573 (1962).
[29] See Chapter 8, p. 133.
[30] See Chapter 3, p. 50.

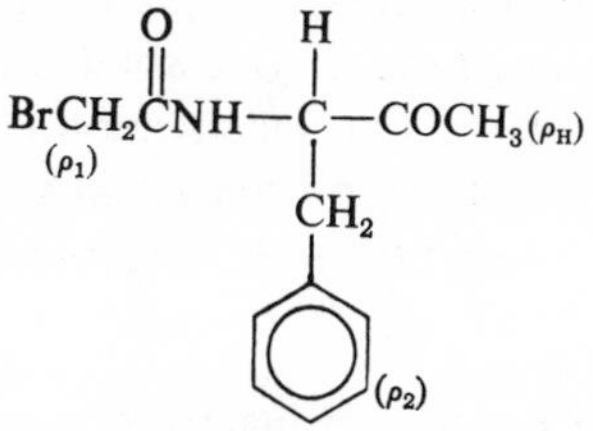

XXIX*A* 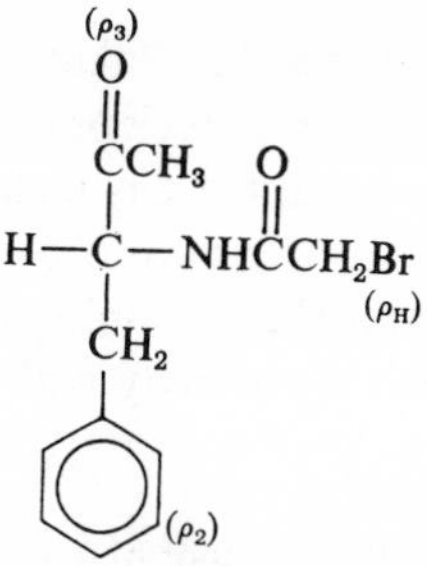   XXIX*B*

alkylate methionine-192—or whether the D isomer is complexed as depicted in XXIX*A*—which would alkylate methionine-192.[31]

Other Inactivations

In an experimentally deficient paper, Kallos[32] investigated the inactivation of chymotrypsin by the L (XXX) and D isomers (XXXI) of *N,O-bis-*

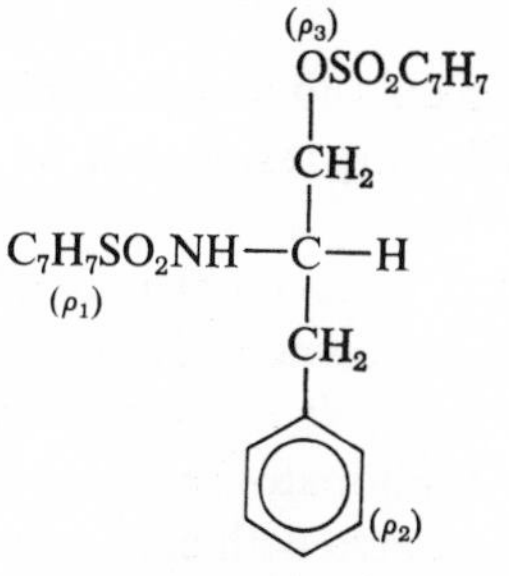

XXX*A* 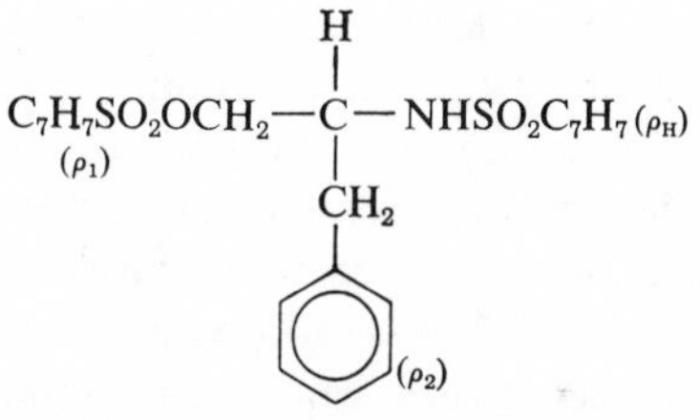   XXX*B*

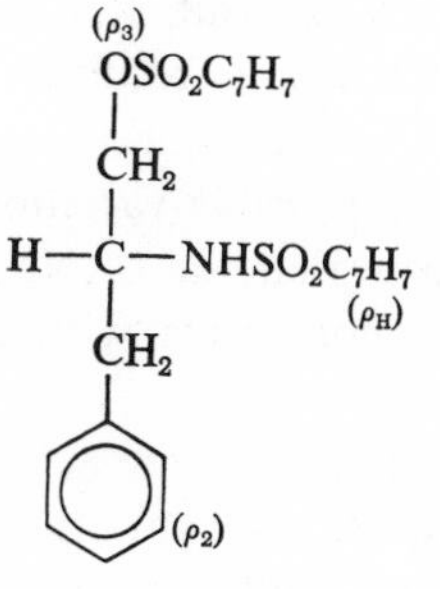

XXXI*A* 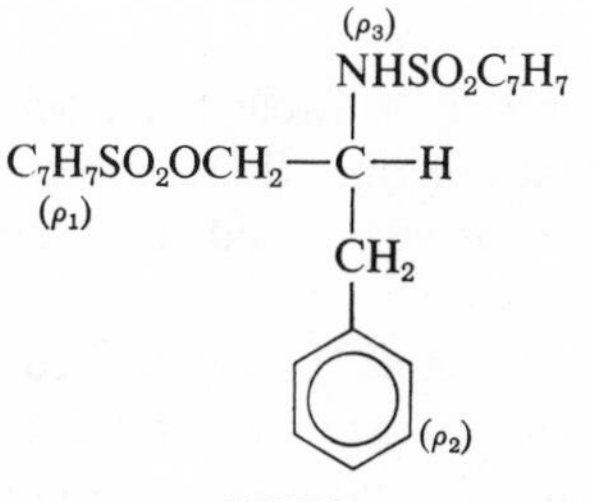   XXXI*B*

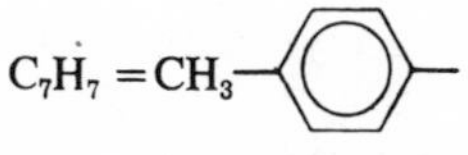

$$C_7H_7 = CH_3-\bigcirc-$$

---

[31] For a discussion of complexing D isomers to chymotrypsin see Chapter 3, p. 55.
[32] J. Kallos, *J. Mol. Biol.*, **7**, 104 (1963).

(*p*-tolylsulfonyl)-phenylalaninol; he proposed that these compounds should attack the enzyme nucleophilic group that catalyzes the ester hydrolysis. He observed that the L isomer inactivated the enzyme about twice the rate of an equal concentration of D isomer and that inactivation leveled off at 60 per cent of the remaining activity with the D isomer and at 20 per cent of the remaining activity with the L isomer; the following information was missing.

1. It was not indicated whether or not further inactivation took place if more of XXX or XXXI was added.
2. The K_i's of the two isomers were not measured to determine the relative rates corrected for the concentration of E····I complex.
3. It was not indicated which amino acid was attacked.
4. It was not determined whether or not a reversible inhibitor would slow the inactivation rate.
5. It was not indicated whether K_m or k_3 or both changed after inactivation ceased.

If it can be assumed that inactivation was complete and that the inhibitor had not been destroyed by solvent, then the following results can be predicted with the ρ area concept.

If histidine-57 or serine-195 had been alkylated, then complete inactivation should have occurred; the fact that there is still some activity—but in different amounts depending on which isomer is involved—suggests that methionine-192 was alkylated. Because an O-sulfonate cannot be an electron acceptor, it will have no affinity for the ρ_3 area with configuration XXXa or XXXIa. However, the tolylsulfonate would have an affinity for the ρ_1 area in conformations XXX*B* and XXXI*B*; such conformations would alkylate methionine-192 with a resultant change in K_m or k_3 or both. As was noted with various alkylating agents for methionine-192 in Table 8-1, there is still considerable variation in the activity that remains; thus, one could anticipate that the D (XXXI) and L (XXX) isomers would give modified chymotrypsins with differing residual activity.

Westheimer et al.[33] have devised a method of labeling the active-site of chymotrypsin that theoretically would not require a neighboring nucleophilic group. Reaction of chymotrypsin (X) with *p*-nitrophenyl diazoacetate (XXXII) gives a stable acylated chymotrypsin (XXXIII) more akin to pivaloyl chymotrypsin[34] than acetyl chymotrypsin; similar to the former,

[33] A. Singh, E. R. Thornton, and F. H. Westheimer, *J. Biol. Chem.*, **237**, PC 3006 (1962).
[34] See Reference 18, p. 133.

XXXIII could be regenerated to active chymotrypsin (X) with hydroxyl-amine at pH 8. The acylated enzyme (XXXIII) was then photolyzed at 370 mμ, the absorption peak of the diazoacetyl group, which could be expected to generate the carbene, XXXV; they theorized that this very reactive species could then either solvolyze to XXXIV or insert into a C—C bond (as in XXXVI*B*) or a C—H bond (as in XXXVI*A*). When

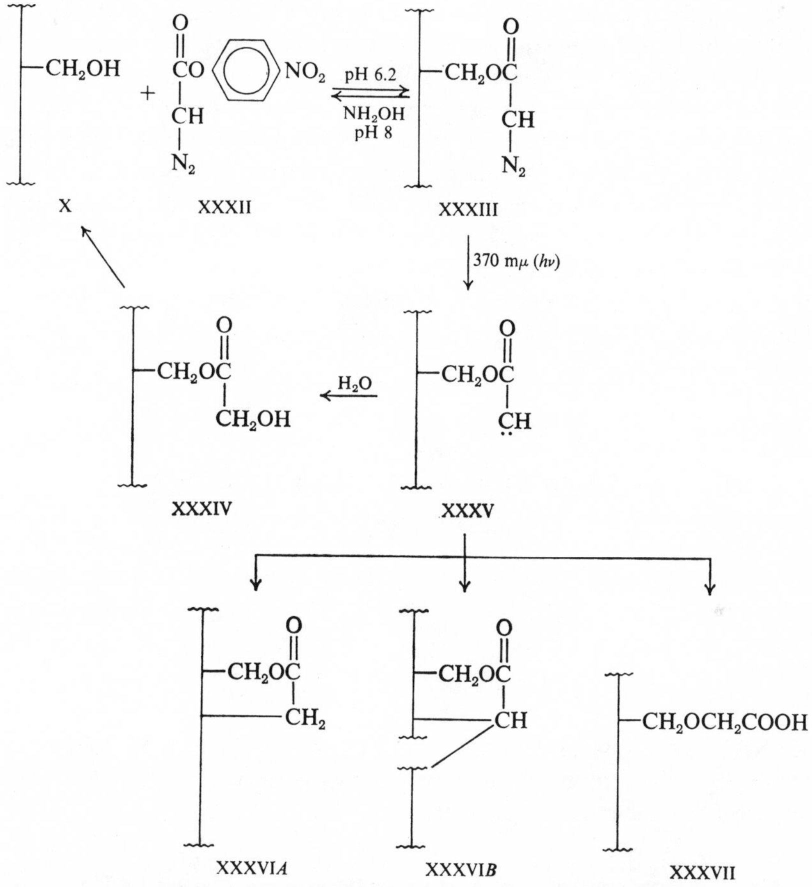

photolyzed, 75–80 per cent of the enzyme (X) was regenerated *via* XXXIV; the remaining 20–25 per cent of inactivation was presumably due to insertion reactions as followed by C^{14} labeled XXXII; because the rate of reaction was not affected by the concentration of XXXIII, the reaction was intramolecular.

A neighboring nucleophilic group is not necessary for this type of active-site labeling; if the carbene is not in a noncontact area,[35] then one or more

[35] See Chapter 1, p. 18 and Chapter 7 for a further discussion of noncontact areas.

C—C and C—H groups are bound to be close to the carbene atom; such a labeling technique is likely to work with any enzyme if the carbene can bridge to an enzymic carbon. Because no specific bridging is required, this technique can unfortunately be predicted to be quite nonspecific; that is, a number of amino acids in the vicinity of the carbene atom are likely to be attacked. Such a nonspecific labeling would make subsequent identification of C^{14} products quite difficult. In a later paper[36] Westheimer et al. showed that the bulk of the labeling and inactivation was due to rearrangement of the carbene to an O-carboxymethyl derivative of serine-195; apparently in the case of this enzyme, the carbene is not in contact with any C—C or C—H group of the enzyme, for the same O-carboxymethyl-serine is also obtained by photolysis of the urea denatured enzyme. At pH 4 in the dark a 16 per cent yield of 1-carboxymethylhistine is obtained; the yield of this histidine derivative is "greatly increased" when the decomposition is run in formic acid in the dark. If the attack is on histidine-57, it would appear that the carbene (XXXV) generated from XXXIII cannot attack histidine, but with acid, XXXIII is converted to a diazonium salt (XXXIII*B*), which can form the carbonium ion

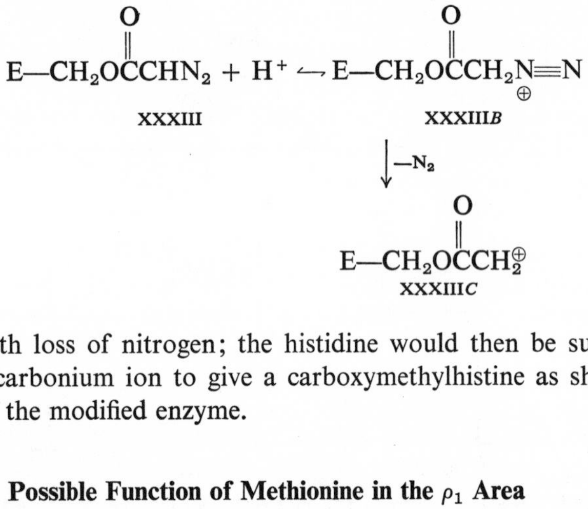

$$\text{E—CH}_2\text{OCCHN}_2 + \text{H}^+ \leftrightharpoons \text{E—CH}_2\text{OCCH}_2\overset{\oplus}{\text{N}}\equiv\text{N}$$

XXXIII   XXXIII*B*

$$\downarrow -\text{N}_2$$

$$\text{E—CH}_2\text{OCCH}_2^{\oplus}$$

XXXIII*C*

XXXIII*C* with loss of nitrogen; the histidine would then be subject to attack by a carbonium ion to give a carboxymethylhistine as shown by hydrolysis of the modified enzyme.

Possible Function of Methionine in the ρ_1 Area

Little more need be said about the role of histidine-57 in the ρ_3 area; the catalytic role of histidine in the function of esterases and amidases for hydrolysis has received solid support.[37]

[36] J. Shafer, P. Baronowsky, R. Laursen, F. Finn, and F. H. Westheimer, *J. Biol. Chem.*, **241**, 421 (1966).
[37] T. C. Bruice and S. J. Benkovic, *Bioorganic Mechanisms*, W. A. Benjamin, New York, 1966, Vol. I.

The implication that methionine-192 is in the ρ_1 area is strong, and the evidence has been presented. The possible function of a methionine in the ρ_1 area is indicated by the change in K_m noted in Table 8–1. Because K_m is changed, it is possible that either the methylthioethyl group of methionine is involved in binding in the ρ_1 area, or alkylation of this methionine causes hindrance to binding by other amino acids in the ρ_1 area. We can conclude that steric hindrance of binding to another amino acid is not a likely explanation from the activity of chymotrypsin that has been modified by oxidation of methionine-192 to a sulfone; the sulfone shows an increase in K_m of 4–5-fold.[38] The methionine-192 modifications in Table 8–1, which are considerably larger structural changes than the sulfone, gave only 10–30-fold increases in K_m.

As a working hypothesis, assume that methionine is the primary amino acid responsible for binding in the ρ_1 area. The possible modes of complexing to the methionine were discussed in detail in Chapter 2; these are (a) by donation of electrons from an electron pair of the sulfur to an acceptor group on a substrate or inhibitor and (b) hydrophobic bonding with the accompanying van der Waals forces by the methyl and ethylene moieties of methionine. Is there any evidence to support such a hypothesis, and what additional evidence would be worth obtaining?

In Table 8–2 are listed some structural variants of the ρ_1 binding area; these inhibitors were selected because they are also slow substrates, the tyrosineamide corresponding to XXXIX being hydrolyzed about 240 times as fast as XXXIX. The fact that XXXIX is a slow substrate strongly indicates that it is complexed normally with the enzyme, the slow rate being primarily due to the slower rate of chemical hydrolysis of an *N*-methylamide compared to an amide. Because a bromoacetamido group in the ρ_1 area is attacked by the sulfur electron pair of methionine 192, it is clear that the methylene group of an *N*-acetyl such as that of XXXIX is juxtaposed next to the methionine-192 sulfur. Furthermore, the sulfur atom of a thioether is hydrophobic, but it is somewhat less hydrophobic than a methylene group.[39] Therefore some hydrophobic binding between the sulfur of methionine-192 and the methyl group of XXXIX should take place.

Note that the formyl group of XXXVIII gives twice as good an inhibitor as the acetyl group of XXXIX. The formyl group has its hydrogen juxtaposed to the sulfur atom and therefore would have little or no hydrophobic bonding. Then how can a formyl group be complexed more strongly than an acetyl group? A steric interaction with the enzyme is possible but un-

---

[38] D. E. Koshland, Jr., *Science*, **142** 1533 (1963).
[39] T. Fujita, J. Iwasa, and C. Hansch, *J. Am. Chem. Soc.*, **86**, 5175 (1964).

Table 8–2. Inhibition of Chymotrypsin by

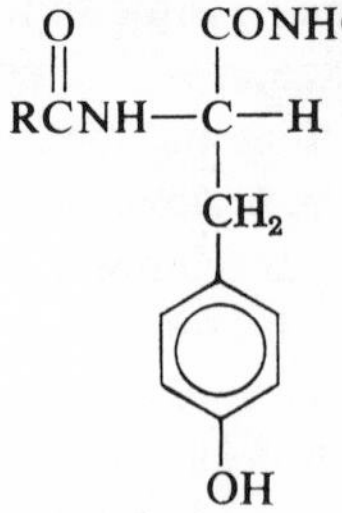

$$
\underset{\substack{|\\ \text{CH}_2\\ |\\ \text{(p-hydroxybenzyl)}}}{\overset{\substack{\text{O}\qquad \text{CONHCH}_3\\ \parallel\qquad\quad |\\ \text{RCNH}-\text{C}-\text{H}}}{}}
$$

No.	R	$K_i \times 10^{3a}$	Reference
XXXVIII	H	31 ± 8	b
XXXIX	CH_3	61 ± 7	b
XL	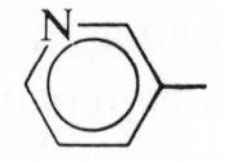 (pyridyl)	8.8 ± 1	b
XLI	C_6H_5—	6.4 ± 1.6	b
XLII	$NO_2C_6H_4$—	$< 6?$	
XLIII	$N{\equiv}CC_6H_4$—	$< 6?$	
XLIV	$CH_3OC_6H_4$—	$> 6?$	
XLV	$(CH_3)_2NC_6H_4$—	$> 6?$	
XLVI	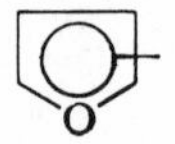 (furyl)	$> 6?$	
XLVII	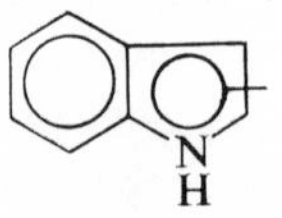 (indolyl)	$> 6?$	

---

[a] With *N*-acetyl-L-tryosineamide as substrate.
[b] W. E. M. Lands and C. Niemann, *J. Am. Chem. Soc.*, **81**, 2204 (1959).

likely in view of the fact that the *N*-benzoyl derivative (XLI) is an even better inhibitor than *N*-formyl (XXXVIII). The hydrogen of a formyl group is more electron deficient—due to electron withdrawal by the polarization of a carbonyl group—than an ordinary CH bond of a methyl. Therefore a donor-acceptor interaction of the following type could occur:

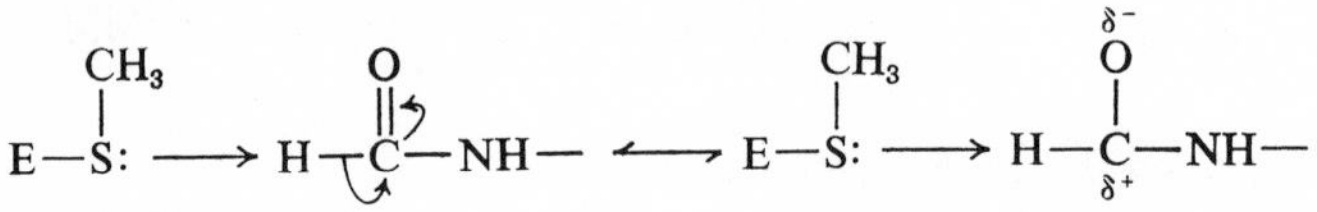

$$
\text{E}-\text{S}: \longrightarrow \text{H}{-}\overset{\text{CH}_3}{\underset{}{\text{C}}}\overset{\text{O}}{\overset{\parallel}{\text{C}}}{-}\text{NH}{-} \longleftrightarrow \text{E}-\text{S}: \longrightarrow \text{H}{-}\overset{\text{CH}_3}{\underset{}{\text{C}}}\overset{\overset{\delta-}{\text{O}}}{\underset{\delta+}{\text{C}}}{-}\text{NH}{-}
$$

The benzene ring of XLI could have good hydrophobic bonding to the methylthioethyl group of methionine-192 and, in addition, a weak donor-acceptor interaction; therefore the phenyl of XLI should give a better inhibitor than either the acetyl (XXXIX) or the formyl (XXXVIII). The nicotinyl derivative (XL) should form a better donor-acceptor complex than the benzoyl derivative but may have poorer hydrophobic bonding due to the water solvation of the polar ring nitrogen; therefore, the sum of the two effects should be about equal, as is indicated by the nearly equal binding of phenyl and 3-pyridyl.

As another useful study it would be valuable to evaluate the various benzene position isomers of XLII–XLV, where two have electron-withdrawing groups and two have electron-donating groups; it would also be useful to measure an isonicotinyl group to see if there is more or less repulsion of the water-solvated ring nitrogen, as well as the *N*-methyl derivatives of both pyridine isomers. If compounds XL–XLVII were then subjected to a Hansch analysis,[40,41] it might be possible to measure the relative electronic and hydrophobic effects to see if this information would correlate with the expected binding properties of the methylthioethyl group of methionine-192.

A number of other studies would aid in this interpretation. The compounds in Table 8–2 should be measured as inhibitors of chymotrypsin that has been *S*-benzylated on methionine-192 (Table 8–1). Such a modified methionine with a sulfonium group should now be an acceptor group—in contrast to the donor properties of the unmodified thioether—thus resulting in opposite donor-acceptor affinities with the compounds in Table 8–2; it should not be too difficult to sort out any steric effects by the *S*-benzyl group. Furthermore, a compound such as XLVIII*A* or *B* might

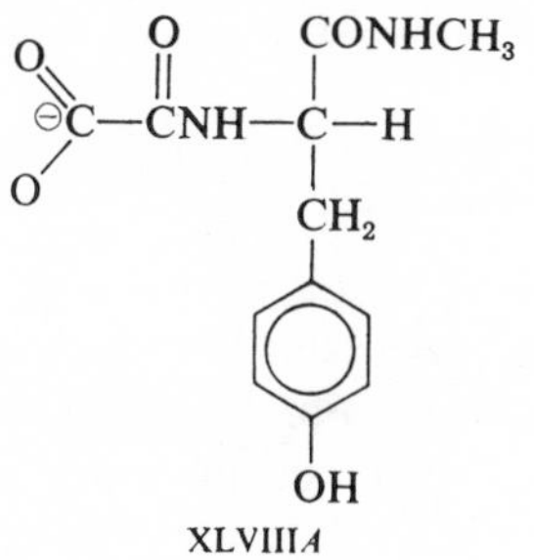

XLVIII*A* 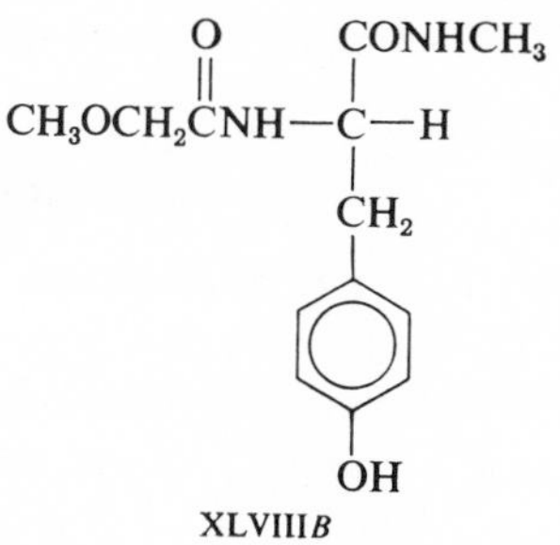   XLVIII*B*

have a strong donor affinity for the juxtaposed sulfonium group of the *S*-benzylated methionine, but poorer affinity for unmodified chymotrypsin.

[40] C. Hansch and A. R. Steward, *J. Med. Chem.*, 7, 691 (1964).
[41] See Reference 39, p. 145.

Although the acylamido group would have one major conformation when complexed to methionine-192, an infinite number of possibilities for this conformation exist; three extreme conformations are shown in

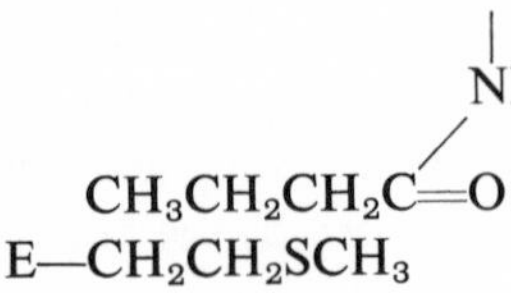

$$\overset{\displaystyle |}{NH} \qquad \overset{\displaystyle |}{HN}$$

$$CH_3CH_2CH_2C\!=\!\!O \qquad\qquad O\!=\!\!CCH_2CH_3$$
$$E\!-\!\!CH_2CH_2SCH_3 \qquad\qquad E\!-\!\!CH_2CH_2SCH_3$$

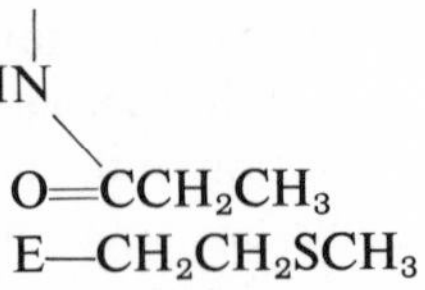

$$\text{XLIX} \qquad\qquad\qquad\qquad \text{L}$$

$$\overset{\displaystyle CH_3}{\underset{\displaystyle |}{\overset{\displaystyle |}{CH_2}}}$$

$$E\!-\!\!CH_2CH_2S\!-\!\!CH_3$$
$$\overset{\displaystyle |}{C\!=\!\!O}$$
$$\overset{\diagdown\quad\diagup}{NH}$$

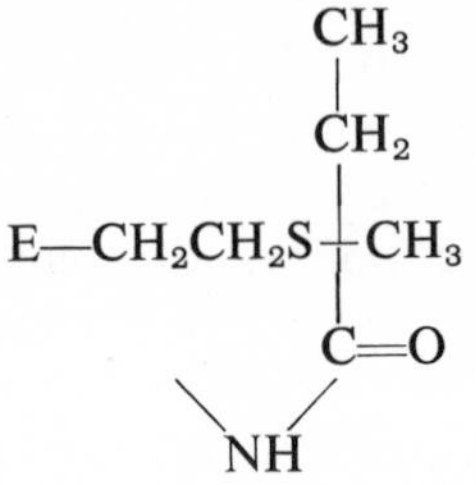

$$\text{LI}$$

XLIX–LI, where XLIX and L have maximum interaction, but where only the sulfur atom and one methylene group interact in LI. If conformation LI is the proper one, then no further increase in binding may occur in proceeding from acetyl to propionyl to butyroyl; the binding of the latter two might even be poorer due to steric interaction. If the maximum interaction conformations XLIX or L exist, then in the latter case, the propionyl should be a better inhibitor than acetyl and butyroyl either equal or less effective inhibitor than propionyl. In contrast, with conformation XLIX, the inhibitory powers should be butyroyl > propionyl > acetyl.

Alkylation of Other Amino Acids

In addition to the alkylation of histidine-57 in the ρ_3 area and methionine-192 in the ρ_1 area, it should be possible to attack other amino acids by other active-site-directed irreversible inhibitors. For example L isomers such as LII and LIII should be investigated with various bridge lengths between an alkylating function and the benzene ring in order to determine if labeling in or near the ρ_2 area can be achieved. The LII type would be easier to synthesize, but it might undergo enzymatic hydrolysis at too fast a rate to allow the active-site-directed irreversible inhibition to occur; if such is the case, we could use a methyl ketone such as LIII (or the corresponding *N*-tolylsulfonyl derivative) or an α-methyl *p*-nitrophenyl ester of a type related to LII and the irreversible inhibitor (XI) of Lawson and Schramm.[42]

The ρ_H area could be similarly investigated with D isomers such as LIV where the bridge length is varied. Types LV and LVI would be good candidates to find functionalized amino acids in the ρ_3 area other than

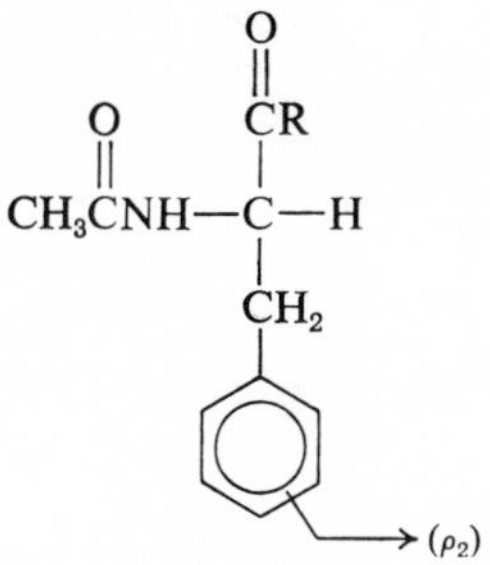

LII, R = NHCH₃
LIII, R = CH₃

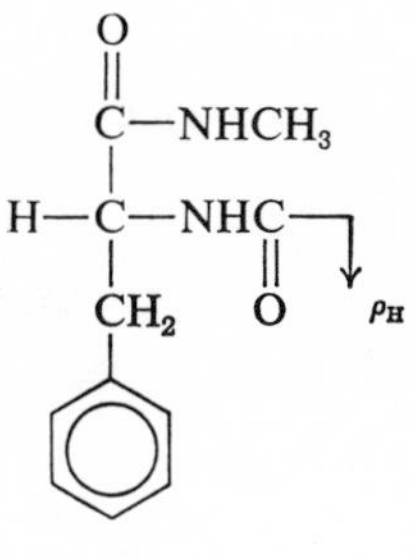

LIV

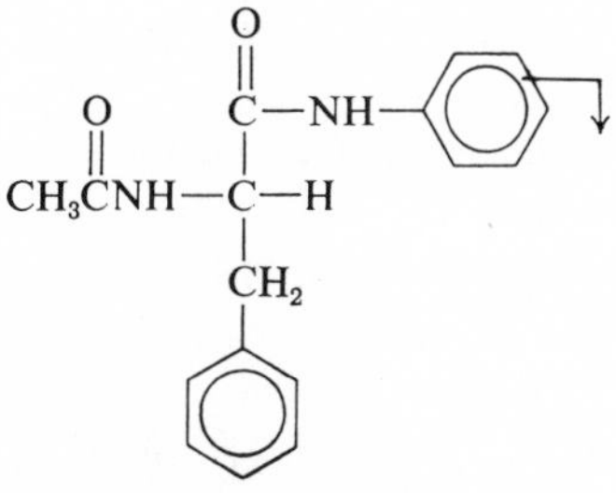

LV

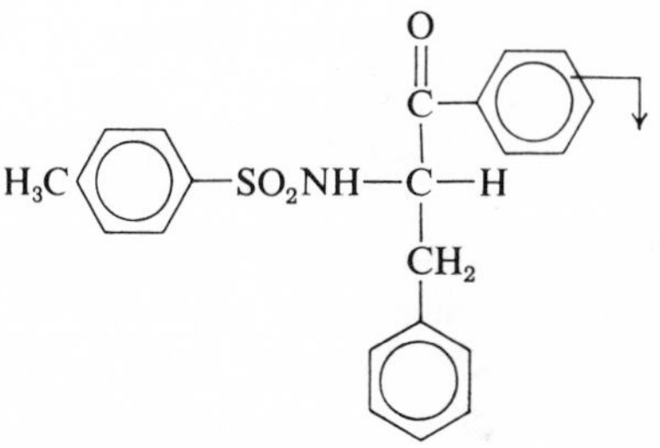

LVI

⌐ = covalent forming group

histidine-57, such as histidine-40. Finally, placing the various lengths of the alkylating functions on the benzenesulfonyl group of LVI might give a reaction with other amino acids in or near the ρ_1 area other than that at methionine-192.

TRYPSIN

In Chapter 3, a comparison of the mode of binding substrates and inhibitors to trypsin and chymotrypsin was made; the catalytic site of the two enzymes (the histidine loop) is almost identical, but the ρ_2 areas differ drastically in binding—thus accounting for the difference in their specifi-

[42] See Chapter 8, p. 133.

city. A posteriori, it is not too surprising that an analog (LVII, TLCK) of the irreversible inhibitor (III, TPCK) of chymotrypsin would give the same result on trypsin; that is, TLCK can complex with trypsin and

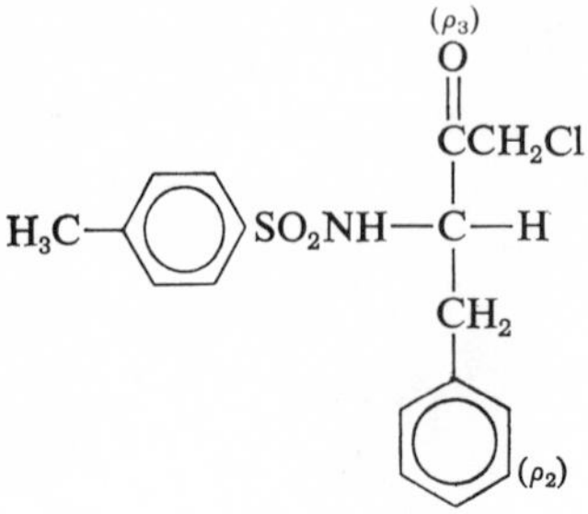

III (TPCK) 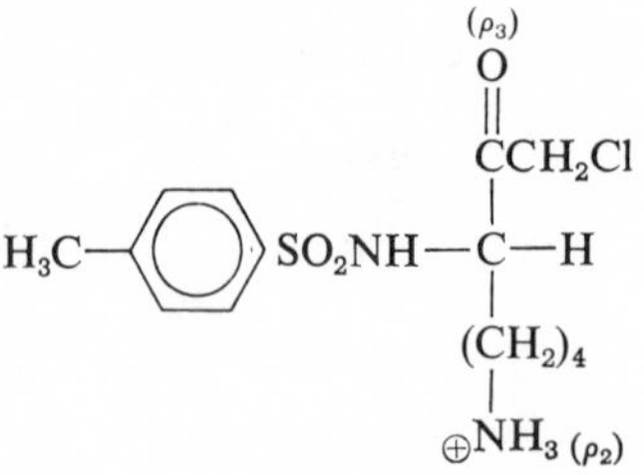   LVII (TLCK)

alkylate a histidine, but it has no effect on chymotrypsin due to the lack of complex formation; to the contrary, TPCK does not complex with trypsin and therefore does not inactivate it.[43]

The criteria applied by Shaw et al. with TLCK was similar to the earlier study with TPCK and chymotrypsin. TLCK at 6×10^{-4} M gave 50 per cent inactivation of trypsin in about eight minutes at pH 6 and essentially 100 per cent inactivation at completion. At completion one of three histidines in trypsin was no longer present as such; 3-carboxymethyl-L-histidine was identified after oxidation with performic acid, then hydrolysis.[44] The reversible inhibitor, benzamidine, slows the rate of inactivation. In the presence of 8 M urea there was no alkylation of trypsin by H[3]—TLCK, which was indicated by the lack of radioactivity after dialysis.

This study suffers the same shortcomings as the earlier study on chymotrypsin and TPCK, that is, failure to correlate the rate of inactivation with the concentration of reversible E····I complex and to relate further the amount of protection with the K_i of benzamidine. Although one histidine is selectively alkylated at N^3, exactly which of the three histidines was alkylated has not yet been announced; its identity should be forthcoming soon.

It should be possible to construct active-site-directed irreversible inhibitors for the ρ_1 and ρ_H areas of this enzyme—as well as the attack on other amino areas in the ρ_3 area—by proper ρ modification of types LIV–LVI; to attack the ρ_2 area would be more difficult with trypsin from a synthetic standpoint, due to the necessity for a cationic moiety to bind in this area.

[43] E. Shaw, M. Mares-Guia, and W. Cohen, *Biochemistry*, **4**, 2219 (1965).
[44] P. H. Petra, W. Cohen, and E. N. Shaw, *Biochem. Biophys. Res. Commun.*, **21**, 612 (1965).

However by use of disubstituted guanidines such as LVIII, it might be possible to achieve such an irreversible inhibitor.

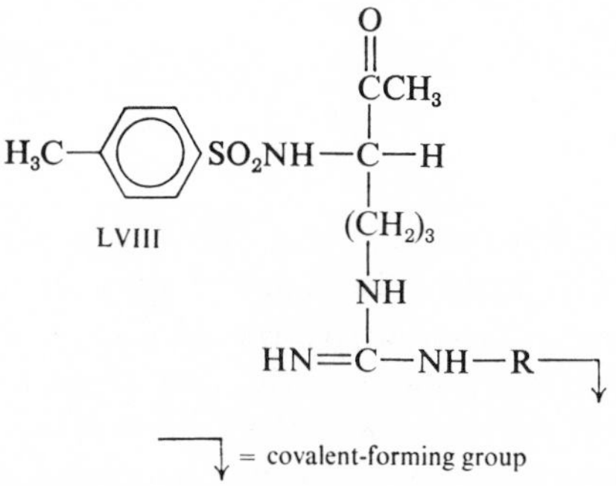

$$
\begin{array}{c}
O \\
\parallel \\
\overset{C-CH_3}{\underset{|}{}} \\
H_3C-\bigcirc-SO_2NH-C-H \\
| \\
(CH_2)_3 \\
| \\
NH \\
| \\
HN=C-NH-R-
\end{array}
$$

LVIII

$\downharpoonright$ = covalent-forming group

Trypsin can be slowly inactivated by iodoacetamide, presumably via a bimolecular reaction. The rate of alkylation by iodoacetamide is increased about six-fold in the presence of 0.4 *M* methylguanidine, a reversible inhibitor, but the rate is decreased to about one half the rate by the larger reversible inhibitor, *n*-butylguanidine, at the same concentration.[45,46] Alkylation on N^3 of a histidine took place. Again, this study would have been more complete if Inagami[45] had related the rate of inactivation by iodoacetamide to the amount of enzyme-methylguanidine complex.[47] Nevertheless, this study does show that it is possible for an inhibitor to cause a conformational change that more greatly exposes a group on the enzyme to attack.[47]

An interesting side observation was also reported by Inagami; that is, inactivation of trypsin by DFP was completely absent in the presence of methylguanidine under conditions that gave 60 per cent inactivation in the

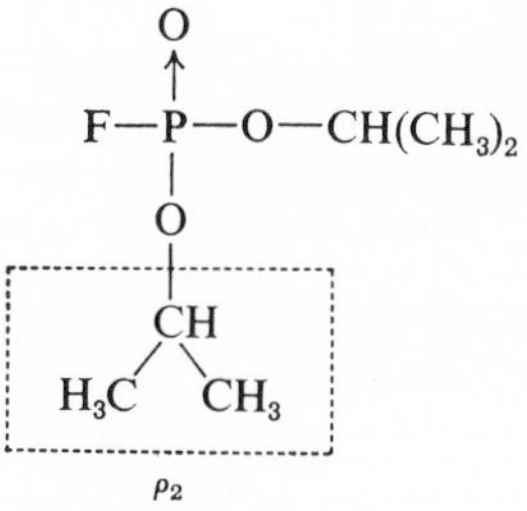

$$
\begin{array}{c}
O \\
\uparrow \\
F-P-O-CH(CH_3)_2 \\
| \\
O \\
| \\
CH \\
H_3C \quad CH_3
\end{array}
$$

ρ_2

LIX

[45] T. Inagama, *J. Biol. Chem.*, **240**, PC 3453 (1965).

[46] For a more detailed discussion on the mode of binding of these alkylguanidines to trypsin see Chapter 3, p. 65.

[47] See Chapter 8, p. 124 for the kinetic parameters of such experiments.

absence of methylguanidine. Because methylguanidine is complexed in the ρ_2 area, it follows that DFP is also partially complexed in the ρ_2 area by hydrophobic bonding, as indicated in LIX (hydrophobic bonding to trypsin in the ρ_3 area was discussed in Chapter 3).

OTHER ENZYMES

Papain is a proteolytic enzyme that favors hydrolysis of the peptide linkage at the carboxyl end of basic amino acids; in this regard, it is like trypsin in specificity.[48] Some derivatives of glycine and leucine are also hydrolyzed, such as *N*-tosylglycine ethyl ester.[49] Papain differs from trypsin in that the acyl enzyme intermediate in papain is an acylated cysteine,[50] in contrast to an acylated serine in trypsin. Husain and Low[51] therefore investigated LX as an irreversible inhibitor of papain; no kinetic information was presented. With ^{14}C-labeled LX essentially only one amino acid was labeled, a cysteine. Partial digestion and isolation of a radioactive heptapeptide showed that cysteine-25 had been labeled. This cysteine is presumably in the catalytic site.

Enzymes with substrate specificity similar to trypsin should be attacked irreversibly by TLCK (LVII), such as thrombin, plasmin, kallikrein, papain, and ficin.[52] Shaw et al.[52] observed that papain was inactivated by both TLCK (LVII) and TPCK (III), but thrombin was attacked by

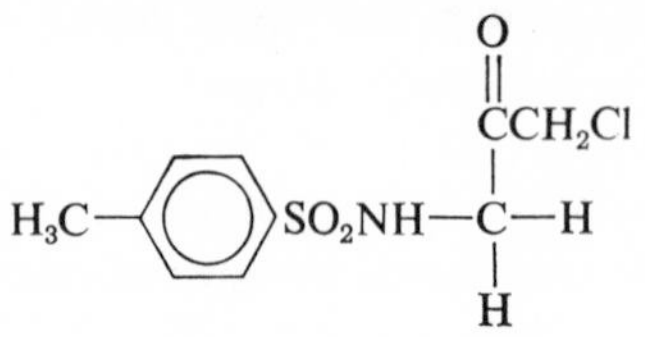

$$H_3C-\underset{}{\bigcirc}-SO_2NH-\underset{\underset{H}{|}}{\overset{\overset{O}{\overset{||}{CCH_2Cl}}}{|}}{C}-H$$

LX

TLCK and not TPCK; amino acid analyses are pending and will be awaited with interest, particularly to see if the cysteine-25 of papain was attacked by both TLCK (LVII) and TPCK (III).

Bulk tolerance studies on thymidine kinase, thymidine phosphorylase, and guanine deaminase were discussed in Chapter 7; further studies on

[48] For a summary see M. Dixon and E. C. Webb, *Enzymes*, Academic Press, New York, 1958, p. 272

[49] G. Lowe and A. Williams, *Biochem. J.*, **96**, 194 (1965).

[50] G. Lowe and A. Williams, *Biochem J.*, **96**, 189 (1965); M. L. Bender and L. J. Brubacker, *J. Am. Chem. Soc.*, **86**, 5333 (1964).

[51] S. S. Husain and G. Lowe, *Chem. Commun.*, **15**, 345 (1965).

[52] See Reference 43, p. 150.

development of active-site-directed irreversible inhibitors of these enzymes, as well as succinoadenylate kinosynthetase (Chapter 5), are in progress in this laboratory.

COMBINING REGIONS OF ANTIBODIES

An approach similar to active-site-directed irreversible inhibition has been taken by Wofsy et al.[53] for covalently attaching groups to the combining regions of antibodies, a process which they termed "affinity labeling." It has been known for a number of years that when a protein is coupled with a diazonium salt such as diazotized arsanilate to give LXIII*A*, then injected into a rabbit, antibodies (LXI*A*) were produced that had specific combining regions dependent upon the character of the attached azo grouping; the grouping was called a hapten (LXIII). The use of other compounds attached to the same protein (LXIII) gave antibody molecules (LXI) that were specific for the particular haptenic determinate in forming insoluble complexes (LXII). It was also known that the hapten (LXIII*A*)-antibody (LXI*A*) complexing to give the insoluble LXII*A*, could be decreased if the combining region of LXI*A* was complexed with a small molecule such as *p*-nitrobenzene arsonic acid. Wofsy et al. chose this system for studying the nature of the combining regions by covalently attaching specific reagents that were related in structure to the hapten; this system has the advantage that haptenic combining regions can be designed more or less to order.

Wofsy et al. reasoned that the diazonium salt (LXIV), from which the original modified protein (LXIII) was prepared, could combine with the specific antibody (LXI) to form a reversible complex (LXV), then undergo irreversible reaction by formation of a covalent linkage as depicted in LXVI. The following evidence supports their affinity labeling of antibody combining regions:

1. The antibody for azobenzene arsonic acid (LXI*A*) reacted rapidly at 0° with the arsonic diazonium salt (LXIV*A*) to form a colored azo derivative (LXVI*A*) (the rate of formation was followed spectrophotometrically). Of the three types of azo compounds that can be formed in a protein—namely, azohistidine, azolysine, and azotyrosine—only the latter was formed with a peak at about 475 mμ. No azohistidine peak was observed.

2. Normal γ-globulin reacted with the arsonic diazonium salt (LXIV*A*) at one four-hundredth the rate of LXI*A*. With the assumption that there

[53] L. Wofsy, H. Metzger, and S. J. Singer, *Biochemistry*, 1, 1031 (1962); *Biochemistry*, 2, 979 (1963); *Abstr. 141st Am. Chem. Soc. Meeting* (March 1962), p. 18C.

was only one tyrosine in each of two active-sites on the antibody molecule (LXI*A*), but that there were 60 tyrosine residues in a normal γ-globulin molecule, the enhancement of the rate of reaction with LXI*A* was about 10,000; "Such a large enhancement is explicable only by the mechanism of initial reversible complex formation (LXV*A*), according to the theory proposed."

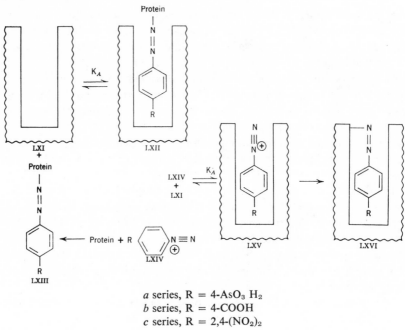

a series, R = 4-AsO₃ H₂
b series, R = 4-COOH
c series, R = 2,4-(NO₂)₂

3. The heterologous reagent *p*-carboxybenzene diazonium salt (LXIV*B*), reacted with the arsonic antibody (LXI*A*) at the same slow rate it reacted with normal γ-globulin, thus showing that there is not a uniquely reactive tyrosine in the arsonic antibody (LXI*A*); these results were consistent with the concept of affinity labeling; that is, when an initial reversible complex (LXV) is formed, the rate of azo reaction is greatly accelerated by an anchimeric reaction.

4. When the combining region (LXI*A*) of the arsonic antibody was protected by initial complexing with *p*-nitrobenzene arsonic acid, then LXI*A* reacted at the same slow rate with either the arsonic diazonium salt (LXIV*A*) or the carboxybenzene diazonium salt (LXIV*B*) at other regions than the haptenic site.

5. An antibody (LXI*C*) specific for the 2,4-dinitrophenyl hapten reacted with a 5 mole ratio of 2,4-dinitrobenzenesulfonyl chloride resulting in a 50 per cent loss of antibody activity in two hours at 25°. In the presence of

a 50 mole ratio of ε-(2,4-dinitrophenyl)-lysine, no loss of antibody activity occurred due to the protective effect of the latter by complex formation.

6. Treatment of the antiarsonic antibody (LXI*A*) with a 10 mole ratio of 2,4-dinitrobenzene sulfonyl chloride under the conditions described in the preceding paragraph gave no loss of antibody activity.

7. Kinetic studies showed that increasing the concentration of diazonium reagent (LXIV) increased the rate of reaction with antibody (LXI) clearly less markedly than would be expected for a simple second-order reaction for the formation of the labeled antibody (LXVI). They demonstrated "that the concentration dependence is entirely accounted for by the unimolecular mechanism" via the obligatory formation of a reversible complex (LXV); that is, the rate of reaction was dependent on the concentration of LXV.

9 | Modus Operandi.
I. Lactic and Glutamic
Dehydrogenases

GENERAL CONSIDERATIONS

In order to design an active-site-directed irreversible inhibitor that operates by the exo mechanism,[1] the following *modus operandi* has been developed:

Phase 1. The binding points on a reversible inhibitor that complex to the enzyme should be determined; some binding points can be eliminated if they are compensated for by a structural change that will give stronger binding at some other point (Chapters 2–6).

Phase 2. Areas on the inhibitor should be determined in which bulky groups can be placed without interfering with the ability of the inhibitor to complex with the enzyme—called either bulk tolerance within the enzyme-inhibitor complex or a noncontact area between inhibitor and enzyme within the complex (Chapter 7).

Phase 3. Once the noncontact area is found, then a group that forms a covalent bond should be placed in the noncontact area. If the dimensions between the reversible complexing region on the enzyme and an enzyme nucleophilic group are correct, then irreversible inhibition by a facile neighboring-group reaction will occur; these dimensions can, as yet, only be found by trial and error with candidate active-site-directed irreversible inhibitors. In this phase, the most general type of electrophilic group, such as bromoacetamido or chlormethyl ketone, should be used (Chapter 8).

[1] See Chapter 1, p. 20 for a definition; see also Fig. 1–3.

Phase 4. The irreversible inhibitor should then be modified to take advantage of the bridge principle of specificity[2-4] until the desired tissue specificity for a given enzyme is found; such variables as distance and steric differences between the reversible complexing region and the covalent-bond forming region on the enzyme, hindrance to the transition state, and inhibitors with more specifically reacting electrophilic groups should be studied.[4]

At each step of each phase the many synthetic compounds needed for the *modus operandi* should be measured for inhibition of the target enzyme; based on the inhibition observed, further synthesis is then undertaken.

The first three phases were discussed in Chapters 2–8, but the work described either had an objective different from chemotherapy or the work had not yet reached Phase 4. There are two major fields of interest through Phase 3, namely, the use of an active-site-directed irreversible inhibitor for (a) covalent reaction with one amino acid specifically in a pure enzyme, then determination of which amino acid in the sequence had become covalently bound—which, in turn can be related to the distance of this specifically labeled amino acid from the reversible complexing region, (b) the study of isozyme specificity (Phase 4) for tissues or species in order to develop a chemotherapeutic agent.

Thus the *modus operandi* for labeling a specific amino acid of a pure enzyme or for chemotherapeutic use is essentially identical through the first three phases. Phase 4 in the two fields differs radically in both objective and methodology. Phase 4, the study of tissue or species specificity for a given enzyme, involves further structural modification of the irreversible inhibitor by synthetic procedures, followed by comparative evaluation of the irreversible inhibitors on the given enzyme from different tissues or species; in contrast, Phase 4 in studies of protein structure involves no further synthetic work—other than getting a radioactive inhibitor—but involves partial hydrolysis of the enzyme to polypeptides, followed by separation and determination of linear peptide sequences in order to establish exactly which specific amino acid in the enzyme chain had become labeled.

In order to develop the *modus operandi* through Phase 4 for chemotherapeutic use, several enzymes will be traced through the first three Phases in the chapters that follow, where the *modus operandi* was deliberately used that started at Phase 1. In this chapter the *modus operandi*

[2] B. R. Baker, *J. Med. Pharm. Chem.*, **5**, 654 (1962); B. R. Baker, *Biochem Pharmacol.*, **11**, 1155 (1962).
[3] B. R. Baker, *Biochem. Pharmacol.*, **12** 293 (1963); B. R. Baker and R. P. Patel, *J. Pharm. Sci.*, **53**, 714 (1964).
[4] For a review see B. R. Baker *J. Pharm. Sci.*, **53**, 347 (1964).

with lactic and glutamic dehydrogenases will be described, which has been carried through Phase 4; these two enzymes are mechanistically quite closely related because each involves dehydrogenation at the α position of a carboxylate.

BINDING POINTS

The enzymatic reactions catalyzed by lactic dehydrogenase (LDH) and glutamic dehydrogenase (GDH) are shown in Figs. 9–1 and 2, respectively. From pH profile and fluorescence spectral studies, Novoa and Schwert[5] have indicated that (a) an imidazole is in the active site of LDH, (b) lactate

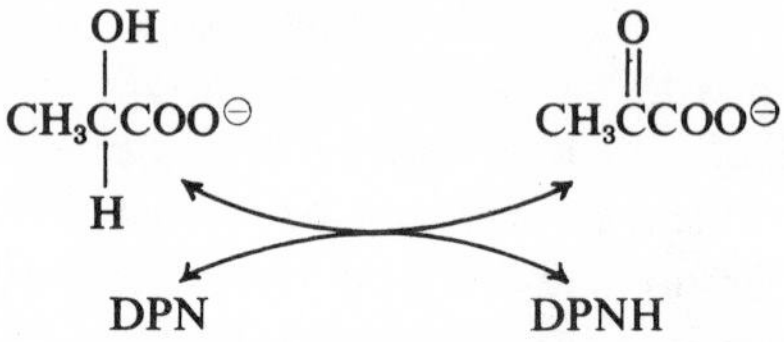

OH
CH3CCOO⊖
H
O
CH3CCOO⊖
DPN
DPNH

Fig. 9–1. The reversible oxidation of L-lactate to pyruvate by DPN catalyzed by lactic dehydrogenase.

NH3⊕
⊖OOCCH2CH2CCOO⊖
H
⊕
NH2
⊖OOCCH2CH2CCOO⊖
O
⊖OOCCH2CH2CCOO⊖
DPN
DPNH
H2O
NH4⊕

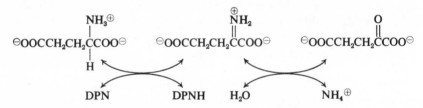

Fig. 9–2. The reversible oxidation of L-glutamate to ammonium ion and α-oxoglutarate by DPN catalyzed by glutamic dehydrogenase.

cannot complex unless DPN is present, and (c) pyruvate cannot complex unless DPNH is present. This compulsory order of binding indicates that one of the binding points of lactate is actually to the DPN part of the DPN-enzyme complex; a similar conclusion can be drawn with pyruvate and DPNH. One possible function of the imidazole in the active-site is to donate to or accept from the substrate a proton; therefore one binding point of lactate is probably between the hydroxylic hydrogen and the imidazole lone electron pair in a donor-acceptor complex. A similar complex between the ketonic oxygen of pyruvate and a protonated imidazole

[5] W. B. Novoa and G. W. Schwert, *J. Biol. Chem.*, **236**, 2150 (1961) and references therein.

can be pictured; as a result of study of the inhibition of LDH by a large number of compounds, the three-dimensional working model in Fig. 9–3 was proposed.[6]

Oxamate (II) is an excellent inhibitor of the reduction of pyruvate (I) to

$$
\begin{array}{cc}
\text{O} & \text{O} \\
\parallel & \parallel \\
\text{CH}_3\text{CCOO}^{\ominus} & \text{NH}_2\text{CCOO}^{\ominus} \\
\text{I} & \text{II}
\end{array}
$$

lactate catalyzed by LDH[7,8]; II represents a structural change at the transfer position[9] because an amide is much more difficult to reduce than a

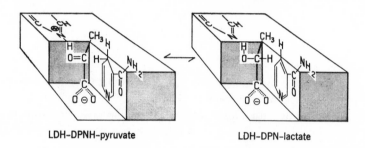

LDH–DPNH–pyruvate   LDH–DPN–lactate

Fig. 9–3. Three-dimensional working model of the active-site of lactic deydrogenase. From B. R. Baker, W. W. Lee, W. A. Skinner, A. P. Martinez, and E. Tong, *J. Med. Pharm. Chem.*, **2**, 633 (1960).

ketone. Oxamate (II) binds better to the enzyme than pyruvate (I), for the $[I/S]_{0.5}$ for 50 per cent inhibition[10] is 0.3.[8]

Glutamic dehydrogenase (Fig. 9–2) is mechanistically closely related to lactic dehydrogenase since both enzymes perform a dehydrogenation α to an anionic group on their substrates; therefore it is not unlikely to assume that there is also an imidazole in the active-site of GDH and that there is a compulsory order of binding where DPN must be complexed before L-glutamate (III). Because glutarate (IV) can bind as well to the enzyme as III,[8,11] it follows that the NH_3^+ group of III is not necessary for binding.

[6] B. R. Baker, W. W. Lee, W. A. Skinner, A. P. Martinez, and E. Tong, *J. Med. Pharm. Chem.*, **2**, 633 (1960).

[7] A. D. Winer and G. W. Schwert, *J. Biol. Chem.*, **234**, 1155 (1959); W. B. Novoa, A. D. Winer, A. J. Glaid, and G. W. Schwert, *J. Biol. Chem.*, **237**, 1143 (1959).

[8] See Reference 6, p. 159.

[9] See Chapter 6.

[10] $[I/S]_{0.5}$ is defined as the ratio of inhibitor to substrate giving 50 per cent inhibition.

[11] W. S. Caughey, J. D. Smiley, and L. Hellerman, *J. Biol. Chem.*, **224**, 591 (1957).

Because isophthalate (V) can bind as well as L-glutamate,[12,13] but benzoate binds only one fiftieth as well,[13] it follows that both carboxylates of isophthalate and, in turn, L-glutamate are complexed to GDH; furthermore, because isophthalate (V) has a fixed staggered conformation between the carboxylate groups, it follows that L-glutamate has the ground-state staggered conformation when complexed to GDH.[12] Although the $NH_3^\oplus$ group of L-glutamate does not appear to bind to GDH, there is a definite

$$\overset{\overset{\displaystyle NH_3^\oplus}{\displaystyle |}}{^\ominus OOC-CH_2CH_2CCOO^\ominus} \qquad ^\ominus OOCCH_2CH_2CH_2COO^\ominus$$

$$\text{III} \qquad\qquad\qquad\qquad \text{IV}$$

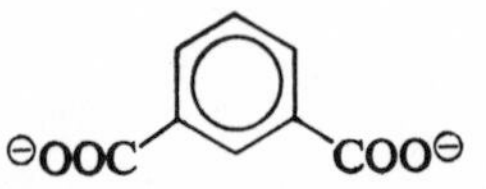

$$\text{V}$$

binding point for ammonium ion when α-oxoglutarate is converted to L-glutamate in the reverse reaction (Fig. 9–2).[12,14]

Based on results with a large number of inhibitors, a three-dimensional working model for the active-site of GDH (Fig. 9–4) has been proposed.[15]

BULK TOLERANCE

Hellerman et al.[16] observed that isophthalate was complexed to GDH as well as the substrate, L-glutamate (III); thus one side of the isophthalate (V) represents a considerable change in gross structure compared to the substrate. The top side of the benzene ring is probably not in contact with the enzyme.[17,18] A structure that still allows inhibition after undergoing such a gross change has been termed a nonclassical antimetabolite.[17,18] Although GDH had a bulk tolerance for the flat benzene ring of isophthalate, poor tolerance was noted when the isophthalate was substituted by 5-methyl[17,19] or 4- or 5-acetamido.[16,19]

[12] See Reference 11, p. 159.

[13] See Reference 6, p. 159.

[14] H. F. Fisher and L. L. McGregor, *Biochem. Biophys. Res. Comm.*, 3, 629 (1960).

[15] B. R. Baker, W. W. Lee, E. Tong, L. O. Ross, and A. P. Martinez, *J. Theoret. Biol.*, 3, 446 (1962).

[16] See Reference 11, p. 159.

[17] B. R. Baker, *Cancer Chemotherapy Reports*, 4, 1 (1959).

[18] See Reference 4, p. 157.

[19] See Reference 6, p. 159.

Phenoxyacetate was reported to be a good inhibitor of the LDH-catalyzed oxidation of L-lactate,[20] the inhibitor being complexed about one third as well as the substrate.[19] The phenyl ring of phenoxyacetate could be substituted by a variety of groups, some of which—such as

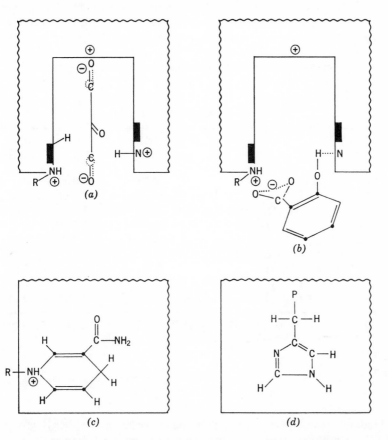

Fig. 9–4. A proposed three-dimensional working model of the GDH active-site; (*a*) top view of binding of α-oxoglutarate to active-site; (*b*) top view of binding of salicylate to active-site; (*c*) and (*d*) side view of (*a*) (looking from right to left) of the dihydronicotinamide and imidazole moieties, respectively where P = enzyme. From B. R. Baker, W. W. Lee, E. Tong, L. O. Ross, and A. P. Martinez, *J. Theoret. Biol.*, **3**, 446 (1962).

2,4,5-trichloro—increased inhibition and some—such as 4-hydroxy—decreased inhibition; thus the enzyme showed bulk tolerance for a variety of groups on the phenoxy moiety.

[20] P. Ottolenghi and O. F. Denstedt, *Can. J. Biochem. Physiol.*, **36**, 1075 (1958).

Because oxamate is an excellent inhibitor of the LDH-catalyzed reduction of pyruvate,[21,22] bulk tolerance for *N*- substituents on oxamate was investigated (Table 9–1).[23] *N*- Substitution by phenyl (VI) led to appreciable loss in binding; part of this loss could be regained by substituting an amide or ketone function at the 3- position of the benzene ring, thus showing that after the initial loss of binding there was bulk tolerance for the groups on the phenyl. Substitution of *N*-benzyl (XII) gave less loss in

Table 9–1. Inhibition of Lactic and Glutamic Dehydrogenases by

$$\underset{\text{RNHCCOOH}}{\overset{\overset{\displaystyle O}{\|}}{}}$$

No.	R	LDH[a] $[I/S]_{0.5}^{c}$	GDH[b] $[I/S]_{0.5}^{c}$	$\dfrac{\text{GDH}^d}{\text{LDH}}$
II	H—	0.30	9.0	30
VI	C_6H_5—	14	19	1.4
VII	$3\text{-}(CH_3CO)C_6H_4$—	3.5	5.5	1.6
VIII	$3\text{-}NO_2C_6H_4$—	2.0	1.7	0.85
IX	$3\text{-}(BrCH_2CO)C_6H_4$—	1.5	0.75	0.50
X	$3\text{-}(ICH_2CONH)C_6H_4$—	0.5	2.0	4.0
XI	$3\text{-}NH_2C_6H_4$—	10.5	22	2.1
XII	$C_6H_5CH_2$—	4.5	13	2.9
XIII	$2,4\text{-}Cl_2C_6H_3CH_2$—	3.5	2.2	0.63

Data from B. R. Baker, W. W. Lee, E. Tong, L. O. Ross, and A. P. Martinez, *J. Theoret. Biol.*, 3, 446 (1962).
[a] Pyruvate to lactate.
[b] Glutamate to α-oxoglutarate.
[c] $[I/S]_{0.5}$ is the ratio of inhibitor to substrate giving 50 per cent inhibition.
[d] Ratio of $[I/S]_{0.5}$ for the two enzymes.

binding than *N*-phenyl (VI), presumably because the phenyl group of XII is out of the plane of the amide function and is better tolerated than in in-plane phenyl group of VI.

Because the binding of L-lactate and pyruvate to LDH appeared to be through the carboxylate group and α-oxygen function, salicylate (XIV) (Table 9–2) was predicted and found to be an inhibitor of the enzyme.[22] That the enzyme could tolerate bulk on the benzene ring of salicylate was demonstrated by a variety of substituents (Table 9–2), some of which caused an increase in affinity for the enzyme.

[21] See Reference 7, p. 159.
[22] See Reference 6, p. 159.
[23] See Reference 15, p. 160.

That salicylic acid could inhibit GDH as effectively as LDH was initially surprising; even more surprising was the fact that either 3- (XVII), 4- (XVIII), or 5-methylsalicylate (XX) were even more effective inhibitors of GDH than salicyate[24] (Table 9–2), particularly in view of the fact that a

Table 9–2. Inhibition of Lactic and Glutamic Dehydrogenases by

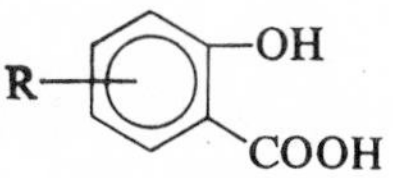

R—⟨benzene ring⟩—OH / COOH

No.	R	LDH[a] $[I/S]_{0.5}{}^c$	GDH[b] $[I/S]_{0.5}{}^c$	$\dfrac{\text{GDH}^d}{\text{LDH}}$
XIV	H	19	20	1.0
XV	5-Br	5.5	1.8	0.33
XVI	3,5-Br$_2$	1.4	0.30	0.21
XVII	3-CH$_3$	12	9	0.75
XVIII	4-CH$_3$	37	14	0.37
XIX	4-CH$_3$-5-Br	5	1.2	0.30
XX	5-CH$_3$	13	9.5	0.75
XXI	4-CH$_3$CONH	3.5	9.0	2.6
XXII	5-CH$_3$CONH	6.0	3.3	0.58
XXIII	4-ICH$_2$CONH	6.6	6.0	0.88
XXIV	5-ICH$_2$CONH	2.0	2.8	1.4

Data from B. R. Baker, W. W. Lee, E. Tong, L. O. Ross, and A. P. Martinez, *J. Theoret. Biol.*, **3**, 446 (1962).

[a] Pyruvate to lactate.
[b] L-Glutamate to α-oxoglutarate.
[c] $[I/S]_{0.5}$ = ratio of inhibitor to substrate giving 50 per cent inhibition.
[d] Ratio of $[I/S]_{0.5}$ for the two enzymes.

40-fold loss in binding occurred when a 5-methyl group (XXV) was substituted on isophthalate (V). These results indicated that isophthalate (V) and salicylate (XIV) did not complex to GDH in the same way. It has been suggested that salicylate complexes to GDH in the same manner as it complexes to LDH, that is, by its carboxylate to the pyridine nitrogen of DPN and its hydroxyl to the supposed imidazole in the active-site (see Fig. 9–4b)[24]; in contrast, it was proposed that isophthalate was complexed to the same two points of GDH that complexes the two carboxylate groups of L-glutamate.[24,25]

Similarly, the *N*- substituted oxamates (Table 9–1) were also as effective

[24] See Reference 15, p. 160.
[25] See Reference 11, p. 159.

Table 9–3. Inhibition of Lactic and Glutamic Dehydrogenases by Bicyclic Oxo Carboxylic Acids

No.	Structure	LDH[a] $[I/S]_{0.5}$	GDH[b] $[I/S]_{0.5}$	$\dfrac{\text{LDH}^c}{\text{GDH}}$
XXVI	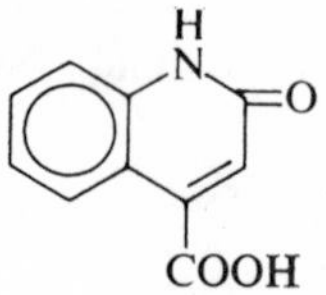	0.60	1.2	2.0
XXVII	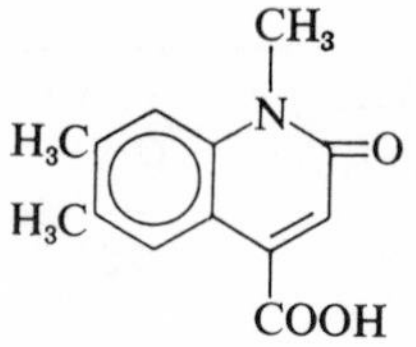	0.20	0.45	2.3
XXVIII	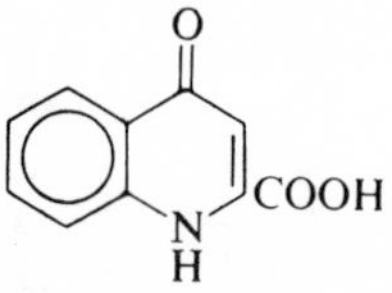	0.19	0.38	2.0
XXIX	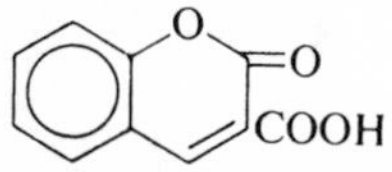	1.7	1.0	0.59
XXX	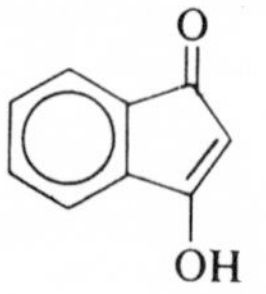	1.5	2.0	1.3
XXXI	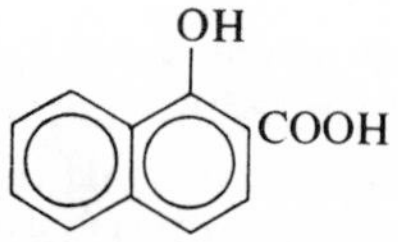	A[d,e]	0.10[e]	

Data from B. R. Baker, W. W. Lee, E. Tong, L. O. Ross, and A. P. Martinez, *J. Theoret. Biol.*, **3**, 446 (1962), unless otherwise indicated.

[a] Pyruvate to lactate.

[b] L-Glutamate to α-oxoglutarate.

[c] Ratio of $[I/S]_{0.5}$ for the two enzymes; $[I/S]_{0.5}$ is the ratio of concentration of inhibitor to substrate giving 50 per cent inhibition.

[d] For lactate to pyruvate, $[I/S]_{0.5}$ was 0.062, compared to salicylate with an $[I/S]_{0.5}$ ratio of 0.75.

[e] Data from B. R. Baker, W. W. Lee, W. A. Skinner, A. P. Martinez, and E. Tong, *J. Med. Pharm. Chem.*, **2**, 633 (1960).

as inhibitors of GDH as they were of LDH, again probably because binding similar to salicylate, as indicated in Fig. 9–4–*b*, occurred.

Some bicyclic structures were complexed to GDH and LDH even more strongly than were the respective substrates; for example, the quinolones

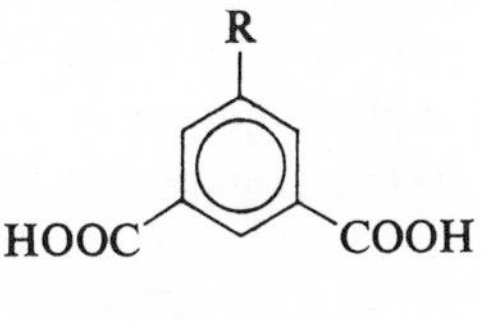

V, R = H($[I/S]_{0.5}$ = 1)
XXV, R = CH_3($[I/S]_{0.5}$ = 40)

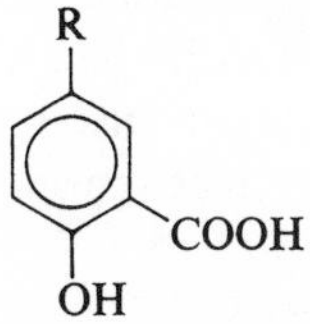

XIV, R = H$[I/S]_{0.5}$ = 20)
XX, R = $CH_3[I/S]_{0.5}$ = 9.5)

(XXVI–XXVIII) were predicted to be good inhibitors because of the 1,2 or 1,3- relationship of carboxyl and oxo functions. At this point it should be noted that the *N*- substituted oxamates (Table 9–1), the substituted salicylates (Table 9–2), and the bicyclic structures (Table 9–3) showed little selectivity of inhibition between LDH and GDH.

ACTIVE-SITE-DIRECTED IRREVERSIBLE INHIBITORS

As was discusssed in the preceding section, the active sites of both LDH and GDH displayed a tolerance for bulky groups on salicyclic acid; thus reversible complex formation would still be possible with a bulky group of the type needed for a neighboring group reaction within the enzyme-inhibitor complex. A likely candidate for active-site-directed irreversible

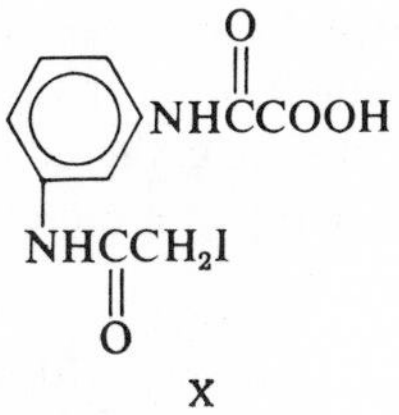

X

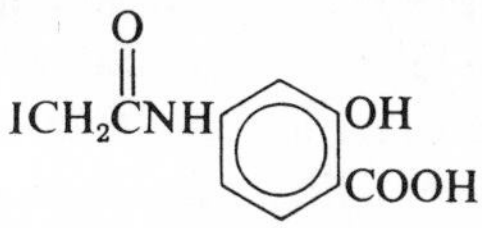

XXIII
(4–ISA)

inhibition was 4-(iodoacetamido)-salicylic acid (XXIII) (Table 9–2). For similar reasons, 3-(iodoacetamido)-oxanilic acid (X) (Table 9–1) was also a potential candidate. The results with XXIII on GDH will be presented first.

In Fig. 9–5 is shown the rate of inactivation of GDH by 2 mM 4-ISA (XXIII); at 37°, the half life of inactivation was 11 minutes.[26] Note that

26 B. R. Baker, W. W. Lee, and E. Tong, *J. Theoret. Biol.*, 3, 459 (1962).

4.48 mM iodoacetamide gave no inactivation in 14 minutes; the higher concentration of iodoacetamide was employed, for the halogen of XXIII was 2.24 times as reactive as that of iodoacetamide towards thiosulfate.[26] If XXIII had inactivated GDH by a bimolecular mechanism,[27] then iodoacetamide should also have inactivated GDH; therefore XXIII inactivates GDH by a different mechanism, presumably by a neighboring group reaction within an enzyme-inhibitor complex. To prove unequivocally that this latter mechanism is operative is not possible by kinetic means

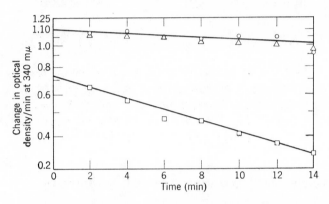

Fig. 9–5. Comparison of 4-ISA (XXIII) and iodoacetamide in inactivating GDH·DPNH: ○, GDH·DPNH control; △, 4.48 mM iodoacetamide; □, 2 mM 4-ISA. The change in optical density per minute is a measure of the relative GDH concentration. From B. R. Baker, W. W. Lee, and E. Tong, *J. Theoret. Biol.*, **3**, 459 (1962).

because kinetics can only differentiate between two possible mechanisms to eliminate a false one, but it does not prove the second one; as is the case for all kinetic experiments, an as yet unthought-of mechanism may be the true one.[28] Several lines of evidence were therefore gathered that eliminated all the yet-thought-of mechanisms except active-site-directed irreversible inhibition, as follows:

1. If the 4-ISA (XXIII) is inactivating GDH only within the complex by the active-site-directed mechanism, then a "rate-saturation effect" should be observed; that is, doubling the concentration should not double the rate, for the rate is dependent upon the relative concentration of enzyme-inhibitor complex, according to the following equations[27]:

$$[EI] = \frac{E_t}{(K_i/I) + 1} \quad \text{and} \quad \frac{r_2}{r_1} = \frac{[EI]_2}{[EI]_1}$$

[27] See Chapter 8, Kinetic Parameters.
[28] See Reference 26, p. 165.

where [EI] is the concentration of reversible enzyme-inhibitor complex, E_t is the total active enzyme both free and reversibly complexed, K_i is the enzyme-inhibitor reversible dissociation constant, I is the inhibitor concentration, and r is the rate of inactivation.

By the reciprocal plot method it was determined that 4-ISA (XXIII) had $K_i = 0.7$ mM; therefore at 1 mM concentration of 4-ISA 59 per cent of the total active enzyme is reversibly complexed, and at 2 mM concentration 74 per cent of total active enzyme is reversibly complexed. It follows that $r_2/r_1 = 0.74/0.59 = 1.26$, In Fig. 9–6 this "rate-saturation" effect is

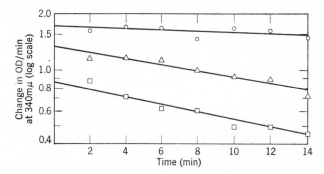

Fig. 9–6. "Rate saturation" effect during inactivation of GDH·DPNH by 4-ISA (XXIII): ○, GDH·DPNH control; △, 1 mM 4-ISA; □, 2 mM 4-ISA. The change in optical density per minute is a measure of the relative GDH concentration. From B. R. Baker, W. W. Lee, and E. Tong, *J. Theoret. Biol.*, 3, 459 (1962).

shown; the observed ratio of slopes was 1.23, in good agreement with the calculated value of 1.26.

The fact that a "rate saturation" was observed does not prove that the active-site-directed mechanism of irreversible inhibition was operational. The same kinetics are observed by a mechanism called "bimolecular reaction with self-protection"[29]; the latter mechanism is eliminated by the fact that iodoacetamide does not inactivate GDH.

2. Because the rate of inactivation by the active-site-directed mechanism is dependent upon the concentration of reversible enzyme-inhibitor complex, it follows that a stronger reversible inhibitor should give the same amount of E····I complex if there is a lower concentration of inhibitor (I), providing other factors are not operational, such as a change in distance between the reversible binding points of the inhibitor and the leaving group on the inhibitor. For example, 4-(iodoacetamido)-benzoic acid (XXXII) should not be as good a reversible inhibitor of GDH as 4-ISA (XXIII) for the hydroxyl binding point is missing in XXXII. However the binding

[29] See Chapter 8, Kinetic Parameters.

distance between the carboxylate binding point and the iodo leaving group is identical in XXIII and XXXII; therefore, at equal concentrations, XXIII should inactivate more rapidly than XXXII because the latter would form a lower concentration of the rate-determining enzyme-inhibitor reversible complex. Because XXXII has $K_i = 5.3$ mM, it can be

XXIII
(4–ISA)

XXXII

calculated that at a 2 mM concentration of XXXII, 26 per cent of the total active enzyme is in a reversible complex, in contrast to XXIII where 74 per cent of the total active enzyme is in a reversible complex. Therefore XXIII should inactivate GDH at $0.74/0.26 = 2.9$ times the rate that XXXII will inactivate; the observed difference was eightfold.[30] As can be predicted, the use of more potent reversible carriers for the leaving groups would be expected to operate irreversibly at a lower concentration of the inhibitor; such a study was successful.[31]

    3. 4-Acetamidosalicylic acid (XXI, Table 9–2) was a reversible inhibitor of GDH, but it showed no inactivation of GDH when incubated; thus the inactivation of GDH by 4-ISA (XXIII) requires the halogen leaving group, and the inactivation is not due to some chelation phenomenon of the 4-acetamidosalicylic acid (XXI) structure.[30]

    4. The possibility that traces of heavy-metal ions caused inactivation of GDH was unlikely because there was no correlation between the trace heavy-metal content of XXIII, XXXII, and 4-acetamidosalicylic acid (XXI) with their relative abilities to inactivate[30]; for example, XXI had 1 ppm of copper, but XXIII had less than 0.5 ppm.

    5. When a competitive inhibitor protects an enzyme against inactivation by an irreversible inhibitor, it is considered to be strong evidence that the effect of the irreversible inhibitor involves the active site.[32,33] Such an interpretation is dependent upon the validity of the assumption that a competitive inhibitor complexes at the active-site; this assumption is not necessarily valid because the mathematical derivation merely states that when an inhibitor forms an E⋯I complex, the substrate cannot form an E⋯S complex; that is, binding by substrate and inhibitor to the enzyme is

---

[30] See Reference 26, p. 165.

[31] B. R. Baker, R. P. Patel, and P. I. Almaula, *J. Pharm. Sci.*, **52**, 1051 (1963).

[32] J. A. Thoma and D. E. Koshland, Jr., *J. Mol. Biol.*, **2**, 169 (1960).

[33] For additional references see Chapter 8.

mutually exclusive.[34] Other mechanisms will give competitive kinetics. For example,[34] (a) when the inhibitor is complexed to the enzyme—but not at the active-site—a conformational change in enzyme structure may take place that does not allow the substrate to complex at the active-site, (b) the inhibitor not complexed at the active-site may sterically hinder the approach of the substrate, or (c) the inhibitor when it is not complexed at the active-site may change the electrical properties of the active-site.

The minimum valid interpretation that can be given to a protection experiment of the type described above is that some functional group essential for enzymatic activity cannot be attacked by the irreversible inhibitor when the enzyme is complexed with a reversible inhibitor, whether competitive or not competitive.

Isophthalate (V) is a competitive inhibitor of the DPN oxidation of L-glutamate catalyzed by GDH, but it is noncompetitive in the reverse direction[35]; it is difficult to believe that isophthalate is not complexed in the same region of the enzyme when the reverse reaction is in effect.[36] Regardless of the difficulties in interpretation, if the active-site-directed mechanism is operational for the inactivation of GDH by 4-ISA (XXIII), then isophthalate should slow the rate of inactivation; this was indeed

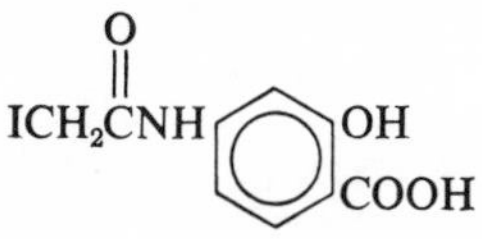

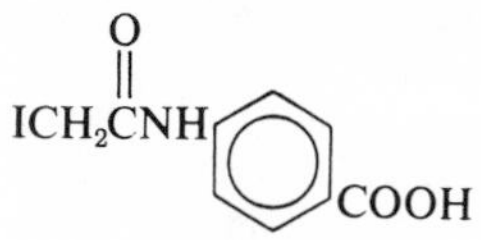

observed experimentally and the protective effect was not due to a chemical interaction between 4-ISA (XXIII) and isophthalate (V).[36]

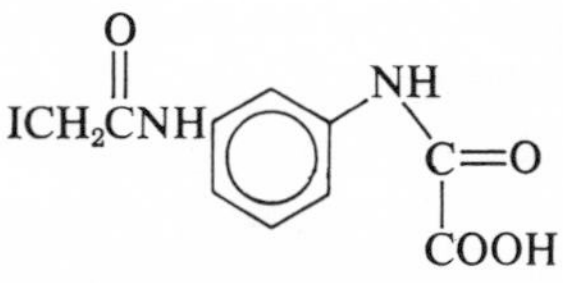

When LDH was incubated with 4-ISA (XXIII) at 37°, the enzyme was inactivated.[37] When inactivated with 2 mM 4-ISA its half-life was about 50 minutes (Fig. 9–7), about one fifth the rate at which GDH was inactivated.

[34] J. M. Reiner, *Behavior of Enzyme Systems*, Burgess Co., Minneapolis, Minn., 1959, p. 152.
[35] See Reference 11, p. 159.
[36] See Reference 26, p. 165.
[37] See Reference 26, p. 165.

Half of this fivefold difference can be attributed to the greater reversible binding of 4-ISA to GDH than LDH; 2 mM 4-ISA (XXIII) gives a ratio of enzyme-inhibitor complex of 2.2 for GDH over LDH. In Fig. 9–7 the "rate-saturation" effect is shown by comparing the rates of inactivation

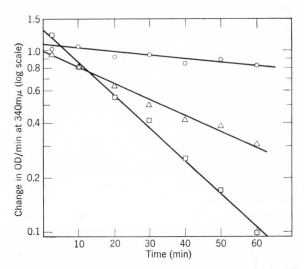

Fig. 9–7. "Rate saturation" effect during inactivation of LDH-DPNH by 4-ISA (XXIII): ○, LDH-DPNH control; △, 1 mM 4-ISA; □, 3 mM 4-ISA. The change in optical density per minute is a measure of the relative LDH concentration. From B. R. Baker, W. W. Lee, and E. Tong, *J. Theoret. Biol.*, **3**, 459 (1962).

by 1 mM and 3 mM 4-ISA (XXIII); the observed ratio of the slopes (rate of inactivation) was 2.0–2.1 in two runs, compared to a calculated ratio of 1.9 from $K_i = 2.6$ mM.[38]

In contrast to GDH, LDH showed appreciable inactivation with iodoacetamide (Fig. 9–7). Because iodoacetamide showed no reversible inhibition of LDH it inactivated LDH most probably by means of the bimolecular mechanism. This was further supported by the absence of a "rate-saturation" effect; that is, increasing the concentration of iodoacetamide by threefold gave a 2.7–3.0-fold increase in rate of inactivation. A direct comparison of 4.48 mM iodoacetamide with 2.00 mM 4-ISA (XXIII) in Fig. 9–8 showed that XXIII inactivated LDH at about twice the rate of iodoacetamide; the higher concentration of iodoacetamide was used because the halogen of XXIII is 2.24 times as active towards thiosulfate as is the halogen of iodoacetamide.

Because iodoacetamide could inactivate LDH, presumably by the bimolecular mechanism, the possibility existed that 4-ISA (XXIII) was inactivating

[38] See Chapter 8, Kinetic Parameters.

LDH entirely by (a) the bimolecular mechanism, (b) entirely by active-site direction through a complex, or (c) a combination of both. That the bimolecular inactivation of LDH was due to 4-ISA (XXIII) was highly unlikely because (a) 3-(iodoacetamido)-oxanilic acid (X), which is an even

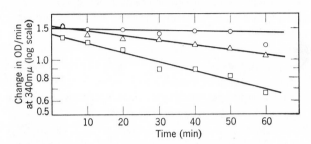

Fig. 9–8. Comparison of 4-ISA (XXIII) and iodoacetamide in inactivating LDH-DPNH: ○, LDH-DPNH control; △, 4.48 mM iodoacetamide; □, 2 mM 4-ISA. The change in optical density per minute is a measure of the relative LDH concentration. From B. R. Baker, W. W. Lee, and E. Tong, *J. Theoret. Biol.*, 3, 459 (1962).

better reversible inhibitor of LDH than XXIII, showed no inactivation in 60 minutes,[39] and (b) 4-ISA (XXIII) inactivated LDH at 3.0–3.1 times the rate observed with 4-(iodoacetamido)-benzoic acid (XXXII). The relative rates of XXIII and XXXII at a concentration of 2 mM agreed with the calculated ratio of reversible enzyme-inhibitor complex of 2.7. If the bimolecular inactivation mechanism of 4-ISA were operating, then 4-ISA (XXIII) and the corresponding benzoic acid derivative XXXII should have inactivated LDH at identical rates due to the fact that (a) the halogens of XXIII or XXXII have identical reactivity towards thiosulfate and (b) XXXII is a smaller molecule than XXIII, thus not giving any additional hindrance to bimolecular inactivation.

The reversible inhibitor of LDH, oxamate, slowed the inactivation of LDH by 4-ISA (XXIII); in the presence of 0.3 mM oxamate and 2 mM 4-ISA the rate was slowed by a factor of 4.0–4.1. From the ratio of the relative amounts of enzyme-4-ISA reversible complex in the presence and absence of oxamate, the calculated ratio was 3.0.[40]

Similarly, the rate of inactivation of LDH by iodoacetamide was decreased by a factor of 3.8–4.3 in the presence of 0.3 mM oxamate; the calculated ratio,[40] based on an enzyme that was not complexed with oxamate, was 4.5.

How much specificity can be expected from an inhibitor such as 4-ISA

[39] B. R. Baker, *J. Med. Pharm. Chem.*, 5, 654 (1962); *Biochem. Pharmacol.*, 11, 1155 (1962).
[40] See Chapter 8, Kinetic Parameters.

(XXIII)? That it is not a general enzyme poison was shown by its failure to show any inactivation of hexokinase[41] in 60 minutes at 37°; in contrast, hexokinase has been reported to be inactivated by ethyl iodoacetate[42] and by sulfur mustard.[43] That 4-ISA (XXIII) can inactivate other enzymes is indicated by its inactivation of glucose-6-phosphate dehydrogenase,[41] an enzyme requiring TPN. These results suggest that any oxidation or reduction enzyme utilizing DPN or TPN (or their reduced forms) such as the dehydrogenases for α-glycerophosphate, malate, isocitrate, 6-phosphogluconate and glyceraldehyde phosphate,[41] and an anionic substrate could be logically studied. From the models of sites of LDH (Fig. 9–3) and GDH (Fig. 9–4b), it is possible that salicylate can complex reversibly in a manner similar to that displayed by other oxidoreductases.

The inactivation of glutamic dehydrogenase[41] by 4-ISA (XXIII) and the fact that 4-ISA had become commercially available[44] suggested to Petrakis and Nielands[45] that 4-ISA (XXIII) should be investigated as an irreversible inhibitor of $\triangle^1$-pyrroline-2-carboxylate reductase, the enzyme that reductively cyclizes α-keto-δ-aminovalerate to proline with TPNH as a cofactor. Preliminary results indicated a 50 per cent inactivation of the enzyme in 15 minutes at 25° with a concentration of 3.6×10^{-6} M 4-ISA (XXIII); doubling the concentration increased the rate of inactivation about 1.3-fold, indicating a "rate-saturation" effect. Iodoacetamide at about 10^{-2} M showed no inactivation; salicylic acid at 3.3×10^{-6} M showed little, if any, irreversible inhibition, but it did show about a 25 per cent reversible inhibition. These preliminary data indicate that the enzyme is being inactivated by the active-site-directed mechanism; final data, including a reversible binding constant, will be awaited with interest.

Can further selectivity with molecules such as 4-ISA (XXIII) be achieved? By application of the bridge principle of specificity the answer is yes—as will be discussed in the following section.

THE BRIDGE PRINCIPLE OF SPECIFICITY

As was pointed out in Chapter 1, the first two milestones in the understanding of active-site-directed irreversible inhibition were established by studying the biological mechanism of the action of DFP and azaserine. The main concern of subsequent investigators—except for the author's

---

[41] See Reference 26, p. 165.
[42] M. Dixon and E. C. Webb, *Enzymes*, Academic Press, New York, 1958, p. 380.
[43] M. Dixon and D. Needham, *Nature*, **158**, 432 (1946).
[44] Nutritional Biochemical Corp., Cleveland, Ohio, U.S.A.
[45] P. H. Petrakis and J. Nielands, unpublished.

laboratory—was to use the phenomenon to label active-sites of pure enzymes or of specific, though heterogeneous, antibodies. Depending upon the goal of the particular investigator, two different criteria for specificity can be envisioned. If the investigator wishes to label the active-site of a pure protein, then he is concerned with finding a reagent that will react specifically with the active-site and have a near-zero effect on other parts of the pure protein. In contrast, if the investigator wishes to use "active-site-directed irreversible inhibitors" in chemotherapy, the problem is less concerned with exactly how a given enzyme becomes inactivated and more concerned with the specific inactivation of a single enzyme in an intracellular mixture of enzymes in a functioning cell.

That these two apparently different goals initially converge into one approach becomes apparent if you realize that the specificity required for inactivation of one enzyme in an intracellular mixture of enzymes must logically reside in the more or less subtle differences in the active-site of enzymes that perform different—but at times mechanistically closely related—enzymic reactions. Once the labeling reagent for an active-site has been found, the experimental approaches to the two goals then diverge dramatically in methodology.

The purpose of studying the labeling of the active-site of a pure enzyme is to determine the amino acid sequence surrounding the label in order to learn what part of the sequence is at (or close to) the active-site (mapping the active-site). In chemotherapy, the problem is different because the labeling reagent must now be studied to determine how specific it may be in reacting with only one of a number of mechanistically closely related enzymes; it is the latter problem to which we have been devoting our attention, and more specifically to the problem of how an active-site-directed irreversible inhibitor may be modified to build in further specificity. This problem has been approached by use of the bridge principle of specificity[46,47]: "Compared to a reversible inhibitor, the active-site-directed type of irreversible inhibitor can have an extra dimension of specificity; this extra specificity is dependent upon the ability of the reversibly bound inhibitor to bridge to and form a covalent bond with a nucleophilic group on the enzyme surface and upon the nucleophilicity of the enzymic group being covalently linked."

Nucleophilic Sites

The bridge principle can be envisioned by inspection of Fig. 1–3. Group B of an active-site-directed irreversible inhibitor can form a covalent bond with a nucleophilic group adjacent to the reversible binding region where

---

[46] See Reference 26, p. 165.
[47] See Reference 39, p. 171.

Group A is reversibly complexed. In order for this covalent bond to form (shown by the arrow), there must be a proper distance between the A and B regions of the inhibitor so that bridging can take place; in addition, the electrophilic group B and the enzymic nucleophilic group must have the ability to interact, for it is obvious that not all electrophilic groups react with all nucleophilic groups. Furthermore, the approach of the electrophilic group to the enzymic nucleophilic group must meet the combined steric and conformational requirements of the active-site, the nucleophilic site, and the environment in between these two sites. These dual site requirements are obviously far more restrictive than the mere additive requirements of each site alone.[47]

Therefore, the use of the bridge principle should make it possible to obtain highly selective irreversible inhibitors within any group of enzymes that are closely related by the nature of their substrates. Furthermore, it should be noted that an irreversible inhibitor will have a much greater effect on the operation of an enzyme than a reversible inhibitor. The enzyme molecule is still more or less operational in the presence of the reversible inhibitor and substrate, but an irreversibly inhibited enzyme molecule can be completely inoperative. Because theoretically only one irreversible inhibitor molecule is necessary to inactivate one enzyme molecule, and because one active enzyme molecule can convert many substrate molecules to product, an irreversible inhibitor will be far more effective than a reversible inhibitor. Thus, an inhibitor will be more effective on an enzyme that can be first reversibly, then irreversibly inhibited than on a closely related enzyme that is only reversibly inhibited, for enzymes have an estimated concentration of 10^{-8} to 10^{-12} M, whereas substrates have a concentration in the range of 10^{-3} to 10^{-6} M.

Conformational and Steric Aspects

For the initial studies on the bridge principle, Baker[49] selected the mechanistically closely related enzymes, GDH and LDH in view of the fact that an earlier study of a variety of reversible inhibitors showed that almost all of the compounds that inhibited GDH also inhibited LDH (Tables 9–1, 2, 3)[48,49]; because these two enzymes perform similar reactions, that is, dehydrogenation at the α position of an anionic substrate, and are therefore by mechanistic necessity closely related, it is not surprising that the two enzymes are inhibited by similar compounds. In contrast, the adjacent nucleophilic sites would most likely be dissimilar because these nucleophilic sites probably have no function in the mechanistic operation of the enzymes; rather they are probably part of the protein molecule necessary

[48] See Reference 26, p. 165.
[49] See Reference 15, p. 160.

for the integrity of the protein's secondary-tertiary structure. Thus, it was anticipated that relatively minor changes in inhibitor structure could greatly influence the bridging ability of the irreversible inhibitor.

Previously 4-(iodoacetamido)-salicylic acid (XXIII) had been shown[48] to be an irreversible inhibitor of both LDH and GDH. A number of closely related compounds were then investigated as irreversible inhibitors of the two enzymes in a search for irreversible specificity.[50] When the length of the bridge was increased as in XXXIII (Table 9–4), both GDH and skeletal muscle LDH were inhibited both reversibly and irreversibly, thus showing no irreversible specificity. However, two other compounds showed a cross-over in selectivity of irreversible inhibition. Although 3-(iodoacetamido)-oxanilic acid (X) was a better reversible inhibitor of skeletal muscle LDH than 4-ISA (XXIII), the former showed no irreversible inhibition of skeletal muscle LDH; in contrast, X was just as good an irreversible inhibitor of GDH as XXIII. A direct antithesis of irreversible inhibition pattern was shown with XXXVI; although skeletal muscle LDH was irreversibly inhibited by XXXVI, the latter showed no irreversible inhibition of GDH (Table 9–4).

It was previously noted[51] in a crude model of the active-site of LDH that the oxanilic-LDH complex does not appear to have sufficient space for the complete free rotation of the phenyl group; in addition, it can be demonstrated with molecular models that the iodomethylene group of the

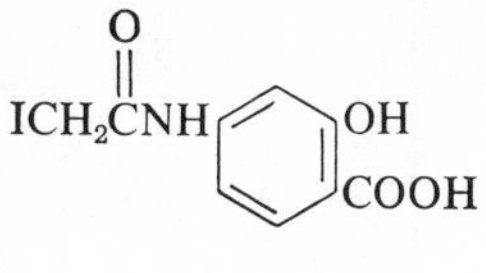

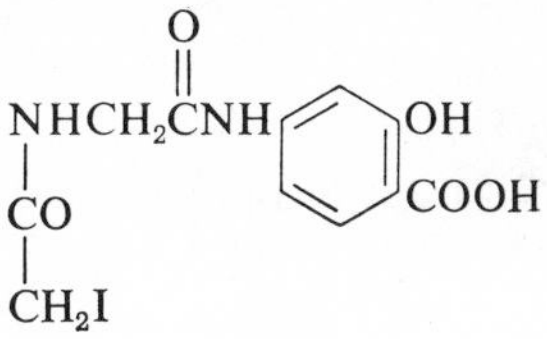

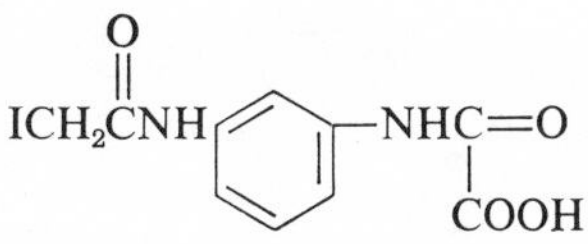

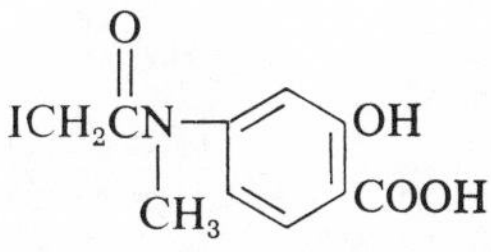

oxanilate (X) can approach any point in space that the iodomethylene group of XXIII (4-ISA) can approach when the respective enzyme-binding points of the inhibitors are anchored. Therefore, the conformation necessary for the iodomethylene group of X to bridge to the nucleophilic site

[50] See Reference 39, p. 171.
[51] See Reference 6, p. 159.

Table 9–4. Selective Irreversible Inhibition of Lactic and Glutamic Dehydrogenases by Substituted Salicyclic Acids

No.	Compound[a]	Glutamic dehydrogenase K_i (mM)	Per cent rev. EI[b]	Rate of inactivation[c]	Skeletal muscle LDH K_i (mM)	Per cent rev. EI[b]	Rate of inactivation	Reference
XXIII	4-ICH$_2$CONH—SA	0.85	70	1.0[d]	1.7	54	1.0[d]	g
XXXIII	4-ICH$_2$CONH—GSA	1.8	53	1.6	0.40	83	0.57	h
XXXIV	4-ICH$_2$CON—SA (—CH$_3$)	3.3	38	0	3.3	38	1.4	h
X	3-ICH$_2$CONH—OA	2.3	47	1.1	0.13	93	0	h
XXXV	5-C$_6$H$_5$OCONH—SA	0.40	83	1.7	1.5	57	0	i
XXXVI	4-C$_6$H$_5$OCONH—SA	0.85	70	0	1.1	65	0.8	i
XXXVII	5-C$_6$H$_5$OCONH—GSA	0.16	93	1.5	0.59	77	0	i
XXXVIII	6-C$_6$H$_5$OCONH—QA	0.23	36[e]	0[e]	0.11	54[e]	0[e]	f
XXXIX	6-C$_6$H$_5$OCONH—CA	0.24	45[f]	2.0[f]	0.24	45[f]	0[f]	f
XL	4-cis-HOOCCH=CHCO SA—NH	4.3	32	0	1.8	52	0.9	k
XLI	maleanilic acid	—	—	—	8.3	19	0	k

[a] Abbreviations used: SA = salicylic acid, OA = oxanilic acid, GSA = glycylamido-salicylic acid; QA = 4-hydroxyquinoline-3-carboxylic acid; CA = 2-hydroxycinchoninic acid.

[b] Per cent of active enzyme in reversible EI complex with 2 mM inhibitor unless otherwise indicated; see Chapter 8, Kinetic Parameters, for calculation.

[c] Compared to 4-ISA (XXIII) as a standard; relative rate corrected to equal concentration of reversible EI complex.

[d] Arbitrary standard that is not the same for GDH and LDH.

[e] With 0.13 mM inhibitor.

[f] With 0.20 mM inhibitor.

[g] B. R. Baker, W. W. Lee, E. Tong, and L. O. Ross, J. Am. Chem. Soc., **83**, 3173 (1961); B. R. Baker, W. W. Lee, and E. Tong, J. Theoret. Biol., **3**, 459 (1962).

[h] B. R. Baker, Biochem. Pharmacol., **11**, 1155 (1962).

[i] B. R. Baker and R. P. Patel, Biochem. Biophys. Res. Commun., **9**, 199 (1962); J. Pharm. Sci., **52**, 927 (1963).

[j] B. R. Baker, R. P. Patel, and P. I. Almaula, J. Pharm. Sci., **52**, 1051 (1963).

[k] B. R. Baker and P. I. Almaula, J. Pharm. Sci., **52**, 914 (1963).

for reaction within the enzyme-inhibitor complex may not be tolerated due to a restriction of rotation.

The carbonyl carbon of the iodoacetyl group and the N-methyl groups of XXXIV have a fixed relationship between them; when the iodomethylene group of XXXIV attempts to bridge to the nucleophilic site within the GDH-inhibitor reversible complex, there is apparently insufficient space for the counterbalancing N-methyl group and bridging for inactivation cannot be completed.

Inactivation via the Carbophenoxy Group

The second corollary of the bridge principle of specificity is based on the difference in nucleophilicity of the enzymic group being attacked. It is also at this point that the approach for labeling the active-site of a pure enzyme and the approach to chemotherapy become divergent. The α-halogen carbonyl group of an iodoacetamide such as that of 4-ISA (XXIII), or a chloroketone, have little functional specificity. Of about 15 amino acids in proteins containing a third functional group, a majority of them—such as methionine, histidine, arginine, lysine, cysteine, cystine, tyrosine, aspartic acid, and glutamic acid—have the nucleophilic ability to become alkylated. The α-halogen carbonyl compounds, therefore have the broadest utility in labeling the active-site of a pure enzyme, the selectivity of reaction being controlled by the initial complexing between the inhibitor and the active-site; this very broadness of utility for a pure enzyme may be undesirable for the mixture of enzymes in a cell involved in chemotherapy. Ideally, for chemotherapy the greatest selectivity should be obtained by using an attacking group for the enzymic nucleophilic group that is specific for a single amino acid of the group of 15, thus affording a further dimension of specificity. The phenyl ester group such as that of 5-(carbophenoxyamino)-salicylic acid (XXXV) apparently can react best with a primary amino group,[52] and possibly slowly react with a serine or threonine hydroxyl group by *trans* esterification.

5-(Carbophenoxyamino)-salicylic acid (XXXV) inactivated GDH at 1.7 times the rate of the standard, 4-(iodoacetamido)-salicylic acid (XXIII); in contrast, XXXV showed no irreversible inhibition of skeletal muscle LDH (Table 9–4). A crossover specificity was noted with XXXVI, which inactivated skeletal muscle LDH at about the same rate as the standard (XXIII), but showed no inactivation of GDH. The peptide, XXXVII, with a longer side chain still inactivated GDH, presumably by folding the chain back to the point in space equivalent to the position of the carbophenoxy

[52] B. R. Baker and R. P. Patel, *Biochem. Biophys. Res. Commun.*, **9**, 199 (1962); J. *Pharm. Sci.*, **52**, 927 (1963).

group of XXXV. Although XXXVII can also fold back to the point in space equivalent to the position of the carbophenoxy group of XXXVI, XXXVII failed to show the inactivation of LDH that XXXVI showed; this difference is attributed to hindrance to the transition state, which is dis-

XXXV

XXXVI

XXXVII

XXXVIII

XXXIX

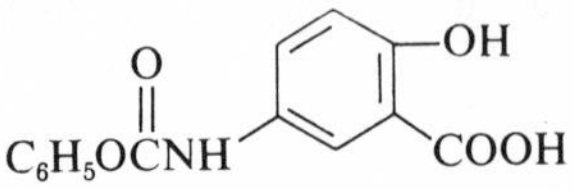

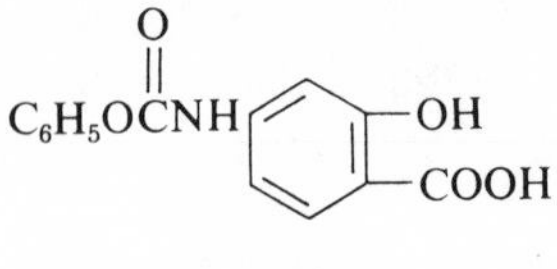

cussed in a later section. In contrast, XXXVIII failed to inactivate either LDH or GDH, showing that the fixed position of the carbophenoxy group in XXXVIII cannot bridge to the available enzymic group. That a bicyclic compound could inactivate GDH at a low concentration was shown with XXXIX, which inactivated GDH at about the rate of XXXV using one tenth the concentration of XXXIX; again LDH was not inactivated by this compound.

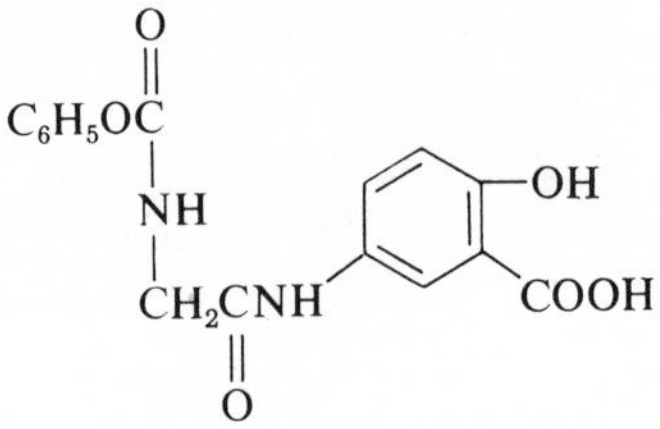

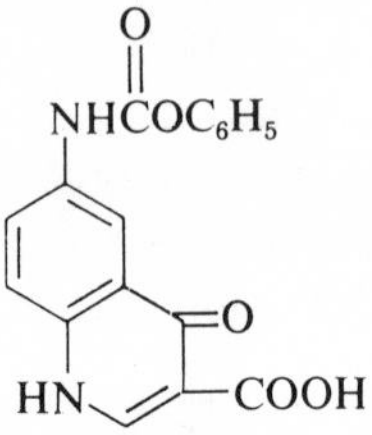

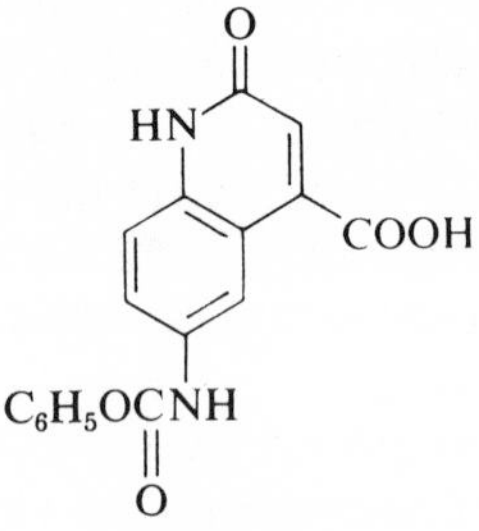

Inactivation via the Maleamyl Group

The α, β-unsaturated system of XLII should react in general most rapidly with SH groups, much more slowly with amino groups, and extremely slowly with hydroxyl groups by a Michael addition reaction. For initial studies, 4-(maleamyl)-salicylic acid (XL) was selected. 4-(Maleamyl)-salicylic acid (XL) inactivated skeletal muscle LDH at about the same rate

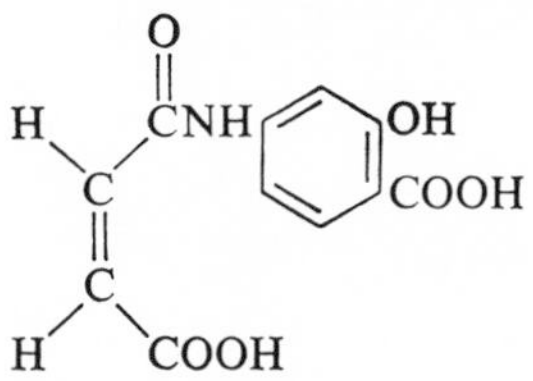

as the standard compound, 4-ISA (XXIII) (Table 9–4); however XL failed to inactivate GDH, thus showing the selectivity of the maleamyl group. That a reversible complex between XL and skeletal muscle LDH appeared to be an obligatory intermediate to inactivation was strongly indicated by the failure of maleanilic acid (XLI) (Table 9–4), which does not have the necessary groups for proper reversible binding, to inactivate skeletal muscle LDH. Preliminary studies have shown that 4-(acrylamido)-salicylic acid (XLII), (R = H) irreversibly inhibited both GDH and skeletal muscle LDH[53]; further studies on the selectivity that might be obtained by varying the R groups of XLII would be useful.

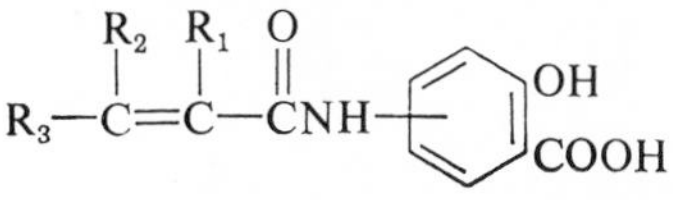

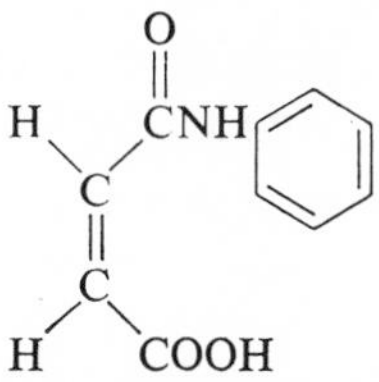

Hindrance to the Transition State

In a displacement reaction of the S_N2 type, whether bimolecular or intramolecular, the transition state appears to be planar (XLIII).[54] Therefore the attacking group should not be hindered by a bulky leaving group because the two groups are on opposite sides of the carbon atom undergoing reaction; this has been indicated experimentally.[55] When such an

[53] Unpublished work by B. R. Baker and D. V. Santi.
[54] E. S. Gould, *Mechanism and Structure in Organic Chemistry*, Holt, Rinehart, and Winston, New York, 1959, p. 129, 251.
[55] E. L. Eliel and R. P. Gerber, *Tetrahedron Letters*, 1961, 473.

intramolecular reaction takes place in an enzyme-inhibitor reversible complex, the enzymic nucleophilic group which is attacking in the displacement reaction is part of the extremely large (compared to inhibitor)

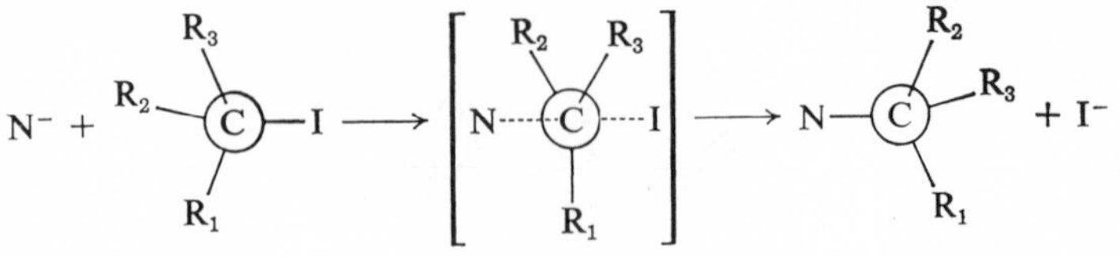

$$N^- + R_2-C(R_3)(R_1)-I \longrightarrow [N\cdots C(R_2)(R_3)(R_1)\cdots I] \longrightarrow N-C(R_2)(R_3)(R_1) + I^-$$

XLIII

enzyme molecule; as a result, there may be hindrance to the formation of the transition state by steric interaction of the enzyme and a bulky leaving

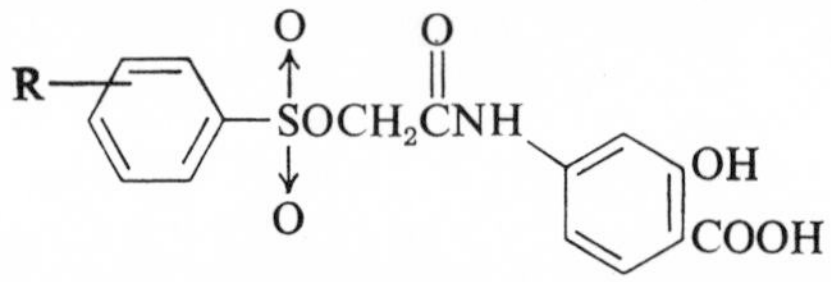

XLIV

group. Such a study could be made with the sulfonate leaving group (XLIV); when $R = Me$, XLIV is an irreversible inhibitor of GDH and skeletal muscle LDH.[56] Studies with bulky R groups would also be worthwhile.

Another type of reaction which may be subject to specificity dependent upon the transition state is the means of inactivation used by phenyl esters such as XXXV and XXXVII (Table 9–4). The enzyme (XLV) initially forms a reversible complex with the inhibitor (XLVI) through the binding area A (see Fig. 1–3). In order for an amine on the enzyme surface in the complex (XLVII) to form a covalent bond, it is necessary that the transition state XLIX be formed; XLIX can then lose the phenoxy group resulting in the mixed urea, XLVIII, and the inactivated enzyme. For this reaction to proceed, there can be no steric interaction between the leaving phenoxy group and the enzyme surface. Stated in another way, the leaving phenoxy group in the transition state must not be in contact with the enzyme in order for the transition state to form, otherwise the transition state could not form.

5-(Carbophenoxyglycylamido)-salicylic acid (XXXVII) fails to inactivate skeletal muscle LDH, whereas XXXVI can inactivate this enzyme

---

[56] Unpublished work by B. R. Baker and K. Sachdev.

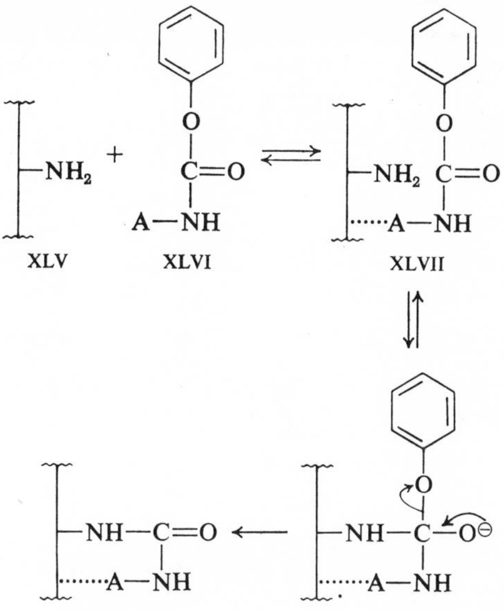

(Table 9–4). Because the carbonyl in the carbophenoxy group of **XXXVII** can reach any point in space that the carbonyl group of **XXXVI** can reach when the reversible binding groups of the salicylic acid structure are anchored, the carbophenoxy group of **XXXVII** most probably cannot approach this critical point to the transition state due to a steric interaction between the phenoxy group and the enzyme. A useful system for studying the possible specificity by the steric interaction of the phenoxy leaving group and the enzyme could be that of the inactivation of both GDH and heart LDH by 5-(carbophenoxyamino)-salicylic acid (**XXXV**) (Table 9–4). A number of related compounds with substituents on the phenoxy group should be evaluated to determine if such a specificity of the irreversible reaction between these two enzymes can be found.

In another approach to find selectivity, compounds related to 4-(iodoacetylglycylamido)-salicylic acid (**XXXIII**) having optically active D and L forms of alanine instead of the glycine residue should be evaluated; there is a possibility for asymmetric tolerance of the bulky group of the substituted glycine residue in the enzyme-inhibitor reversible complex that may influence the probability that the bridge can be completed as in Fig. 1–3. For example, only a D isomer may be an irreversible inhibitor of one enzyme, such as LDH, and only an L isomer an irreversible inhibitor of a closely related enzyme, such as GDH.

Bridging Phenomenon with Chymotrypsin

In Chapter 8 we discussed the ability of α-haloacylamidoacylchymotrypsin (L) to undergo intramolecular alkylation of methionine-192 to give LI. That the proper bridge length is necessary for the reaction to occur is

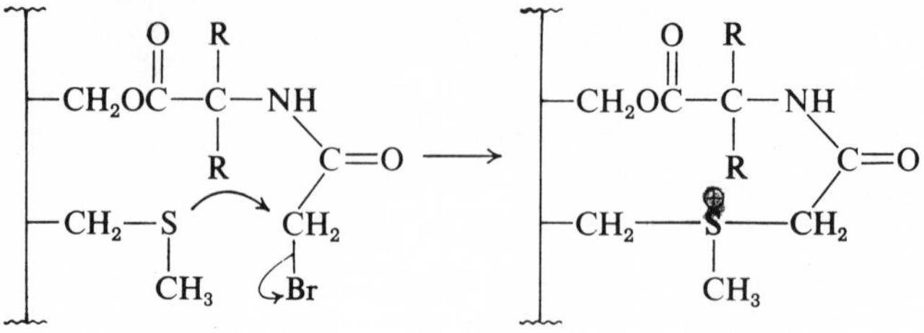

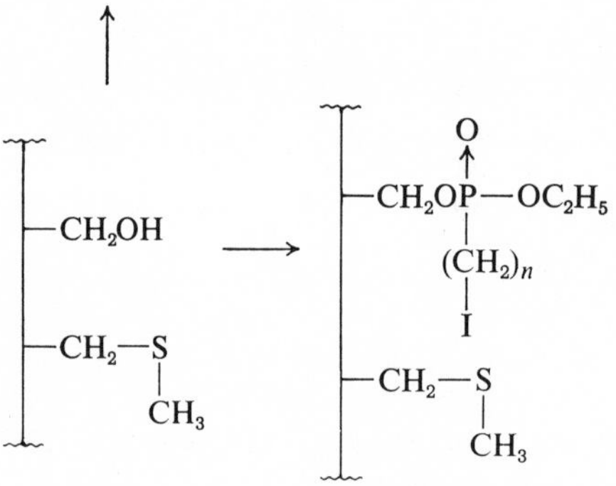

shown by the fact that iodoacetylchymotrypsin does not undergo such an intramolecular reaction with methionine or any other amino acid of chymotrypsin.[57]

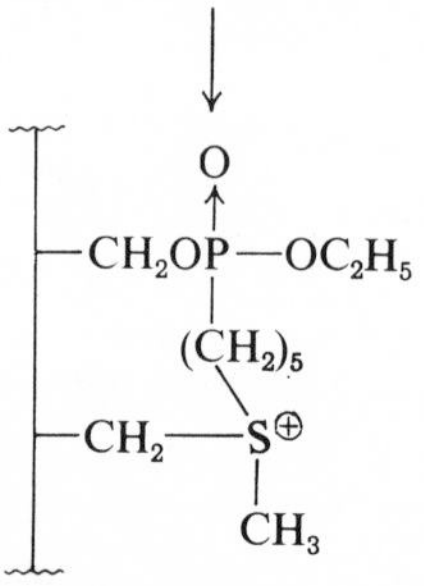

In preliminary studies with ethyl 5-iodopentylphosphonofluoridate, Gold[58] has shown the phosphonylchymotrypsin (LIII, $n = 5$) undergoes

[57] B. S. Hartley and E. S. Awad, *Brookhaven Symp. Biol.*, **15**, 124 (1962).
[58] A. M. Gold, *Brookhaven Symp. Biol.*, **15**, 125 (1962).

loss of iodide, presumably by an internal alkylation reaction; the ethyl 5-iodopentylphosphonofluoridate does not release bound iodine under the same conditions without enzyme. Furthermore, LIII with shorter or longer alkyl groups did not release any iodide in the presence of enzyme. It is probable that the same methionine attacked intramolecularly in the acylated chymotrypsin of type L is also attacked in this case to give LIV because the bridging distance is nearly the same.

That azaserine inactivates the appropriate enzyme (Chapter 1) while diazoacetylchymotrypsin (Chapter 8) is stable, unless photolyzed, or protonated, is an interesting comparison. The diazo group of diazoacetylchymotrypsin certainly has the capacity to react with a carboxyl, phenolic hydroxyl, or mercapto group; apparently such a group on the enzyme is not within bridgeable distance to the diazomethyl group.

Isozyme Specificity

The enzymic nucleophilic site that covalently binds an active-site-directed irreversible inhibitor can be, but is not necessarily adjacent to the active-site in the secondary-tertiary structure of the protein (see Fig. 1–3). The substrate-identical enzyme from different tissues frequently gives no cross-reaction with specific antisera,[59,60] indicating differences in tertiary structure. Therefore, Baker[61] suggested that it may be possible to obtain highly selective irreversible inhibition of the substrate-identical enzyme from different tissues by use of the bridge principle.

By antisera cross-reaction studies[60,62] and by amino acid analysis,[62] it has been shown that LDHs from heart and skeletal muscle in the same animal are quite different, but that heart LDHs from different species are more similar; also skeletal muscle LDHs from different species are more similar. As a first approximation, a study on selective irreversible inhibition of LDHs from rabbit skeletal muscle and beef heart was undertaken.[63,64]

The standard compound for irreversible inhibition of skeletal muscle LDH, 4-(iodoacetamido)-salicylic acid (XXIII), failed to inhibit heart LDH irreversibly (Table 9–5). When the bridge distance was lengthened (as in the peptide XXXIII) both LDHs were irreversibly inhibited, but at different absolute rates. For further work, XXXIII was used as a standard for heart LDH. Selectivity of action was shown with 5-(carbophenoxyamino)-salicylic acid (XXXV), which could inactivate heart LDH, but

[59] W. F. Henion and E. S. Sutherland, *J. Biol. Chem.*, **224**, 477 (1957).
[60] R. D. Cahn, N. O. Kaplan, L. Levine, and E. Zwilling, *Science*, **136**, 962 (1962).
[61] B. R. Baker, *Biochem. Pharmacol.*, **11**, 1155 (1962).
[62] T. Weiland and G. Pfleiderer, *Angew. Chem. Intern. Ed. Engl.*, **1**, 169 (1962).
[63] B. R. Baker, *Biochem. Pharmacol.*, **12**, 293 (1962).
[64] B. R. Baker and R. P. Patel, *J. Pharm. Sci.*, **53**, 714 (1964).

failed to inactivate skeletal muscle LDH. A cross-over in specificity was noted with the 4- isomer (XXXVI), which inactivated skeletal muscle LDH, but not heart LDH. It was previously noted that 4-(maleamyl)-salicylic acid (XL) could inactivate skeletal muscle LDH; in contrast, heart LDH is not inactivated by XL.

The only other compound found to inactivate heart LDH was the coumarin carboxylic acid LV, but no isozyme specificity was obtained. By

comparison of XXXIII or LV with 4-ISA (XXIII), it appears that the latter does not have sufficient bridge length to inactivate heart LDH. The fact that 5-(carbophenoxyamino)-salicylic acid (XXXV), with its short bridge, will inactivate heart LDH indicates that XXXV and XXXIII probably attack different amino acids of the heart LDH.

Although 5-(carbophenoxyamino)-salicylic acid (XXXV) showed a "rate-saturation" effect with heart LDH, which is compatible with active-site-directed irreversible inhibition, 4-(carbophenoxyamino)-salicylic acid (XXXV) did not show a "rate-saturation" effect with skeletal muscle LDH. In fact, doubling the concentration of XXXV more than doubled the rate; only one kinetic situation has yet been thought of that agrees with such a result, namely, that an enzymic group exposed by conformational change in the enzyme-inhibitor complex is now subject to bimolecular attack.[65] Such a proposition can be further verified, but it has not been done in this case.

If this irreversible specificity for substrate-identical enzymes from different tissues can be transposed to such critical areas for cell division as (a) purine or pyrimidine biosynthesis or (b) the folic cofactor area, the benefits that could accrue to chemotherapy would be obvious. The start of such studies in area (a) is described in Chapters 4, 5, and 7, and the studies in area (b) are discussed in the next two chapters.

ENZYME EVOLUTION

The evolution of enzymes is a recent, rapidly developing field ancillary to the use of active-site-directed irreversible inhibitors for chemotherapy;

[65] See Chapter 8, Kinetic Parameters.

Table 9–5. Selective Irreversible Inhibition of Lactic Dehydrogenase from Different Tissues

No.	Compound[a]	Skeletal muscle LDH K_i (mM)	Skeletal muscle LDH Per cent rev. EI[b]	Skeletal muscle LDH Rate of inactivation[c]	Heart LDH K_i (mM)	Heart LDH Per cent rev. EI[b]	Heart LDH Rate of inactivation[d]	Reference
XXIII	4-ICH_2CONH—SA	1.7	54	1.0[e]	4.5	31	0	j
XXXIII	4-ICH_2CONH—GSA	0.40	83	0.57	2.5	44[f]	1.0[e,f]	j
X	3-ICH_2CONH—OA	0.13	93	0	1.2	62	0	j
XXXV	5-C_6H_5OCONH—SA	1.5	57	0	1.4	59[g]	0.4[g]	j
XXXVI	4-C_6H_5OCONH—SA	1.1	65	0.8	1.9	51[f]	0[f]	j
XXXVII	5-C_6H_5OCONH—GSA	0.59	77	0	1.8	53	0	j
XL	4-*cis*-HOOCCH=CHCO │ SA—NH	1.8	52	0.9	3.0	40[f]	0[f]	k,l
LV	6-ICH_2CONH—CC	0.31	56[h]	0.5[h]	0.96	51[i]	0.6[i]	j
LVI	5-ICH_2CONH—GSA	2.3	47	2.2	3.4	54[f]	0.8[f]	j

[a] Abbreviations used: SA = salicylic acid; GSA = glycylamidosalicylic acid; OA = oxanilic acid; CC = coumarin-3-carboxylic acid.
[b] Per cent of active enzyme in reversible EI complex with 2 mM inhibitor, unless otherwise indicated; see Chapter 8, Kinetic Parameters, for calculation.
[c] Compared to 4-ISA (XXIII) as a standard; relative rate corrected to equal concentration of reversible EI complex.
[d] Compared to XXXIII as a standard; relative rate corrected to equal concentration of reversible EI complex.
[e] Arbitrary standard that is not the same for two isozymes.
[f] 4 mM inhibitor. [g] 3 mM inhibitor. [h] 0.4 mM inhibitor. [i] 1 mM inhibitor.
[j] B. R. Baker and R. P. Patel, *J. Pharm. Sci.*, **53**, 714 (1964).
[k] B. R. Baker and P. I. Almaula, *J. Pharm. Sci.*, **52**, 914 (1963). [l] Unpublished.

this new field seeks answers to the question, "In what structural way do substrate-identical enzymes become different through evolutionary mutation?"

Once the pure enzyme is isolated it is relatively simple to show gross differences. For example, although phosphoglucomutase from *E. coli* B and rabbit muscle show only slight differences in K_m and V_{max}, after trypsin digestion two-dimensional paper chromatography of the resultant "tryptic peptides" gives "peptide-maps" that are chromatographically different[66,67]; however, the amino acid sequence about the active-site was similar. Furthermore, injection of *E. coli* B phosphoglucomutose into the rabbit elicited antibody formation, but—as expected—injection of rabbit muscle phosphoglucomutase into the rabbit did not.

The most extensive studies on species differences in the linear sequence of a protein have been done on cytochrome c[68] and myoglobin.[69] The linear sequence of cytochrome c from horse heart was the first of the cytochrome c's to be determined.[70,71] Thereafter the sequences of cytochrome c of man, pig, chicken, baker's yeast, cow, sheep, tunafish, rhesus monkey, domestic rabbit, an insect, a marsupial, and rattlesnake were determined.[68] If hog heart is used as the baseline, then the sequence in cytochrome c from beef, horse, human, tuna, and baker's yeast differed by 0, 3, 10, 17, and 43 amino acid residues, respectively, out of a total of about 104 amino acids.[72] In Table 9–6 are shown three examples using cytochrome c from man as the baseline. Some changes by "like" amino acids such as isoleucine-11 for valine, tyrosine-46 for phenylalanine, serine-47 for threonine, and aspartate-62 for glutamate would not be expected to cause much change in protein structure; in contrast, serine-15 for alanine represents a loss of possible hydrogen bonding properties by the serine hydroxyl, isoleucine-58 for threonine represents a possible loss in hydrophobic bonding properties, glycine-60 for lysine represents a change to increased bulk and charge, and alanine-92 to glutamate also represents a change to increased bulk and charge. With the latter type of drastic

[66] J. G. Joshi and P. Handler, *J. Biol. Chem.*, **239**, 2741 (1964).

[67] J. G. Joshi, T. Hashimoto, K. Hanabusa, H. W. Dougherty, and P. Handler in *Evolving Genes and Proteins*, V. Bryson and H. J. Vogel, eds., Academic Press, New York, 1965, pp. 207–220.

[68] For a review see E. Morgoliash and E. L. Smith in *Evolving Genes and Proteins*, V. Bryson and H. J. Vogel, eds., Academic Press, New York, 1965, pp. 221–242.

[69] For a review see E. Zuckerkandl and L. Pauling, *ibid.*, pp. 97–166.

[70] E. Margoliash, J. R. Kimmel, R. L. Hill, and W. R. Schmidt, *J. Biol. Chem.*, **237**, 2148 (1962); E. Margoliash and E. L. Smith, *J. Biol. Chem.*, **237**, 2151 (1962); E. Margoliash, *J. Biol. Chem.*, **237**, 2161 (1962).

[71] H. Tuppy and G. Kreil, *Monatsh. Chem.*, **92**, 780 (1962).

[72] J. W. Stewart and E. Margoliash, *Fed. Proc.*, **24**, 2224 (1965).

**Table 9–6. Amino Acid Replacements in Heart Cytochrome *c*
of Man, Horse, and Dog**

Amino acid number	Human	Horse	Dog
11	Ileu	Val	Val
12	Met	Gln	Gln
15	Ser	Ala	Ala
46	Tyr	Phe	Phe
47	Ser	Thr	Ser
50	Ala	Asp	Asp
58	Ileu	Thr	Thr
60	Gly	Lys	Gly
62	Asp	Glu	Glu
83	Val	Ala	Ala
88	Lys	Lys	Thr
89	Glu	Thr	Gly
92	Ala	Glu	Ala
103	Asn	Asn	Lys

Data from H. Matsubara and E. L. Smith, *J. Biol. Chem.*, **238** 2732 (1963); M. A. McDowall and E. L. Smith, *J. Biol. Chem.*, **240**, 4635 (1965).

changes, Matsubara and Smith[73] have logically suggested that "it is likely that such [amino acid] residues play no major role in function or in conformation of the protein."

In an elegant study, Margoliash and Smith[74] have compared the changes that exist between species. The amino acid residues can be divided into two groups (a) those residues that are invariant and cannot be replaced, and (b) those residues that can be replaced. Zuckerkandl and Pauling[75] have summarized the possible reasons and given examples why an amino acid residue may not be exchanged (else the protein would be nonfunctional).

1. Inside of the protein tertiary structure, there would be relatively no space for an increase in bulk; furthermore, an exchange of a hydrophobic amino acid on the inside of the tertiary structure for a polar amino acid (or vice versa) could also unstabilize the tertiary structure.

2. A notable change in polarity at the outside of the protein tertiary structure could alter the solubility [or the binding characteristics] of the protein.

3. Substitution at bends in the structure could tend to unstabilize the bend, thus tending to convert a random sequence into a straight helix.

[73] H. Matsubara and E. L. Smith, *J. Biol. Chem.*, **238**, 2732 (1963).
[74] See Reference 70, p. 186.
[75] See Reference 69, p. 186.

4. In contrast to paragraph 3, any substitution in a helix that could unstabilize the helix would alter the tertiary structure.

5. Changes at sites where conformational specificity are particularly high, such as catalytic sites or binding sites, could give an inoperable protein.

In cytochrome *c*, about half of the amino acid residues remain constant in all the species; these constancies are not random, but lie in rather specific areas. For example, the three prolyl residues (positions 30, 71, and 76) and 11 glycine residues (positions 1, 6, 23, 24, 29, 34, 37, 41, 45, 77, and 84) are strictly conserved and may play a role in permitting a particular conformation of the polypeptide chains by the prolines acting as helix breakers and the glycines at locations where the polypeptide chains approach closely and cannot tolerate bulky groups. The amino acids at positions 70 through 80 remain remarkably constant.

The amino acid substitutions may be divided into (a) conservative substitutions by a "like" amino acid and (b) radical substitution such as a polar amino acid for a hydrophobic amino acid or a basic amino acid for an acidic amino acid. Examples of conservative substitution are either lysine or arginine at position 13, either tryosine or phenylalanine at position 46, and serine or threonine at position 47; other examples occur in the hydrophobic regions at residues 9 through 12, 32 through 36, 46 through 48, 57 through 59, 64 through 68, 74 through 75, 80 through 85, and 96 through 98, which contain all but three of the hydrophobic amino acids. In these hydrophobic regions, a hydrophobic constancy is maintained, but the individual hydrophobic amino acid residues do vary.

Let us now consider enzyme evolution with respect to active-site-directed irreversible inhibitors and utilization of the bridge principle of specificity. As is indicated schematically in Fig. 9–8, an irreversible inhibitor operating by the exo mechanism must first be able to complex with the enzyme—presumably, but not necessarily, at the active-site; a properly positioned covalent-bond forming group can then attack a nucleophilic group on the enzyme adjacent to the reversible complexing region.

Little structural change can be expected to occur in the "active-site" of an enzyme, which is defined to include the complexing regions for the substrate and coenzyme (if any) as well as the amino acid residues catalyzing the enzymic reaction; therefore little specificity from tissue to tissue or species to species can be expected with classical antimetabolites closely related in structure to the substrate. Similarly, irreversible inhibitors operating by the endo mechanism within the complexing region would be expected to have little specificity. In contrast, active-site-directed irreversible inhibitors operating by the exo mechanism (Fig. 9–9) are dependent upon the combined environments of both the active-site and the nucleophilic site as well as the conformational and steric requirements between the two sites.[76] Thus in evolution of the enzyme, with respect to two species, if one of the following changes in amino acid residues occurs *outside the "active-site,"* then the bridge principle of specificity should work.

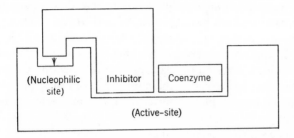

Fig. 9–9. A schematic diagram of an active-site-directed irreversible inhibitor operating by formation of a covalent linkage with an enzymic nucleophilic group outside the "active-site"; the arrow represents the covalent bond-forming group on the inhibitor. From B. R. Baker, *Biochem. Pharmacol.*, **11**, 1155 (1962).

1. The nucleophilic site is different because a nucleophilic amino acid is substituted for a hydrophobic amino acid, such as the exchange of alanine-50 for aspartate in cytochrome *c* (see Table 9–6); in this case, the enzyme with the nucleophilic group could be inactivated, but the other would not be.

2. Exchange of one nucleophilic amino acid for another type of nucleophilic amino acid, such as glutamate-89 for threonine in cytochrome *c* can be utilized. In this case the electrophilic group of the active-site-directed irreversible inhibitor could be modified; for example, a properly positioned sulfonyl fluoride could attack threonine, but threonine would form a readily hydrolyzable mixed anhydride if it was attacked with glutamate; a properly positioned diazomethyl ketone or chloromethyl ketone would attack glutamate much more rapidly than threonine.

3. Suppose a bulkier amino acid, such as valine-83 replaced with alanine in cytochrome *c*, is in the region between the binding region in the "active-site" and the nucleophilic region; then a shorter bridge could inactivate the enzyme with an alanine in this area between the complexing region and the nucleophilic site than with a valine in this area.

Thus the bridge principle of specificity should be able to differentiate substrate-identical enzymes with as little as a single amino acid change, providing this change is in an exploitable area. As will be pointed out in the following section, it is not necessary to know the linear sequence, the tertiary structure, or the differences between substrate-identical enzymes from different species in order to design active-site-directed irreversible

[76] B. R. Baker, *Biochem. Pharmacol.*, **11**, 1155 (1962).

inhibitors and utilize them in chemotherapy with the bridge principle of specificity. The foregoing discussion on enzyme evolution is only intended to indicate that substrate-identical enzymes can have amino acid replacements, particularly outside the active-site. If cytochrome *c* is an example of typical evolution of an enzyme, it is clear that even among mammals a few amino acid residues have been exchanged. It is also clear that nearly half the amino acids are exchanged when cytochrome *c* from man is compared to that from baker's yeast; thus, the farther removed are man and an invading species on the paleontological scale, the greater could be the differences in sequences of the amino acids in their proteins and the easier it should be possible to utilize the bridge principle of specificity for chemotherapy.

The question how different the enzymes structures of a cell are before and after viral infection is considered in Chapter 10 on dihydrofolic reductase. That gross differences in structures of dihydrofolic reductase and thymidylate synthetase exist before and after T_2-phage infection of *E. coli* is clear; what actual amino acid replacements have occurred would be of great interest from both the chemotherapeutic standpoint and the paleontological standpoint.

Did viral particles appear before or after the cell it can infect? Intuitively one would guess the viral particle occurred later on the paleontological scale. In either case there will be exploitable structural differences in the enzymes before and after viral infection of a cell, particularly with regard to the tumorogenic viruses causing cancer? The probability is good that at least some amino acid changes will have occurred in the enzymes induced by viruses, for viruses can certainly mutate, as expressed by the structure of their protein coat present before infection.

EXPERIMENTAL DESIGN FOR UNEXPLORED ENZYMES

Lest the medicinal chemist who has had the patience to read this far be tempted to dash into the laboratory and attach diazoketone, fluorophosphate, halomethyl carbonyl, diazonium, maleamyl, carbophenoxy, or other covalent forming groups to the nearest available substrate or inhibitor, he would be wise to be cautious with the suggestions that follow; otherwise he may be disappointed in his laboratory labors.

The studies described to this point have dealt only with irreversible inhibition of isolated enzymes—a far cry from chemotherapy in a host system. It is obvious that there are a variety of other factors—other than selective irreversible inhibition of isolated enzyme systems—that play important roles in whether the inhibitor would be effective in a host system, among them being the following. (a) Transport to and into the desired target cell from the site of administration of the inhibitor must be achieved. (b) The inhibitor must be reactive enough to give a reasonable rate of inactivation of the target enzyme but not so reactive that insufficient inhibitor reaches the desired cell containing the target enzyme. (c) There must be selectivity of inhibition of an enzyme in the target cell such as a cancer cell or an invading organism.

The main emphasis so far has been on point (c); the other facets will have to be overcome simultaneously for the inhibitor to be a useful drug. If the candidate inhibitor is only studied for effectiveness in a host system, the jackpot of (a), (b), and (c) working at the same time will have to be achieved, a remote possibility predicted mostly on extremely good luck.

The design of an effective agent in a host system is still so nebulous that a successful one is more likely to be achieved by individual study of the three facets, followed by collective use, in order to find eventually chemotherapeutic agents on less of a hit-or-miss basis; that is not to say that synthesis and screening should be discontinued, but the screening approach is a calculated risk of hit or miss that has hit in infectious chemotherapy and has been so much less successful in cancer chemotherapy as to be termed a near miss. In fact, the medicinal chemist will even find it difficult to make a successful guess concerning where to put a covalent-forming group on a substrate or inhibitor to give an active-site-directed irreversible inhibitor for an unexplored enzyme. At this early stage of research in this area, it would appear wise to proceed systematically to determine the binding points of the inhibitor (area A, Fig. 1–3) and the noncontact area of the inhibitor and the enzyme. If the covalent-forming group (B) is unfortuitously placed in area A (Fig. 1–3), then an active-site-directed inhibitor will not be obtained because the reversible complex cannot form.

The logical development of where to place the covalent-forming group B (Fig. 1–3) to make an active-site-directed irreversible inhibitor for an unexplored enzyme can be gleaned by carefully considering the chapters in the following order: (a) the theoretical background, (b) types of inhibitors and points of binding, (c) the noncontact areas, and (d) the bridge principle of specificity. Chapters 9 through 12 follow this continuity and therefore are titled *Modus Operandi*.

10 | Modus Operandi.
II. Dihydrofolic Reductase

FOLATE COFACTOR ENZYMES

The B vitamin, folic acid (I), is reduced enzymatically in the cell to tetra-hydrofolic acid (III) (FAH$_4$)[1] via 7,8-dihydrofolic acid (II) (FAH$_2$). Any one of five enzymes can then be used by a cell to catalyze the attachment of a one-carbon fragment at the formaldehyde or formic acid oxidation level by FAH$_4$ (III) on either N^5 or N^{10} or both (see Chart I). A further six enzymes can then interconvert the oxidation level of the one-carbon fragment or its position on FAH$_4$. Finally, there are four one-carbon transfer reactions, three of which are involved in purine and pyrimidine biosynthesis. In the two reactions involved in purine biosynthesis, the one-carbon fragment is transferred to the substrate with the formation of FAH$_4$; thus, the FAH$_4$ reacts catalytically because the "C"-FAH$_4$ can then be regenerated by the enzymes in the first and second class. The third enzyme, thymidylate synthetase, is unique in that an internal oxidation-reduction of an intermediate takes place when deoxyuridylate (dUMP)[1] is converted to thymidylate (dTMP),[2] that is, the formaldehyde oxidation level of 5,10-methylene-FAH$_4$ is reduced to the methyl oxidation level on dTMP at the expense of oxidation of the FAH$_4$ to FAH$_2$; thus, FAH$_4$ is used stoichiometrically in this reaction, and the FAH$_2$ must then again be reduced to FAH$_4$ by (dihydro)folic reductase. As a result, a blockade of dihydrofolic reductase prevents the coupled thymidylate synthetase from operating, leading to a cellular deficiency of dTMP. Therefore, blockade

---

[1] Abbreviations: FAH$_4$ = 5,6,7,8-tetrahydrofolate; FAH$_2$ = 7,8-dihydrofolate; dUMP = 2'-deoxyuridylate; dTMP = thymidylate; TPNH = reduced triphospho-pyridine nucleotide.

[2] T. H. Jukes and H. P. Broquist in *Metabolic Inhibitors*, R. M. Hochster and J. H. Quastel, eds., Academic Press, New York, 1963, pp. 481–534.

of either thymidylate synthetase or dihydrofolic reductase in a cell will lead to "thymine-less death" if the cell is unable to use the alternate pathway via thymidine with thymidine kinase.[3]

A strong blockade of dihydrofolic reductase is readily achieved with

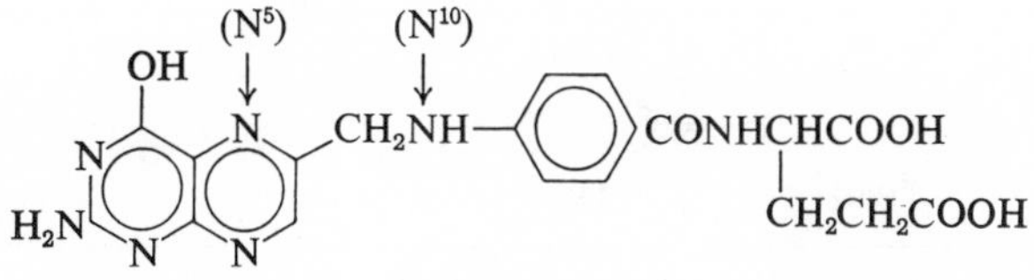

I, FA

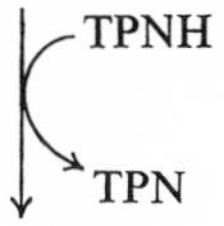

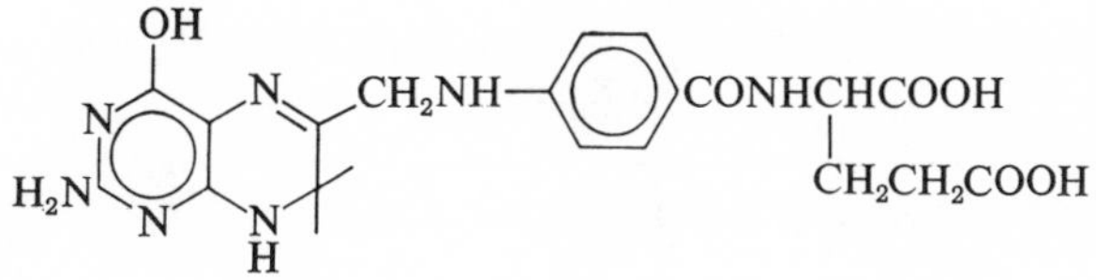

II, FAH$_2$

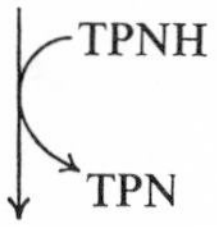

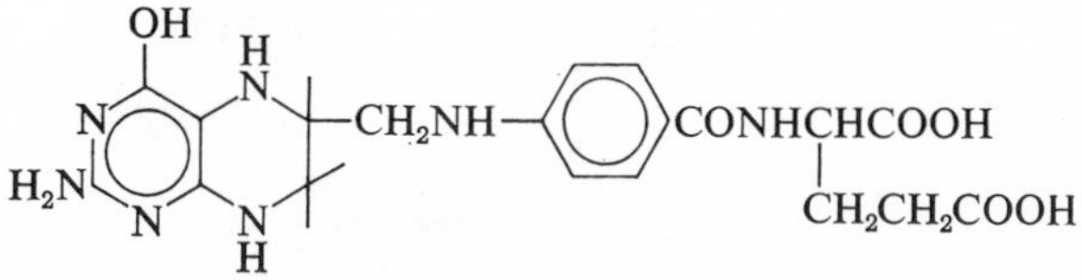

III, FAH$_4$

such 2,4-diamino heterocycles as amethopterin (V) or pyrimethamine (VI); however, the achievement of a more selective blockade of the dihydrofolic reductase of an invading cancer cell than the dihydrofolic reductase of the host tissues has not been achieved to any known degree.

If the tissue specificity observed with active-site-directed irreversible inhibitors of lactic dehydrogenase (see Chapter 9) could be carried over to thymidylate synthetase or dihydrofolic reductase in a given type of tumor

[3] See Reference 2, p. 192.

cell, sufficient specificity might be achieved to create a selective blockade in the tumor cell. The question immediately arises: Can any differences in the primary, secondary, or tertiary structures of dihydrofolic reductase in normal tissues be expected in comparison with those of the dihydrofolic

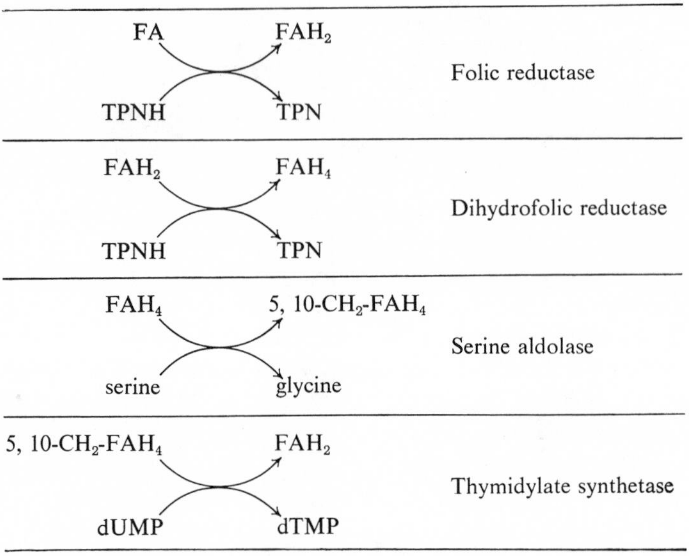

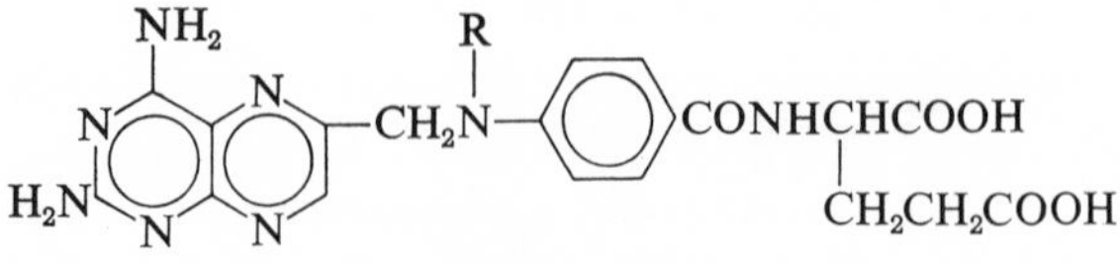

FA → FAH$_2$

TPNH → TPN

Folic reductase

FAH$_2$ → FAH$_4$

TPNH → TPN

Dihydrofolic reductase

FAH$_4$ → 5, 10-CH$_2$-FAH$_4$

serine → glycine

Serine aldolase

5, 10-CH$_2$-FAH$_4$ → FAH$_2$

dUMP → dTMP

Thymidylate synthetase

IV, R = H; aminopterin
V, R = CH$_3$; amethopterin

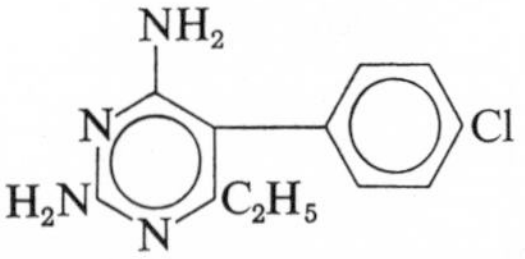

VI, pyrimethamine

reductase in an invading tumor cell? The answer is most probably yes, particularly in the case of virus-induced cancers. When *E. coli* is infected with T$_2$ phage, a rapid 20–50-fold rise in the levels of dihydrofolic reductase and thymidylate synthetase takes place. By kinetic parameters the new enzymes are different from the original enzymes present in the *E. coli*; furthermore, the new dihydrofolic reductase and thymidylate synthetase is genetically controlled by the virus and is not merely an induction of more *E. coli* enzyme.[4] The two thymidylate synthetases are even sufficiently different in charge that they are readily separated with a DEAE-cellulose column.[5]

As a result of the invasion of a normal cell by a tumorigenic virus, the viral coding information becomes an integral part of the original cell. This, in turn, produces a cancer cell containing the genetic information of both the virus and the original cell. In order for the cell to reproduce more rapidly, DNA must be synthesized more rapidly; this requires more dTMP per unit time, which in turn requires more thymidylate synthetase and more dihydrofolic reductase. The new enzymes are presumably coded by the nucleic acid originally present in the virus and therefore could be anticipated to be subtly different in structure from the original two enzymes.

That the dihydrofolic reductases from different species can have readily detectable differences has been shown in numerous cases and will be discussed later in this chapter.

How much difference in protein structure must there be for an active-site-directed irreversible inhibitor to inhibit the tumorigenic cell and not the original normal cell? With the bridge principle of specificity (Chapter 9) a single change of a hydrophobic amino acid such as leucine for valine could be sufficient if this change occurs somewhere between the active-site where the inhibitor is complexed and a nucleophilic site somewhere adjacent to the active-site where covalent linkage with the irreversible inhibitor occurs (see Fig. 1–3). Ordinary classical reversible antimetabolites would not be expected to have more than two- to fourfold differences in effect, for the nature of the active-site cannot change much and continue to convert substrate to product; in contrast, active-site-directed irreversible inhibitors take advantage of the similarity in the active-site for reversible complexing, but in addition they have an extra magnitude of specificity by taking advantage of less functional parts of the enzyme for irreversible covalent bond formation. It is the area outside of the active-site where structural differences of the substrate-identical enzyme in different tissues are likely to occur, for little structural change can be tolerated in the active-site before the enzyme ceases to be functional.[6]

[4] C. K. Mathews and S. S. Cohen, *J. Biol. Chem.*, **238**, 367 (1963); *J. Biol. Chem.*, **238**, PC 853 (1963).
[5] G. R. Greenberg, R. L. Somerville, and S. DeWolf, *Proc. Natl. Acad. Sci. (U.S.)*, **48**, 242 (1962).
[6] See Chapter 9, Enzyme Evolution.

GENERAL CONSIDERATIONS

Substrates

The enzymic reduction of folate (FA) (I) proceeds in two steps, first to dihydrofolate (II), then to tetrahydrofolate (III); the first step is rate limiting; that is, the TPNH reduction of folate (I) is much slower than TPNH reduction of dihydrofolate (II). The same enzyme is involved in reduction of both I and II; if dihydrofolate (II) is used as the substrate, the enzyme is called dihydrofolic reductase, but if folate (I) is used as the substrate, the enzyme can be called folic reductase, even though they are one and the same enzyme.

The most useful assay is the rate of decrease of optical density at 340 mμ because TPNH has a peak at this wavelength and both folate and dihydrofolate have strong absorption; the products TPN and FAH$_4$ have no absorption at 340 mμ.[7] If the enzyme can use folate (I) as a substrate, the resultant tetrahydrofolate (III) will decompose under specified conditions to p-aminobenzoyl-L-glutamate, which can then be assayed[8] by the highly sensitive Bratton-Marshall test for aromatic amines[9]; this assay has about twice the sensitivity of the spectrophotometric assay, but the latter has the distinct advantage of being a continuously recorded assay and in being more rapid.

Apparently all mammalian and avian, but only a few bacterial, dihydrofolic reductases can utilize folic acid (I) as a substrate; the pH maximum with folic acid (I) is 4–5.5 and reduction is near zero at pH 7. The enzymes utilizing folate (I) as a substrate usually show a double maximum with dihydrofolate, one at pH 4–5.5 and the other near pH 7.4; at pH 7.4 folate is a good inhibitor of dihydrofolate, being complexed to the enzyme even better than the substrate. Those bacterial enzymes that cannot utilize folic acid as a substrate have only one pH maximum and that is near pH 7.4. Because many bacteria synthesize dihydrofolate (II) *de novo*— rather than by reduction of folate (I)—there is no reason why these bacteria should have to reduce folic acid; in fact, those bacteria that cannot utilize folic acid, but synthesize dihydrofolate *de novo* from p-aminobenzoic acid are selectively inhibited by sulfonamides because mammalian cells do not use the *de novo* synthesis.[10]

[7] M. J. Osborn and F. M. Huennekens, *J. Biol. Chem.*, **233**, 969 (1958).

[8] S. F. Zakrzewski, *J. Biol. Chem.*, **235**, 1776 (1960); W. C. Werkheiser, *J. Biol. Chem.*, **236**, 888 (1961).

[9] A. C. Bratton and E. K. Marshall Jr., *J. Biol. Chem.*, **128**, 537 (1939).

[10] For reviews on these subjects see Reference 2, p. 192; M. Friedkin, *Ann. Rev. Biochem.*, **32**, 185 (1963); G. H. Hitchings and J. H. Burchall, *Adv. Enzymol.*, **27**, 417 (1965).

Types of Inhibitors

Folate (I) and dihydrofolate (II) have quite complex structures compared to most monomeric substrates in that they have 11 different polar groups and two π-electron systems that can complex with dihydrofolic reductase; it has been estimated that on the order of three to six of these groups would be sufficient for binding to give the observed binding constants.[11]

The mode of binding inhibitors to dihydrofolic reductase is still not completely understood even after intense study in many laboratories. Complications arise when the binding of individual groups on inhibitors are assigned, for strong hydrophobic bonding occurs with the dihydrofolic reductases. This intense hydrophobic bonding has been observed to be as high as 6 kcal/mole, compared with dihydrofolate (II) which has a total binding energy of 7.8 kcal/mole. As a result of this extremely energetic hydrophobic bonding, it is likely that an inhibitor can complex to dihydrofolic reductase in one of several possible rotomeric conformations, depending upon the rotomer giving maximum hydrophobic bonding; therefore studies related to binding of specific groups on an inhibitor are limited to a single type of inhibitor and the conclusions are not general.

To indicate the complexity of the modes of inhibitor binding, some discrepancies will be pointed out which indicate that there is more than one mode of binding depending on the type of inhibitor.

In Table 10–1 are listed some inhibitors of dihydrofolic reductase that are close analogs of folic acid (I) (except pyrimethamine) (VI). Folic acid (I) is an excellent inhibitor of dihydrofolic reductase, being complexed 2–10-fold better than the substrate, dihydrofolate; note that folic acid shows no detectable substrate properties at the pH 7.5 used in these assays. Replacement of the 4-hydroxy group of folate by a 4-amino group, as in aminopterin (IV), gives a tremendous enhancement in binding—about 3000-fold in the pigeon liver assay. Substitution of a methyl group at N^{10} appears not to change the binding properties, although the "lesser than" values could still be quite different absolute values. That the hydrogen on N^{10} does not contribute to binding is clearly shown by the results with 10-formyl folic acid (VII); an actual 16-fold enhancement in binding occurs, which is probably due to the effect of the *N*-formyl group on the pyrimidal

$$CH_2\overset{|}{-}N-C_6H_4$$ moiety of folic acid which is made planar by amide formation. This could result in a more favorable groundstate conformation for binding to the enzyme as an inhibitor[12]; note, however, that 10-formyl folic acid is not a substrate at pH 5.9 where folic acid is a substrate

[11] B. R. Baker, D. V. Santi, P. I. Almaula, and W. C. Werkheiser, *J. Med. Chem.*, 7, 24 (1964).

[12] B. R. Baker, B.-T. Ho, J. K. Coward, and D. V. Santi, *J. Pharm. Sci.*, 55, 302 (1966).

and that 10-formyl dihydrofolic acid is not a substrate at pH 7.4 where dihydrofolate is used as a substrate. The better binding to the enzyme resulting from 10-formylation could indicate that the enzyme has to make a

Table 10–1. Inhibition of Dihydrofolic Reductase by

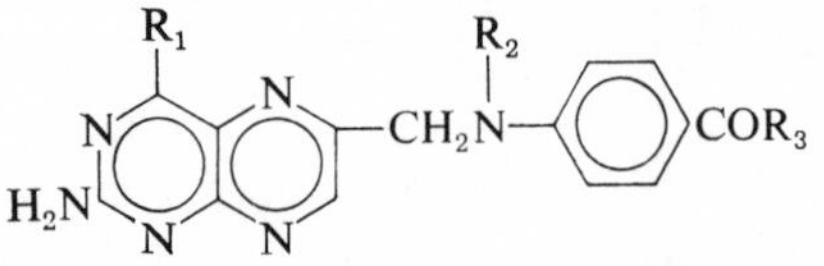

No.	R_1	R_2	R_3	$K_i(M)^a$	I_{50} $(\mu M)^b$
I	OH	H	—NHCHCOOH $\quad\vert$ CH_2CH_2COOH	1.1×10^{-7}	3
IV	NH_2	H	—NHCHCOOH $\quad\vert$ CH_2CH_2COOH	$< 6 \times 10^{-10}$	0.001
V	NH_2	CH_3	—NHCHCOOH $\quad\vert$ CH_2CH_2COOH	$< 6 \times 10^{-10}$	
VII	OH	$\overset{\overset{\textstyle O}{\|\|}}{-CH}$	—NHCHCOOH $\quad\vert$ CH_2CH_2COOH	6×10^{-9}	
VIII	OH	H	OH	8×10^{-6}	
IX^c	NH_2	CH_3	—NHCHCOOH $\quad\vert$ CH_2COOH	2×10^{-9}	
VI			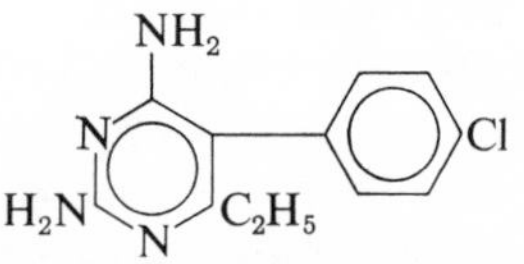	1.7×10^{-8}	

[a] Data from J. R. Bertino, J. P. Perkins, and D. G. Johns, *Biochemistry*, **4**, 839 (1965) unless otherwise indicated; enzyme from Ehrlich ascites cells assayed with dihydrofolate as substrate at pH 7.5; $K_m = 1.3 \times 10^{-6}$ M.

[b] Data from B. R. Baker and J. H. Jordaan, *J. Heterocyclic Chem.*, **2**, 162 (1965) and *J. Pharm. Sci.*, **54**, 1740 (1965); the enzyme was isolated from pigeon liver and assayed with 6 μM dihydrofolate as substrate at pH 7.4; $I_{50} = \mu M$ concentration for 50 per cent inhibition.

[c] Data from J. A. R. Mead, N. H. Greenberg, A. W. Schrecker, D. R. Seeger, and A. S. Tomcufcik, *Biochem. Pharmacol.*, **14**, 105 (1965).

conformational change that requires energy in order to bind folate and dihydrofolate; this conformational change may well cause a juxtaposition-ing of the catalytic site for reaction, as was previously -discussed with trypsin and chymotrypsin.[13]

That the L-glutamate moiety of folic acid (I) contributes to binding is indicated by the 70-fold loss in binding when this group is removed (giving pteroic acid) (VIII). By comparison of the aspartate analog (IX) of amethopterin with amethopterin (V) it can be seen that the γ-carboxyl of IV contributes to binding; however, it cannot be stated whether all of the binding of the L-glutamate moiety is due to the γ-carboxyl group, for the absolute K_i value for amethopterin (IV) is not known. It would be useful to compare the inhibitor constants of pteroyl-L-aspartic acid, pteroylgly-cine, and γ-pteroylaminobutyric acid with dihydrofolate as the sub-strate.

Little is known about the contribution to inhibitor binding by specific groups on the pteridine moiety of folic acid. The fact that 2-desaminofolic acid and N^2,N^2-dimethyl folic acid are not substrates indicates that a free 2-amino group is necessary for substrate properties,[14] but this tells little about binding properties; it would be of interest to measure these com-pounds as inhibitors. The N^2,N^2-dimethyl and N^4,N^4-dimethyl analogs of aminopterin bind 10,000-fold less effectively than aminopterin[15]; these results were interpreted to indicate that hydrogen bonds through the hydrogen of the NH's was a mode of binding.[15] However, these results could also be interpreted as a change in geometry[16] or pK_a[16] or a lack of bulk tolerance for the methyl groups. It would also be of interest to evaluate other analogs such as 4-thiofolic acid, 4-deoxyfolic acid, 5-deazafolic acid, and 8-deazafolic acid.

A particularly potent and useful dihydrofolic reductase inhibitor is pyrimethamine (VI), the antimalarial.[17] VI binds to dihydrofolic reductase about one tenth as well as the aspartate analog, IX, but VI has a consider-ably abbreviated structure. The mode of binding of the chlorophenyl group of VI is an interesting and useful one and will be discussed in a later section; note that the chlorophenyl group can give a 1300-fold enhance-ment in binding in a comparison of X and XI (Table 10–2).[18]

---

[13] See Chapter 3, p. 52.

[14] J. R. Bertino, J. P. Perkins, and D. G. Johns, *Biochemistry*, **4**, 839 (1965).

[15] D. G. Johns, A. C. Satorrelli, A. T. Ianotti, and J. Bertino, *Proc. Am. Assoc. Cancer Res.*, **5**, 32 (1964).

[16] See Reference 10, p. 196.

[17] See Reference 10, p. 196.

[18] A closely related inhibitor is the dihydrotriazine (i), which is also a useful anti-malarial; it showed 50 per cent inhibition of the dihydrofolic reductase from pigeon

Table 10-2. Inhibition of Dihydrofolic Reductase by

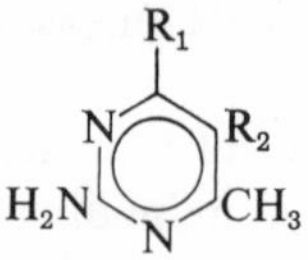

$$\begin{array}{c} R_1 \\ N \diagup \diagdown R_2 \\ H_2N \diagdown \diagup CH_3 \\ N \end{array}$$

No.	R_1	R_2	I_{50} $(\mu M)^a$	Reference
X	NH_2	H	1100	b
XI	NH_2	$p\text{-}ClC_6H_4-$	0.85	c
XII	OH	H	19,000	b
XIII	OH	 $-(CH_2)_3NH-$⟨◯⟩$CONHCHCOOH$ CH_2CH_2COOH	100	d
XIV	OH	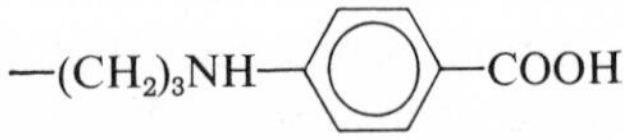 $-(CH_2)_3NH-$⟨◯⟩$-COOH$	77	d
XV	OH	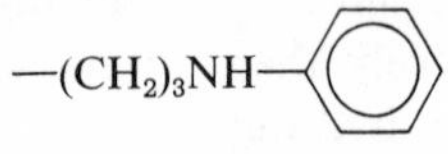 $-(CH_2)_3NH-$⟨◯⟩	800	d,e
XVI	OH	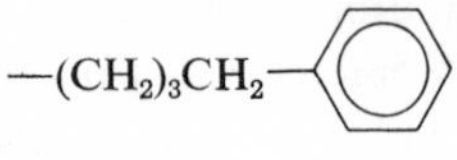 $-(CH_2)_3CH_2-$⟨◯⟩	30	f
XVII	NH_2	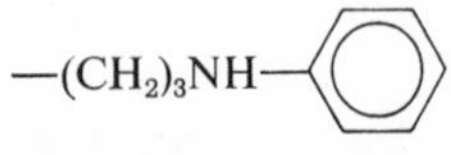 $-(CH_2)_3NH-$⟨◯⟩	2.2	d
XVIII	NH_2	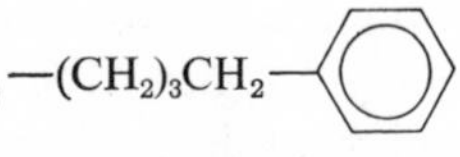 $-(CH_2)_3CH_2-$⟨◯⟩	0.027	g
XIX	NH_2	$-(CH_2)_3CH_3$	2.0	b

[a] Assayed with 6 μM dihydrofolate at pH 7.4 with enzyme from pigeon liver; I_{50} = μM concentration for 50 per cent inhibition.
[b] B. R. Baker, B.-T. Ho and D. V. Santi, *J. Pharm. Sci.*, **54**, 1415 (1965).
[c] B. R. Baker and B.-T. Ho. *J. Pharm. Sci.*, **53**, 1457 (1964).
[d] B. R. Baker and J. H. Jordaan, *J. Med. Chem.*, **8**, 35 (1965); B. R. Baker, D. V. Santi, P. I. Almaula, and W. C. Werkheiser, *J. Med. Chem.*, **7**, 24 (1964).
[e] B. R. Baker, B.-T. Ho, and T. Neilson, *J. Heterocyclic Chem.*, **1**, 79 (1964).
[f] B. R. Baker, B.-T. Ho, and G. B. Chheda, *J. Heterocyclic Chem.*, **1**, 88 (1964).
[g] B. R. Baker and B.-T. Ho, *J. Pharm. Sci.*, **54**, 1261 (1965).

Serious discrepancies in binding occur when comparisons are made between the pyrimidine type inhibitors in Table 10–2 with the pteridine type inhibitors in Table 10–1. The pyrimidylpropyl analog (XIII) of folic acid (I) binds about one thirtieth as well as folic acid; this result could be interpreted to indicate that N^5 or N^8 or both of folic acid and (I) are binding points. The first discrepancy appears when the pyrimidyl analog (XIV) of pteroic acid is compared to the folic acid analog (XIII); the pteroic acid

Table 10–3. Inhibition of Dihydrofolic Reductase by

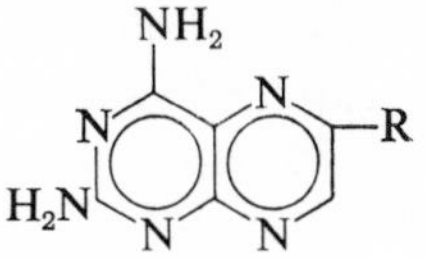

No.	R	I_{50} (μM)[a,b]
IV	 —CH$_2$NH⟨◯⟩CONHCHCOOH CH$_2$CH$_2$COOH	0.001
XX	—CH$_3$	220
XXI	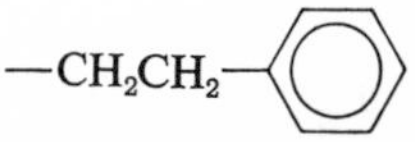 —CH$_2$CH$_2$—⟨◯⟩	4.2

[a] Assayed with 6 μM dihydrofolate at pH 7.4 with enzyme from pigeon liver; I_{50} = μM concentration for 50 per cent inhibition.
[b] Data from B. R. Baker and B.-T. Ho, *J. Pharm. Sci.*, **54**, 1261 (1965).

analog (XIV) actually binds somewhat better than the folic acid analog (XIII), in contrast with the comparison of folic acid (I) with pteroic acid (VIII) (Table 10–1) where folic acid binds 80-fold better. In fact, removal of the entire carboxy-L-glutamate moiety of XIII to give XV only gives an eightfold loss in binding.

liver at a concentration of 0.4 μM in the presence of 6 μM dihydrofolate. Considerably more potent dihydrotriazine inhibitors have been synthetized and will be discussed later.

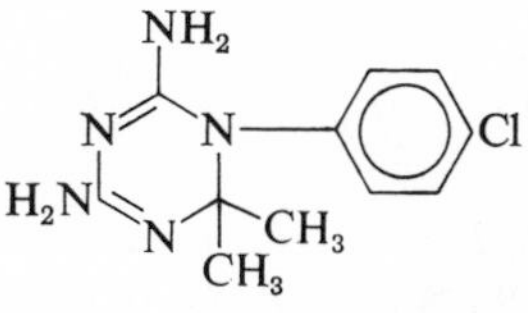

i

Of considerable interest was the enzymic results of replacing the anilino nitrogen of XV with a CH_2 group to give XVI; XVI was a 27-fold better inhibitor of dihydrofolic reductase than XV, and in fact, was nearly fourfold better than the folic acid analog (XIII); furthermore, in the 2,4-diamino series, replacement of the anilino NH of XVII by CH_2 to give XVIII led to an 80-fold enhancement in binding. These results suggested that replacement of the *p*-aminobenzoyl-L-glutamate moiety of aminopterin (IV) by benzyl, as in XXI (Table 10–3), should give an inhibitor better than aminopterin. That such was not the case can be seen in Table 10–3; aminopterin (IV) was a 4200-fold better inhibitor than the phenethylpteridine (XXI). This extremely serious discrepancy was partially resolved by synthesizing and evaluating the simple 5-*n*-butyl pyrimidine, XIX (Table 10–2); the *n*-butyl group of XIX gave a 550-fold increment in binding compared to the corresponding pyrimidine with no 5- substituent (X). Because the *n*-butyl group can only complex to an enzyme by a combination of hydrophobic bonding and van der Waals forces, this observation with XIX led to an extensive study of the hydrophobic bonding to dihydrofolic reductase.

Binding Measurements

With Equation (10–1) it is possible to determine K_i, the enzyme-inhibitor dissociation constant, by a variety of reciprocal plots.[19]

$$\frac{1}{V_I} = \left(1 + \frac{I}{K_i}\right)\frac{K_m}{V_0}\cdot\frac{1}{S} + \frac{1}{V_0} \tag{10–1}$$

When this equation is multiplied through by V_0, then

$$\frac{V_0}{V_I} = \left(1 + \frac{I}{K_i}\right)\frac{K_m}{S} + 1 \tag{10–2}$$

where V_0 is the velocity without inhibitor with an S concentration of substrate, V_I is the velocity with an I concentration of inhibitor, K_i is the enzyme-inhibitor dissociation constant, and K_m is the enzyme-substrate dissociation constant.

By varying the inhibitor concentration I with constant substrate concentration, then plotting V_0/V_I against I, it is possible to determine[20] the I concentration that gives 50 per cent inhibition, that is, the point where $V_0/V_I = 2$. When $V_0/V_I = 2$ is inserted into Equation (10–2), then

$$\left(1 + \frac{I}{K_i}\right)\cdot\frac{K_m}{S} + 1 = 2 \tag{10–3}$$

[19] M. Dixon and E. C. Webb, *Enzymes*, Academic Press, New York, 1958, p. 180.
[20] B. R. Baker, W. W. Lee, W. S. Skinner, A. P. Martinez, and E. Tong, *J. Med. Pharm. Chem.*, **2**, 633 (1960).

which reduces to

$$K_i = \left(\frac{K_m}{S - K_m}\right) \cdot I \qquad (10\text{--}4)$$

If the experimental conditions are set up so that S is at least four times greater than K_m, then K_m becomes negligible compared to S when the experimental error is considered; then Equation (10–4) reduces to

$$K_i = \frac{K_m}{S} \cdot I \qquad (10\text{--}5)$$

or

$$\frac{K_i}{K_m} = \frac{I}{S} = \left[\frac{I}{S}\right]_{0.5} \qquad (10\text{--}6)$$

where $[I/S]_{0.5}$ is the ratio of inhibitor to substrate giving 50 per cent inhibition,[21,22] providing $S > 4K_m$. In the dihydrofolic reductase assays using 6 μM dihydrofolate, $S = 6K_m$.

Because

$$\Delta F = -RT \ln \frac{1}{K_i} = -1300 \log \frac{1}{K_i} \text{ cal/mole} \qquad (10\text{--}7)$$

then the difference in free energy of binding, $\Delta\Delta F$ between two inhibitors is

$$\Delta\Delta F'' = -\Delta F + \Delta F' = +RT \ln \frac{1}{K_i} - RT \ln \frac{1}{K_i'} = RT \ln \frac{K_i'}{K_i} \qquad (10\text{--}8)$$

By combining Equation (10–8) with (10–6)

$$\Delta\Delta F'' = RT \ln \frac{K_m \cdot (I'/S)}{K_m \cdot (I/S)} = RT \ln \frac{I'}{I} = 1300 \log \frac{I'}{I} \text{ cal/mole} \qquad (10\text{--}9)$$

where I and I' are the inhibitor concentrations necessary for 50 per cent inhibition and $S > 4K_m$.[23] It is therefore not necessary to use K_m for the difference in binding of inhibitors. The derivation of Equation (10–9) contains the assumption that a complex between an enzyme and an inhibitor or an enzyme and a substrate are mutually exclusive and does not distinguish "competitive" from "noncompetitive" inhibition. Reiner[24] has pointed out that "competitive" kinetics determined by a reciprocal plot method do not prove that the inhibitor complexes at the active-site— a common misinterpretation—but only that the enzyme-inhibitor complex

---

[21] See Reference 11, p. 197.

[22] B. R. Baker, B.-T. Ho, and D. V. Santi, *J. Pharm. Sci.*, **54**, 1415 (1965).

[23] See Reference 22, p. 203.

[24] J. M. Reiner, *Behavior of Enzyme Systems*, Burgess Co., Minneapolis, Minn., 1959, pp. 151–152.

cannot further complex with substrate, regardless of where the inhibitor is complexed to the enzyme.

HYDROPHOBIC BONDING

General Considerations

Philosophically, we might question why anyone should try to rationalize the mode of binding various moieties of inhibitors to dihydrofolic reductase; it is not sufficient just to synthesize compounds, test them, and avoid the pitfalls of rationalizations on binding that may ultimately prove to be wrong? There are several reasons why it is important to try to understand the mode of binding.

1. We can predict more active structures.

2. It is quite essential to understand the mode of reversible binding in order to design successfully an active-site-directed irreversible inhibitor which might ultimately lead to compounds with tissue specificity.[25]

3. If a rationalization does not predict correctly, then the rationalization is obviously incorrect; however, the compounds resulting from an incorrect rationalization can lead to a more nearly correct rationalization, which, in turn, could have a utility that would be highly unlikely to be discovered by random synthesis and unrationalized testing.

Without the philosophy of trying to rationalize the mode of binding and from it trying to predict better binding, we might still have uncovered the extremely strong hydrophobic bonding region present on folic reductase, but we probably would not know how to proceed further.

The energetics of hydrophobic bonding and van der Waals forces were discussed in Chapter 2. Briefly, this energy can be about 700 cal/mole of $CH_2 \cdots CH_2$ interaction for each mode of bonding or a total of 1.4 kcal/mole, which is about equivalent to one power of ten in a dissociation constant of an enzyme-inhibitor complex.

The magnitude of the free energy of hydrophobic bonding to dihydrofolic reductase can be understood by comparing 2,4-diamino-6-methylpyrimidine (X) with its 5-phenylbutyl derivative (XVIII) (Table 10–2); X gives 50 per cent inhibition at 1100 μM and XVIII at 0.027 μM, an increment of 40,000 in binding. This 40,000-fold increment can be calculated to be a difference in free energy of binding ($\Delta\Delta F$) of 6.0 kcal/mole; the magnitude of this increment becomes more apparent if you consider that the substrate, dihydrofolate, with $K_m = 1 \times 10^{-6}$ M has a total free energy binding of 7.8 kcal/mole; thus the hydrophobic bonding (including the accompanying van der Waals forces) of the phenylbutyl group alone is equivalent to nearly 80 per cent of the binding energy of the substrate.

[25] See Chapter 9; Bridge Principle of Specificity.

In the sections that follow, attempts will be made to answer the following questions.

1. What are the conformational aspects of maximum hydrophobic bonding?

2. Where is the hydrophobic region with respect to the binding region for the substrate, dihydrofolate? Is it between the binding regions for the pyrimidyl and *p*-aminobenzoyl-L-glutamate moieties of dihydrofolate when it is complexed to the enzyme, or is it in some other region than the binding area for dihydrofolate?

3. If the hydrophobic region is not within the dihydrofolate binding region, then what types of side chains on the 5- position of pyrimidines complex in the hydrophobic region and what types of side chains complex at the *p*-aminobenzoyl binding area?

4. Is the large increment in binding shown by the 5-phenyl group of the pyrimethamine (VI) type inhibitor due to hydrophobic bonding?

5. What additional factors must be considered in the design of active-site-directed irreversible inhibitors for dihydrofolic inhibitors in order to avoid or utilize the hydrophobic bonding for tissue specificity?

6. Are there species or tissue differences in hydrophobic bonding? What are the differences from the standpoint of conformation and can these differences be exploited for chemotherapy?

7. Can the strong hydrophobic bonding lead to a variety of rotomers for pyrimidine binding where the hydrophobic bonding determines the particular rotomer that will bind?

Mode of Aryl Binding of 1-Aryl-1,2-Dihydro-*s*-Triazines

The *n*-butyl group of XIX (Table 10–2) gave almost as strong bonding to the dihydrofolic reductase from pigeon liver as the *p*-chlorophenyl group

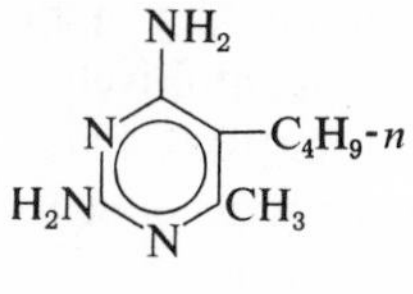

XIX (2.2 μM) 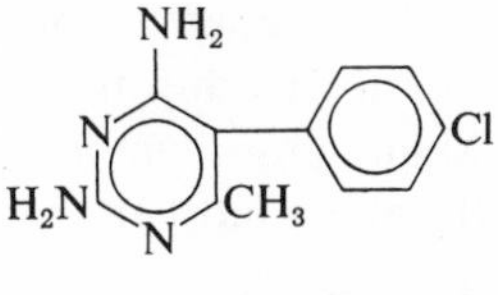   XXII (0.85 μM) 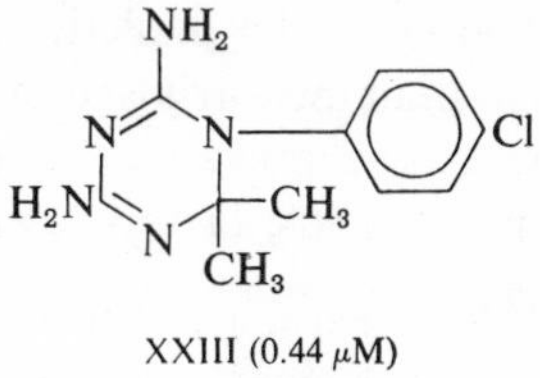   XXIII (0.44 μM)

of XXII.[26] The fact that the *n*-butyl group can only bind by a combination of hydrophobic bonding and van der Waals forces suggested that the mode of binding of the 5-chlorophenyl group of XXII be investigated from the standpoint of hydrophobic bonding. For this study the related 1-aryl-1,2-dihydro-*s*-triazine (XXIII) was investigated because XXIII is simpler to

[26] See Reference 22, p. 203.

synthesize; XXII and XXIII have very similar binding because substitution on the benzene ring has nearly identical effects on both types.[27]

In Table 10–4 are listed the results on inhibition of dihydrofolic reductase by 1-substituted-1,2-dihydro-*s*-triazines. Note that 1-phenyl (XXV) gives 2000-fold more binding than 1-methyl (XXVI) and that isoamyl (XXVII) gives even better binding than phenyl; therefore, the possibility that the phenyl group is complexed by hydrophobic bonding is strong.

The following different ways can be envisioned for the mode of complexing an aryl group of the 1-aryl-dihydrotriazine to dihydrofolic reductase: (a) a charge-transfer complex[28]; (b) an inductive effect of the aryl group on the binding of the 4,6-diamino-*s*-triazine system; (c) van der Waals forces[29]; (d) hydrophobic bonding.[29]

Furthermore, combinations of these four factors could occur. For example, hydrophobic bonding without van der Waals interactions and vice versa is unlikely by the definition that hydrophobic bonding results from the reorientation of water molecules when the hydrocarbon part of an inhibitor or substrate becomes located adjacent to a hydrophobic portion of the enzyme. It is also possible for a combination of hydrophobic bonding and factors (a) and (b) to coexist. At this point the relative energetics of binding by the four classes should be considered because the 1-phenyl-*s*-triazine (XXV) complexes with dihydrofolic reductase about 2000-fold better than the corresponding 1-methyl-*s*-triazine (XXVI) (Table 10–4), a matter of about 4.5 kcal/mole.

Hydrophobic bonding and van der Waals forces can each contribute about 0.7 kcal/mole/methylene group[29]; thus a phenyl group could be anticipated to give a maximum of about 4.2 kcal from each force. The contribution to binding by a charge-transfer complex in a dark unexcited state could be very small because these complexes that could form with any of the electron donors or electron acceptors present in a protein might have dissociation constants in the vicinity of 0.5–1, a negligible amount of energy.[28] The inductive effect of the phenyl ring on the binding of the 4,6-diamino-*s*-triazine system is not readily measured, but intuitively it would be unlikely to increase binding by a factor greater than 10 (1.4 kcal/mole). Thus, factors (a) and (b) alone most probably cannot account for

---

[27] B. R. Baker and B.-T. Ho, *J. Pharm. Sci.*, **53**, 1137 (1964).

[28] E. M. Kosower, *Molecular Biochemistry*, McGraw-Hill Book Company, New York, 1962, pp. 180–195; L. J. Andrews and R. M. Keefer, *Molecular Complexes in Organic Chemistry*, Holden-Day, Inc., San Francisco, 1964; see Chapter 2.

[29] H. Kauzmann, *Advan. Protein Chem.*, **14**, 1 (1959); R. A. Wallace, A. N. Kurtz, and C. Niemann, *Biochemistry*, **2**, 824 (1963); G. Nemethy and H. A. Scheraga, *J. Phys. Chem.*, **66**, 1773 (1962); B. Belleau and G. Lacasse, *J. Med. Chem.*, **7**, 768 (1964); J. B. Jones, T. Kunitake, C. Niemann, and G. E. Hein, *J. Am. Chem.*, **87**, 1777 (1965); see Chapter 2.

Table 10–4. Inhibition of Dihydrofolic Reductase by

$$NH_2 \cdot HCl$$

No.	R	μM conc. for 50 per cent inhibition[a]	Hammett σ constant[b]	Hansch π constant[c]
XXV	C_6H_5—	0.11	0	0
XXVI	CH_3—	220[d]		
XXVII	$i\text{-}C_5H_{11}$—	0.058		
XXVIII	$n\text{-}C_4H_9$—	0.36		
XXIX	$p\text{-}C_6H_4COO^{\ominus}$	1100	0	−0.28[d]
XXX	$m\text{-}C_6H_4COO^{\ominus}$	110	0	−0.28[d]
XXXI	$p\text{-}C_6H_4CH_2NH_3^{\oplus}$	10	weak +	large − [e]
XXXII	$p\text{-}C_6H_4COOC_2H_5$	42	+0.45	−0.01
XXXIII	$p\text{-}C_6H_4CH_2NHCOCH_3$	0.11	weak −	−0.5[f]
XXXIV	$m\text{-}C_6H_4NO_2$	0.072	+0.71	−0.28
XXXV	$m\text{-}C_6H_4CF_3$	0.080	+0.43	+1.1
XXXVI	$p\text{-}C_6H_4C\equiv N$	8.0	+0.66	−0.57
XXXVII	$p\text{-}C_6H_4N(CH_3)_2$	0.98	−0.20	+0.18
XXXVIII	$m\text{-}C_6H_4CH_3$	0.078	−0.07	+0.56
XXXIX	$p\text{-}C_6H_4C_4H_9$—n	0.064	−0.12	+1.9
XL	$p\text{-}C_6H_4$—C_6H_5	160	−0.01	+1.9[g]
XLI	$m\text{-}C_6H_4$—C_6H_5	1.3	+0.06	+1.9
XLII	$m\text{-}C_6H_4Cl$	0.0085	+0.23	+0.71
XXIII	$p\text{-}C_6H_4Cl$	0.44	+0.37	+0.71
XLIII	$m\text{-}C_6H_4Br$	0.0085	+0.22	+0.86
XLIV	$p\text{-}C_6H_4CH_2C_6H_5$	0.040	−0.1[h]	+2.4[i]

[a] Dihydrofolic reductase was isolated from pigeon liver and assayed with 6 μM dihydrofolate and 12 μM TPNH in 0.05 M Tris buffer at pH 7.4; data from B. R. Baker and B.-T. Ho, *J. Heterocyclic Chem.*, **2**, 335 (1965).

[b] For the substituent on the 1-phenyl group of the dihydro-s-triazine; data from M. Charton, *J. Org. Chem.*, **28**, 3121 (1963) and L. P. Hammett, *Physical Organic Chemistry*, McGraw-Hill Book Company, New York, 1940, pp. 184–207.

[c] For the substituent on the 1-phenyl group of the dihydro-s-triazine; data from T. Fujita, J. Iwasa, and C. Hansch, *J. Am. Chem. Soc.*, **86**, 5175 (1964). π is a log function that measures the relative hydrophobic character of the group.

[d] Measurement for COOH; COO⁻, which exists at pH 7.4, would be expected to be much more negative.

[e] This amine group is fully protonated at pH 7.4 and would be expected to have a large negative value.

[f] Estimated from values recorded for CH_3—, C_2H_5—, and CH_3CONH—.

[g] Estimated to be the same as $m\text{-}C_6H_5$—.

[h] Estimated from the relative σ values of p-methyl and p-phenyl (see footnote [b] above).

[i] Estimated by addition of the values for methyl and phenyl[c].

the 4.5 kcal/mole in increased binding when phenyl (XXV) is substituted for methyl (XXVI). Since the *n*-butyl group (XXVIII) can bind one third as well as phenyl (XXV) and isoamyl (XXVII) twice as well as phenyl (XXV) (Table 10–4), it is clear that factors (c) and (d) could readily account for phenyl binding; note that factors (a) and (b) do not exist when methyl is compared with *i*-amyl or *n*-butyl.

If the phenyl group does complex to a nonpolar region of dihydrofolic reductase, then ionized groups attached to the phenyl ring should cause a repulsion from this hydrophobic region. Note that insertion of a *p*-carboxyl group (XXIX) or an *m*-carboxyl group (XXX) causes about a 10,000- and 1000-fold loss in binding, respectively, compared to the parent phenyl analog (XXV); that this repulsion is due to a repulsive interaction of the anionic group on the inhibitor with an electron-donor group on the enzyme is therefore highly unlikely, for such a repulsion should be more position sensitive. Furthermore, if such a coulombic repulsion did exist, then the *p*-aminomethyl derivative (XXXI), which is fully protonated at pH 7.4, should be a more powerful inhibitor than the parent phenyl analog (XXV) due to the attraction of the cationic group of XXXI to the supposed donor group on the enzyme. Rather than being a better inhibitor than the parent phenyl derivative, the aminomethyl analog (XXXI) is actually only about one hundredth as effective; the repulsion of both an anionic or cationic group from the enzyme, which is relatively insensitive to position, is considered to be strong evidence that the phenyl group is complexed hydrophobically; that is, both the solvated anionic (XXIX) or cationic (XXXI) groups are repulsed. When the charge is removed from the *p*-carboxyl group of XXIX by conversion to the ester, XXXII, the ester is about a 260-fold better inhibitor than the carboxylate; similarly, when the charge is removed from the cationic ammonium group of XXXI by acetylation, the acetamido derivative (XXXIII) is a 100-fold better inhibitor than the corresponding amine (XXXI) (Table 10–4).

Inductive effects should be observable if either factors (a) or (b) also contribute to binding; however, it is difficult to separate these effects completely from additional hydrophobic attraction, or repulsion of a hydrophobic group on the inhibitor from the hydrophobic region of the enzyme, or from steric interactions with the enzyme surface. If inductive effects are present, it should be possible to correlate these effects with the Hammett σ values (Table 10–4); the relative hydrophobic or hydrophilic values of the substituents can be estimated from the Hansch π values (Table 10–4). Note that introducing the strong electron-withdrawing nitro (XXXIV) or trifluoromethyl (XXXV) groups or the weakly donating methyl group (XXXVIII) in the *m*-position gave compounds with little change in affinity for the enzyme; in contrast, with the electron-withdrawing chloro (XLII) and bromo (XLIII), binding to the enzyme was increased 13-fold. The two halogen compounds are therefore unique, and there is no correlation between enzyme affinity and either π or σ combinations of the two. Since none of these structural changes caused any detrimental effects to binding, there is apparently no unfavorable interaction with the enzyme caused by these particular *m*- substituents.

The results with *p*- substituents are more difficult to interpret. The possible additional hydrophobic bonding to—or conversely, steric interaction with—the enzyme by *p*-substituents was first studied with the phenyl (XL) and *n*-butyl (XXXIX) groups. The *p-n*-butyl group caused little change in affinity, showing there was neither appreciable additional hydrophobic bonding nor steric interaction with the enzyme. In contrast, the *p*-phenyl group (XL) caused a tremendous 1500-fold loss in binding. Note that this phenyl group is obviously nonpolar $(+\pi)$ and has essentially a zero σ value; further, note that XL has about the same order of binding as the 1-methyl-*s*-triazine, XXVI. Thus, all of the binding of the 1-phenyl group of XXV is lost when the *p*-phenyl group (XL) is introduced. This result can only be attributed to a steric interaction of the *p*-phenyl group with the enzyme. Because the more conformationally flexible, *n*-butyl group (XXXIX) or acetamidomethyl group (XXXIII) do not give any steric interaction with the enzyme, it is clear that the enzyme can tolerate an out-of-plane group in the *p*-position but not a relatively long group in the same plane as the 1-phenyl group; it was also noted that replacement of the 1-phenyl by the 1-(2-fluorenonyl) group, which is planar, also gave an 800-fold loss in binding.[30] Also note that the *p*-benzyl group (XLIV), which places the two phenyl groups out of plane, still is as good an inhibitor as XXV. This planar steric interaction of a phenyl substituent was considerably decreased when the phenyl group was shifted to the *m*- position (XLI); only an 11-fold loss in binding occurred.

It is obvious that the first carbon of a *p*- group does not interact sterically, else the *p*-acetamidomethyl (XXXIII) and the *p-n*-butyl groups (XXXIX) would lower the affinity of XXV for the enzyme; however, the steric interaction of the *p*-phenyl group could begin to occur at any point after the carbon joining to the *p*- position of the 1-phenyl. The *p*-cyano group (XXXVI), which is in the plane of the 1-phenyl, and the *p*-carbethoxy (XXXII), which has its —CO_2— moiety in the plane of the benzene ring, may give poor inhibitors primarily because of this steric interaction. Although it is possible that part of this detrimental effect on binding may be due to the electron-withdrawing properties of the carbethoxy and cyano groups, not all of the effect can be due to this property, otherwise the greater electron-withdrawing cyano group (XXXVI) should have given a

[30] B. R. Baker and B.-T. Ho, *J. Heterocyclic Chem.*, **2**, 72 (1965).

poorer inhibitor than the *p*-carbethoxy group (XXXII), rather than vice versa; the same argument can be advanced for the relative π values of the two groups. The electron-withdrawing *p*-chloro group (XXIII) causes a fourfold loss in binding, which may be attributed to its electron-withdrawing effect on the *p*-position; the main objection to these inductive effects being an important factor still remains the lack of these effects at the *m*-position by the trifluoromethyl (XXXV) and nitro (XXXIV) groups. Furthermore, the electron-donating group, dimethylamino (XXXVII) in the *p*- position also decreases binding by a factor of about ninefold. This result cannot be attributed to hydrophobic repulsion, for the dimethylamino group has a $+\pi$ value and is too weakly basic to be protonated at pH 7.4; because there is no correlation between the dimethylamino and *p*-carbethoxy groups with their opposite σ effects, the only remaining explanation is that the bulky dimethylamino group has some steric interaction when XXXVII is complexed with the enzyme.

In summary, the data in Table 10–4 support the hypotheses (a) that the main contribution to binding by the aryl group of 1-aryl-*s*-triazines is by a combination of hydrophobic bonding and van der Waals forces, (b) inductive effects on enzymic complexing are relatively small, if at all present, and (c) steric inhibition of binding to the enzyme by in-plane substituents at the *p*- position of the 1-phenyl group can be large. It is highly probable that the aryl group of 5-aryl-2,4-diamino-6-alkylpyrimidines of the Daraprim type (VI and XXII) also is complexed with the enzyme mainly by hydrophobic bonding and van der Waals forces.

Further studies on the relative hydrophobic repulsion by the enzyme of a hydrophilic group on the aryl ring and steric interactions of coplanar *p*- substituents by dihydrofolic reductase in other species or tissues might lead to results of considerable value in chemotherapy if differences can be detected; such differences will be described in a later section.

n-Alkyl Binding

Because 5-(*n*-butyl)-2,4-diamino-6-methylpyrimidine (XIX) gave a 550-fold increment in binding over 2,4-diamino-6-methylpyrimidine, an extensive study was made on the maximum hydrophobic bonding by *n*-alkyl groups on 2,6-diamino-4-pyrimidinol (Series A, Table 10–5), 2-amino-6-methyl-4-pyrimidinol (Series B), and 4,6-diamino-1,2-dihydro-*s*-triazine (Series E). Based on the inhibition data of these three series, selected key alkyl derivatives of 2,4,6-triaminopyrimidine (Series C) and 2,4-diamino-6-methylpyrimidine (Series D) were synthesized and evaluated.[31] From Table 10–5 the following comparisons should be noted.

1. Maximum hydrophobic bonding is achieved with a straight-chain

[31] See Reference 22, p. 203.

Table 10-5. Inhibition of Dihydrofolic Reductase by 5-*n*-Alkyl Pyrimidines and 1-*n*-Alkyl-1,2-Dihydro-*s*-Triazines

Series and μM concentration for 50 per cent inhibition[a]

No.	R	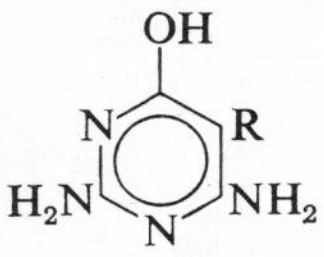 A	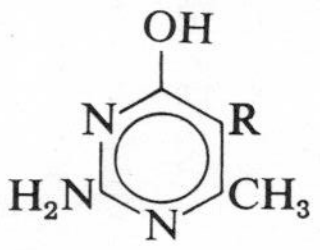 B	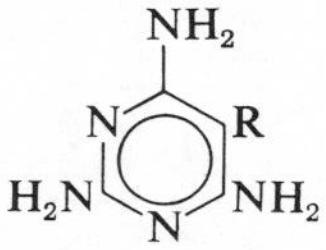 C	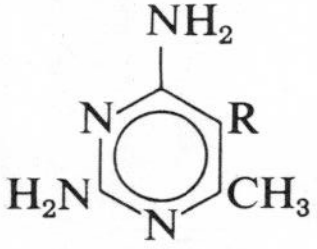 D	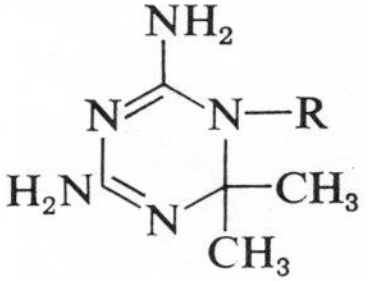 E
XLV	H	13,000	19,000	1200	1100	74
XLVI	CH_3		7,500			220
XLVII	C_2H_5	17,000	2,200			11
XLVIII	$n\text{-}C_3H_7$	450	1,100	300		
XLIX	$n\text{-}C_4H_9$	40	260	23	2.0	0.36
L	$n\text{-}C_5H_{11}$		30		1.0	
LI	$n\text{-}C_6H_{13}$	30	35			0.32
LII	$n\text{-}C_8H_{17}$	48	230			0.14
LIII	C_6H_5	2.1				0.11
LIV	$p\text{-}ClC_6H_4-$				0.85	0.44
LV	$i\text{-}C_5H_{11}$	4.0	8.5	2.1	0.24	0.058
LVI	$(CH_3)_2C=$ $CHCH_2-$	17				

[a] Assayed with pigeon liver dihydrofolic reductase with 6 μM dihydrofolate; data from B. R. Baker, B.-T. Ho, and D. V. Santi, *J. Pharm. Sci.*, **54**, 1415 (1965).

hydrocarbon at *n*-butyl, and it is increased only slightly more at *n*-hexyl and *n*-octyl, except in the case of Series B; with the 2-amino-6-methyl-4-pyrimidinols (Series B) maximum hydrophobic bonding occurs at *n*-amyl and *n*-hexyl, then decreases dramatically with *n*-octyl. The maximum effect with an *n*-alkyl group on binding is 520-fold in Series A, 630-fold in Series B, and 1100-fold in series D. In Series E, only the 1-methyl derivative could be compared with *n*-butyl, because R=H was not accessible; in Series E a 200-fold increment in binding was observed between methyl and *n*-butyl. Only the triamino Series C differed in the magnitude of the maximum increment from hydrogen to butyl, being only 52.

These two discrepancies are of considerable theoretical interest. If it is assumed that in all five series, the heterocyclic ring binds to the same site on the enzyme, it is clear that the 2-amino-4-hydroxy-6-methylpyrimidine Series B is not complexed with exactly the same stereochemistry as in the A, D, and E series. There are at least two ways in which the pyrimidine ring of Series B could be complexed differently from Series A, D, and E. When it is complexed with enzyme, the pyrimidine ring may be able to rotate in the plane of the complex to accommodate maximum binding, depending upon the interaction of the pyrimidine substituents with the enzyme, as noted with the complexing of isoadenosine derivatives with enzymes.[32] Such a rotation of the pyrimidine would be compatible if the pyrimidine is complexed via a charge-transfer complex, a mode of binding which is not likely.[33] It is even less compatible with the four-hydrogen bond formulation of Zakrzewski[34] or a van der Waals or hydrophobic interaction with the enzyme of such a hydrophilic moiety. Similarly, if there is one hydrogen bond interaction between the enzyme and the pyrimidine and one sometimes-weak π-cloud interaction, as has been recently proposed,[33] then the pyrimidine might be able to rotate in the plane of the complex with the enzyme. Another possibility is that there are two hydrogen bonds between the enzyme and the pyrimidine ring, instead of four hydrogen bonds[34]; in such a case, the angle of the plane of pyrimidine ring to the binding locus of the enzyme for the pyrimidine could vary, depending upon substitution at the 6- position and thus vary the distance required to reach the hydrophobic region.

These results led to a more extensive study on the mode of pyrimidine binding which will be discussed in a later section.

The discrepancy in maximum hydrophobic bonding attainable (52-fold) with the 2,4,6-triaminopyrimidine Series C is also of interest. First, there is no difference in binding when R is H (XLV) between Series C and

[32] N. J. Leonard and R. A. Laursen, *Biochemistry*, **4**, 354, 365 (1965).
[33] B. R. Baker and J. H. Jordaan, *J. Heterocyclic Chem.*, **2**, 162 (1965).
[34] S. F. Zakrzewski, *J. Biol. Chem.*, **238**, 1485 (1963).

the 6-methyl Series D. Therefore, it would appear that XLV in Series C is more potent that it should be or that there is some opposing factor to hydrophobic bonding in Series C. Because the compounds in Series C are fairly strong bases (pK_a of XLV in Series C is 6.8) that are about 20 per cent protonated at the assay of pH of 7.4, part of this charge of these protonated species will be localized at the 6-amino group. If the 6- position must approach the hydrophobic region as the 5-alkyl group is complexing with the hydrophobic region, there would be a repulsion of the partially protonated 6-NH_2, which must be overcome at the expense of some of the energy of hydrophobic bonding of the 5-alkyl group. Such a 12-fold repulsion in XLIX of Series C compared to XLIX of Series D would not be out of the range of possibility. Thus, it is possible that the triamino-pyrimidine (XLV in Series C) can rotate so that the repulsion is minimal from any hydrophobic region, but in order to bind, the *n*-butyl group of XLIX in Series C may force the partially protonated 6-amino group into the hydrophobic region with resultant loss in binding energy; it is also possible that the 6-amino group is forced into an electron-acceptor region on the enzyme with a resultant coulombic repulsion.

The relatively weak inhibition by the 2,4-diamino-6-hydroxy of Series A, compared to that of Series D might also be accounted for by the fact that either the hydroxyl or one of the amino groups, both of which are hydrophilic, would be in the 6- position near the supposed hydrophobic region. An alternate explanation has been offered by Zakrzewski[35] that one of the four hydrogen bonds between the enzyme and the pyrimidine is lost in the lowest member of this series (XLV in Series A); however, the four-hydrogen bond hypothesis is untenable with some other results[36] that will be discussed in the section on pyrimidine binding.

2. The same increments per carbon atom in proceeding from H to butyl are not observed in all series. In Series E, the ethyl group is less effective than methyl. Similarly, in Series A, the ethyl group is less effective than hydrogen. In contrast, in Series B, each added methylene group up to amyl gives an added increment in binding. Furthermore, in Series E, the increment in binding between *n*-propyl (XLVIII in Series E) and *n*-butyl (XLIX in Series E) is 30-fold, and the increment between *n*-propyl (XLVIII in Series E) and ethyl (XLVII in Series E) is 20-fold; the maximum increment in binding that could be expected for one methylene group from both hydrophobic bonding and van der Waals forces would be 10-fold. A possible explanation emerges if one considers that the total increment in binding between the methyl (XLVI in Series E) and the *n*-butyl (XLIX in Series E) dihydrotriazines is 200-fold, whereas the maximum for the three

[35] See Reference 34, p. 212.
[36] See Reference 33, p. 212.

methylene groups could be 1000-fold; if a conformational change in the enzyme or a rotational change of the pyrimidine must take place to get maximum hydrophobic binding, there may be some energy barrier to these changes that is only fully overcome when the *n*-butyl side chain (XLIX in Series E) is reached, and then the total free energy change of the four carbons for hydrophobic bonding—minus the energy required for the supposed conformational change—is observed.

Conformational Aspects of Alkyl Binding

In a previous section the experimental evidence for hydrophobic bonding by the aryl group of molecules such as LIII and LIV (Table 10–5) was presented. Note that the *n*-butyltriazine (XLIX in Series E) is almost as effective as the phenyltriazine (LIII in Series E); this three-fold difference is about 600 cal/mole in binding energy. Also note that in the D series the *n*-butyl derivative (XLIX in Series D) has the same magnitude of inhibition as the *p*-chlorophenyl analog (LIV in Series D), although the butyl is somewhat less effective. In the A series, the phenyl analog (LIII in Series A) is about 20-fold more effective than the *n*-butyl analog (XLIX in Series A), a difference of about 1700 cal; however, the isoamyl analog (LV in Series A) has the same order of activity as the phenyl analog (LIII in Series A). Therefore, the possibility was considered that the *n*-butyl group and the phenyl group were both complexed to the same region of the enzyme by hydrophobic bonding.

In order for the *n*-butyl group to assume the conformation of a benzene ring, it would be necessary for the *n*-butyl group to assume an eclipsed conformation. The energy required to shift an *n*-butyl group from the ground-state staggered conformation (LXIV) to the eclipsed conformation (LXV) would require about 5 kcal/mole of energy.[37] Because the total energy of hydrophobic bonding and van der Waals forces available for a butyl group complexing with an enzyme would be about 5600 cal/mole, there would be little net binding energy remaining if the butyl group had to assume such an eclipsed conformation. However, there is no *a priori* reason why it should be assumed that the benzene ring has the optimum conformation for the most hydrophobic bonding. Therefore, the possibility should be considered that a skew conformation (LXVI) of the *n*-butyl group, which requires only 800 cal in energy[37] could approach maximum hydrophobic bonding. The maximum increment in *n*-butyl binding of 550-fold was observed in the D series, thus giving a net free energy of binding of 3600 cal/mole. Because the *n*-butyl group could have a maximum free energy binding of 5600 cal/mole and 800 cal/mole is neces-

[37] W. G. Dauben and K. S. Pitzer in *Steric Effects in Organic Chemistry*, M. S. Newman, ed., John Wiley, New York, 1956, pp. 7–9.

sary to skew the butyl group, a net maximum of 4800 cal/mole remains. This is well above the 3600 cal/mole noted for net binding of the *n*-butyl group of XLIX in Series D.

The hydrophobic bonding of the isoamyl group (LV, Table 10–5) was then studied, for the ground-state conformation would be fixed in a skewed

LXIV (staggered) 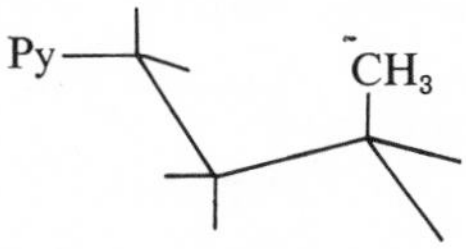   LXV (eclipsed)

LXVI (skew) 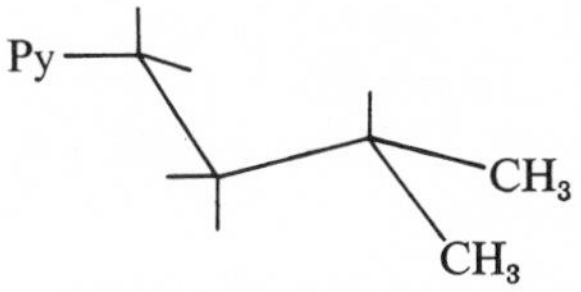   LXVII ("fixed" skew)

conformation, LXVII. Note that in Series A, and C through E, the isoamyl group gives a six- to 11-fold enhancement in binding over the *n*-butyl group; this enhancement is equivalent to a free energy change of 1000–1400 cal/mole, not much above the range of 800 cal required to place the *n*-butyl group in a skew conformation, LXVI. Thus, the results with the isoamyl group could be rationalized on the basis that the extra methyl in the isoamyl group does not necessarily give additional hydrophobic bonding but allows a more skew-like conformation (LXVII) of the remaining methyl group to be at the ground state. It is then noteworthy that the isoamyl group gives the same order of binding as the phenyl in Series A, D, and E.

A peculiarity in the isoamyl hydrophobic bonding still remains in the B series. The isoamyl group (LV in Series B) binds fourfold better than the *n*-amyl group (L in Series B) and 30-fold better than the *n*-butyl group (XLIX in Series B); however, as we discussed previously, maximum straight-chain hydrophobic bonding is not reached in the B series until *n*-amyl. Furthermore, in the B series, the *n*-octyl group (LII in Series B) causes an eightfold loss in the maximal straight-chain hydrophobic bonding, but little change in binding from *n*-butyl (XLIX) to *n*-octyl (LII) occurs in A or E series where maximal straight-chain hydrophobic bonding is reached with the *n*-butyl group.

The 3,3-dimethylallyl side chain (LVI) (Table 10–5) was selected as being one that is fixed in a high-energy eclipsed conformation (LXVIII) similar to benzene (LIII); it was synthesized in the 2,6-diamino-4-pyrimidinol, Series A. However, the angle between the C_2—C_1 and C_1—pyrimidine bonds in the dimethylallyl group is about 25° different from the corresponding angle with the 5-phenylpyrimidine. The 3,3-dimethylallyl pyrimidine (LVI in Series A) was intermediate in activity between the *n*-butyl pyrimidine (XLIX in Series A) and isoamyl pyrimidines (LV in Series A), but was somewhat less effective than the phenyl pyrimidine (LIII in Series A).

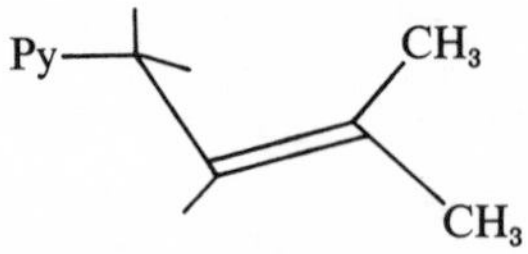

LXVIII ("fixed" eclipsed)

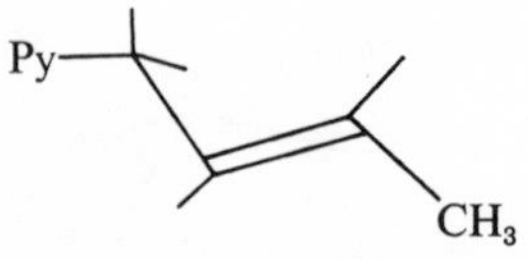

LXIX ("fixed" staggered)

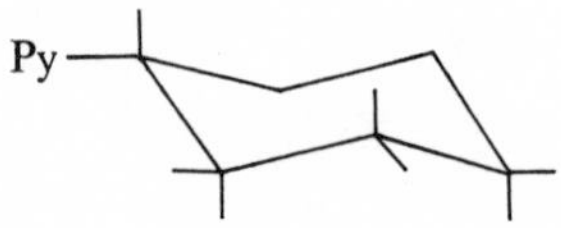

LVII ("fixed" skew)

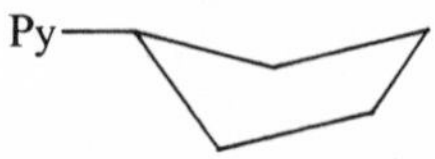

LIX

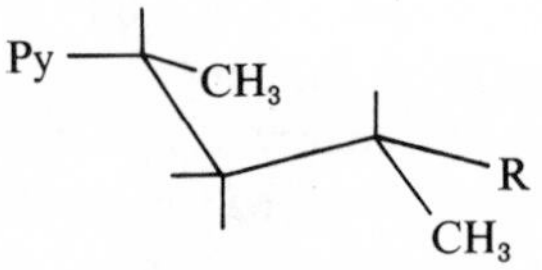

LX in Series A, R = H
LXII in Series A, R = CH$_3$

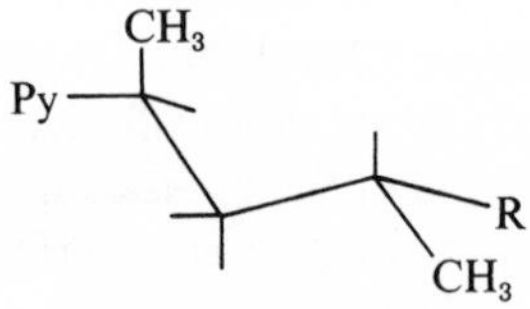

LX in Series B, R = H
LXII in Series B, R = CH$_3$

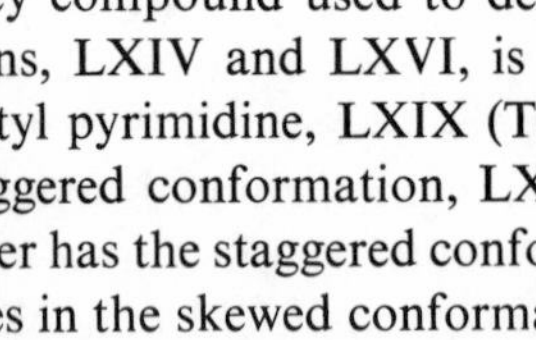

LXIII in Series A

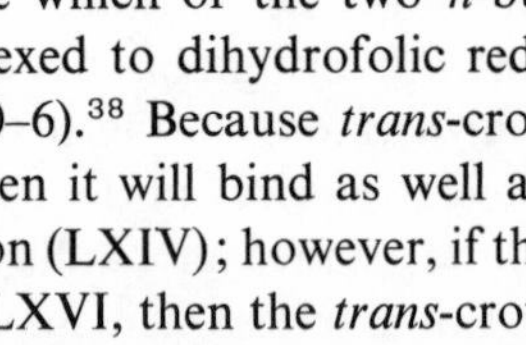

LXIII in Series B

The key compound used to determine which of the two *n*-butyl conformations, LXIV and LXVI, is complexed to dihydrofolic reductase is *trans*-crotyl pyrimidine, LXIX (Table 10–6).[38] Because *trans*-crotyl has a fixed staggered conformation, LXIX, then it will bind as well as *n*-butyl if the latter has the staggered conformation (LXIV); however, if the *n*-butyl complexes in the skewed conformation, LXVI, then the *trans*-crotyl group (LXIX) should bind no better than the 5-*n*-propylpyrimidine (XLVIII in Series A). In Table 10–6 it can be seen that the *trans*-crotylpyrimidine (LXIX) was equally as effective as the *n*-butylpyrimidine, XLIX in Series A; both XLIX in Series A and LXIX were better than 10 times more effective than the *n*-propylpyrimidine (XLVIII in Series A), thus giving

[38] B. R. Baker and G. J. Lourens, *J. Heterocyclic Chem.*, **2**, 344 (1965).

strong experimental support that the *n*-butyl group complexes to dihydrofolic reductase in a staggered conformation (LXIV).

If the *n*-butyl group is complexed to the enzyme in a staggered conformation (LXIV), then the extra methyl group of isoamyl (LXVII)—which is skewed with respect to the staggered butyl chain, LXIV—presumably can give additional hydrophobic bonding. Support for such a hypothesis might be obtainable with a *cis*-crotyl group or a cyclohexyl group. The cyclohexyl

Table 10–6. Inhibition of Dihydrofolic Reductase by

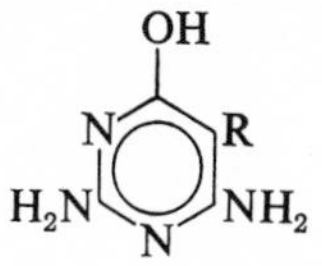

No.	R	μM concentration for 50 per cent inhibition[a]
XLVIII *A*	$n\text{-}C_3H_7-$	450
XLIX *A*	$n\text{-}C_4H_9$	40
LV *A*	$i\text{-}C_5H_{11}$	4.0
LIII *A*	C_6H_5	2.1
LVI *A*	$(CH_3)_2C{=}CHCH_2-$	17
LVII	cyclohexyl	35
LXIX	*trans*-$CH_3CH{=}CHCH_2-$	35
LIX	cyclopentyl	450
LX	$-CH(CH_3)CH_2CH_2CH_3$	82
LXI	$-CH(CH_3)CH_2CH_3$	620
LXII	$-CH(CH_3)CH_2CH(CH_3)_2$	8.1
LXIII	$-CH_2CH(CH_3)CH_2CH_3$	14

[a] Assayed with 6 μM dihydrofolate on dihydrofolic reductase isolated from pigeon liver; data from B. R. Baker and G. J. Lourens, *J. Heterocyclic Chem.*, **2**, 344 (1965).

group (LVII) was chosen because it has skewed carbons between C_1 and C_4 in the ground state; in addition to the *cis*-crotyl group having an eclipsed conformation, it is more difficult to synthesize than the cyclohexylpyrimidine. Note in Table 10–6 that cyclohexyl (LVII) was equivalent in binding to *n*-butyl (XLIX in Series A), thus confirming that a skewed C_4-methyl group can hydrophobically bind to the enzyme.

That there are some conformational restrictions to optimum hydrophobic bonding and that the bonding is not due simply to an extraction phenomenon related to the hydrocarbon content[39] was shown in several ways as follows.

1. Comparison of 1-methylbutyl (LX) with 2-methylbutyl (LXIII) and 3-methylbutyl (isoamyl, LV in Series A) (Table 10–6) shows considerable difference in the order of bindings, LV in Series A being 20 times more effective than LX.

2. Comparison of 3,3-dimethylallyl (LVI in Series A), which has an eclipsed conformation, with the skewed isoamyl group (LV) shows that LV is a fourfold better inhibitor than LVI in Series A.

3. The cyclopentyl group (LIX) is only one hundredth as effective as isoamyl (LV in Series A).

Note that the cyclohexyl group (LVII) is 13 times more effective than the cyclopentyl group (LIX) (Table 10–6) but that the cyclopentyl is equivalent to n-propyl (XLVIII) in binding; this comparison gives strong evidence that only C_1, C_2, and C_3 of the cyclopentyl is hydrophobically bonded, and C_4 and C_5 neither complex nor interfere with complex formation. Furthermore, about the same increment in increased binding occurs from n-propyl to n-butyl as from cyclopentyl to cyclohexyl.

The relative contribution to binding—positive or negative—by methyl substitution on the n-butyl group at C_1, C_2, or C_3 was studied for two purposes; first, it would be of interest to see if there were increased hydrophobic bonding and secondly, if decreased binding due to a steric interaction of the methyl group to binding could occur. If substitution at any of these positions does not give decreased binding, then it might be possible to place a longer branch at that position; this branch might be able to bridge to a hydrophilic area on the enzyme surface; this hydrophilic area might then be subject to attack by a properly positioned covalent-forming group on the inhibitor leading to an active-site-directed irreversible inhibitor of dihydrofolic reductase.

Substitution of a methyl group at the C_1- position (LX) of n-butyl (XLIX in Series A) or at the C_1- position (LXII) of isoamyl (LV in Series A) led to a consistent twofold loss in binding (Table 10–6). A similar, but slightly lesser effect was observed with the propyl series (XLVIII in Series A and LXI). These results would appear to be best rationalized by considering the conformations of the d- and l- forms. One of the enantiomers of LX would have the methyl group above the plane of the pyrimidine ring (LX in Series B) when the n-butyl chain is in the staggered conformation. With the reasonable assumption that there is a relatively flat enzyme interaction with the top of the pyrimidylbutyl moiety, as depicted in LX

[39] A. J. Hymes, D. A. Robinson, and W. J. Canady, *J. Biol. Chem.*, **240**, 134 (1965) and references therein.

in Series A, then one enantiomorph (LX in Series B) will have its methyl group projecting into the enzyme surface, thus interfering with binding. The other enantiomer (LX in Series A) has its methyl group in the plane of the C_1—C_2 bond which should not interfere with binding as noted with cyclohexyl (LVII) and cyclopentyl (LIX). It follows that because one enantiomer could have about the same activity as the alkylpyrimidine unsubstituted at C_1 and because the other enantiomer would be considerably less effective, one could expect the *dl-* pairs (LX) to be one half as effective as *n*-butyl.

A similar explanation can be used for the 1-methyl-isoamyl group (LXII in Series A, LXII in Series B), which is one half as effective as isoamyl (LV*A*). It would be of interest to resolve either LX or LXII and compare the relative ability of the enantiomers to inhibit.

Substitution of a methyl group at C_2 (LXIII) of the *n*-butylpyrimidine (XLIX in Series A) gave a threefold better inhibitor (Table 10–6); however this increment was less than the 10-fold increment observed by C_3- substitution to give the isoamylpyrimidine (LV in Series A). Again you should consider that one (LXII in Series B) of the two enantiomers could have a methyl group projecting away from the enzyme surface, whereas the other enantiomer (LXIII in Series A) has its methyl group nearly in the plane of the pyrimidine ring. Thus if the enzyme is complexed to the butylpyrimidine above the plane of the ring, one might see additional hydrophobic binding from enantiomer LXIII in Series A but no additional binding with enantiomer LXIII in Series B. Such interactions would then predict that the 2-methylbutyl group would be more effective than butyl, but one half or less as effective as the isoamyl group, depending upon whether or not the 2-methyl of LXIII in Series A gives as much hydrophobic bonding as the 3-methyl of LV in Series A.

Aralkyl Binding

When a phenyl group (LXXI) was attached to the terminal carbon of the *n*-butyl moiety (XLIX), increased binding with all five types of the heterocycles, listed in Table 10–7, was achieved. In all but Series D, a five- to ninefold tightening in binding occurred, a matter of 900–1200 cal/mole of free energy. In the D series, a 74-fold better binding was observed. In Series A, C, and E, the magnitude of binding was about the same as the *i*-amyl series (LV); in the B series, the *i*-amyl (LV) was better than phenylbutyl (LXXI), but in the D series the opposite condition was noted. The increment in binding in all but the D series could be accounted for by hydrophobic bonding by one carbon of the benzene ring; in the D series, hydrophobic bonding by two carbons would be required. It is also possible that the phenyl complexes by a charge transfer; however, such a bonding

Table 10–7. Inhibition of Dihydrofolic Reductase by 5-Substituted Pyrimidines and 1-Substituted Dihydro-s-Triazines

		Series and μM concentration for 50 per cent inhibition[a]				
No.	R	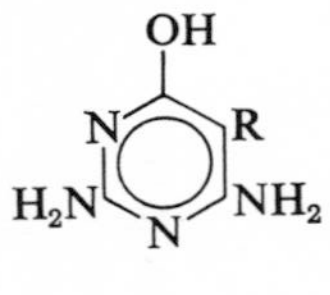 A	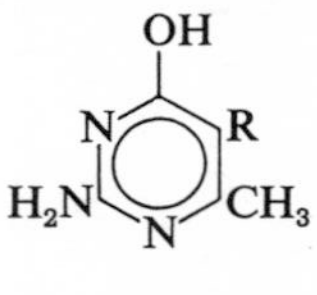 B	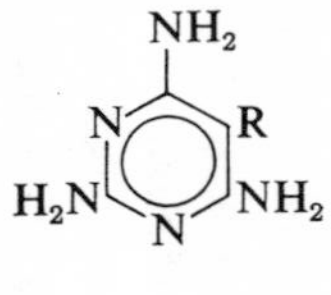 C	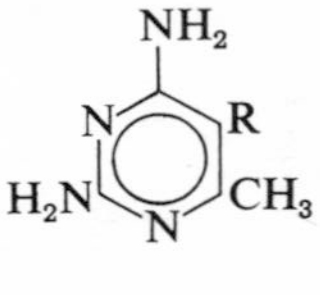 D	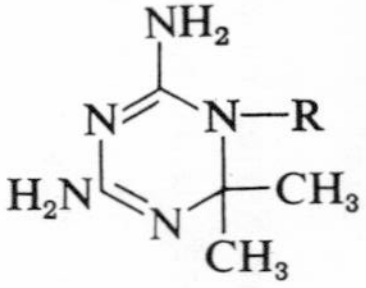 E
XLV	H	13,000	19,000	1,200	1,100	220
XLVII	C$_2$H$_5$	17,000	2,200	300		11
XLVIII	n-C$_3$H$_7$—	450	1,100	23	2.0	0.36
XLIX	n-C$_4$H$_9$	40	260			0.14
LII	n-C$_8$H$_{17}$	48	230			0.058
LV	i-C$_5$H$_{11}$—	4.0	8.5	2.1	0.24	0.028
LXX	C$_6$H$_5$(CH$_2$)$_3$—	60	160	7.1	0.18	0.041
LXXI	C$_6$H$_5$(CH$_2$)$_4$—	8.4	30	3.5	0.027	
LXXII	C$_6$H$_5$NH(CH$_2$)$_3$—		800		2.2	

[a] Assayed with dihydrofolic reductase from pigeon liver with 6 μM dihydrofolate; data from B. R. Baker, B.-T. Ho, and D. V. Santi, *J. Pharm. Sci.*, **54**, 1415 (1965) and references therein.

should also have the accompanying van der Waals forces that should give 100–1000 times the binding. It is noteworthy that the *n*-octyl group (LII) gave little, if any, increase in binding to the enzyme, compared with *n*-butyl (XLIX); thus, these additional four carbons could not assume a flat enough conformation to bind hydrophobically like the phenyl moiety of LXXI, or the phenyl was complexed by a different mode such as charge transfer.

The fact that hydrophobic bonding differed from one series to another indicates again that the pyrimidine ring does not complex identically to the enzyme in all series. This was further amplified when the phenylbutyl series (LXXI) was compared with the phenylpropyl series (LXX); in Series C and E almost identical binding of the two groups was observed, whereas in Series A, B and D, the phenylbutyl (LXXI) was complexed more tightly.

The comparative increase in binding when the *n*-propyl side chain (XLVIII) is substituted by a benzyl group to give the phenylbutyl side chain (LXXI) is enlightening. In Series A, B, and C, a 37–85-fold increase in binding was observed, whereas in Series E the increment was 270-fold; in Series E this increment is larger than expected, but it is most likely due to the larger increment between propyl (XLVIH in Series E) and *n*-butyl (XLIX in Series E). Note that substitution of the benzyl group on the

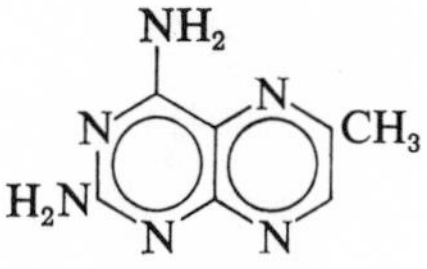

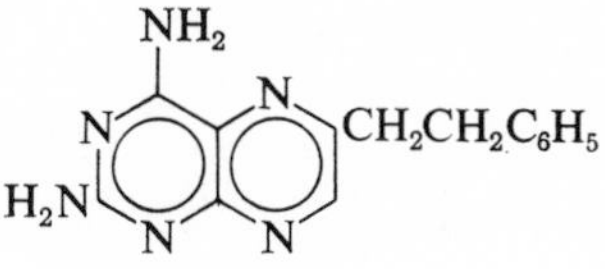

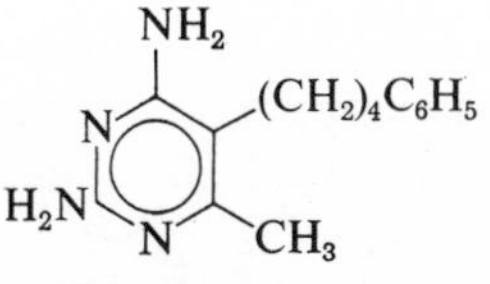

LXXI in Series D = XVIII

methyl of 2,4-diamino-6-methylpteridine (XX) to give XXI affords a 52-fold increment in binding, thus being compatible with the changes between XLVIII to LXXI (Table 10–7). Thus part of the 1600-fold difference in bonding between XXI and LXXID (equivalent to XVIII) discussed at the beginning is due to the difference in hydrophobic bonding between XXI and LXXI in Series D; it is obvious that other important factors contribute to this because the two structures differ only in (a) a replacement of CH_2 by N and (b) ground-state conformational differences.

It is therefore possible that XXI and LXXI in Series D have a conformation in the enzyme-inhibitor complex different than the conformation that is normally assumed by dihydrofolate when it is complexed to the enzyme; this possible difference will be explored in the next section.

The hydrophobic bonding by the phenylbutyl group (LXXI) also explains why the LXXI series is more tightly complexed to the enzyme than the anilinopropyl series (LXXII); not only is one of the methylene groups missing in LXXII, which could give a 10-fold difference in binding, but some repulsion of the polar NH group from the hydrophobic region could occur. If it is assumed that the benzene ring of the anilinopropyl (LXXII in Series B) gives a fivefold increment in binding, then the remaining aminopropyl moiety contributes to binding about as much as an ethyl group (XLVII in Series B).

Position of the Hydrophobic Bonding Area on the Enzyme

The discovery of a hydrophobic bonding region on dihydrofolic reductase creates a serious problem from the standpoint of the design of an active-site-directed irreversible inhibitor, namely, where is the hydrophobic region with respect to the binding region for the *p*-aminobenzoyl moiety of folic acid (I) on dihydrofolic reductase? Is this hydrophobic region between the binding loci for *p*-aminobenzoyl and the pyrimidine moieties

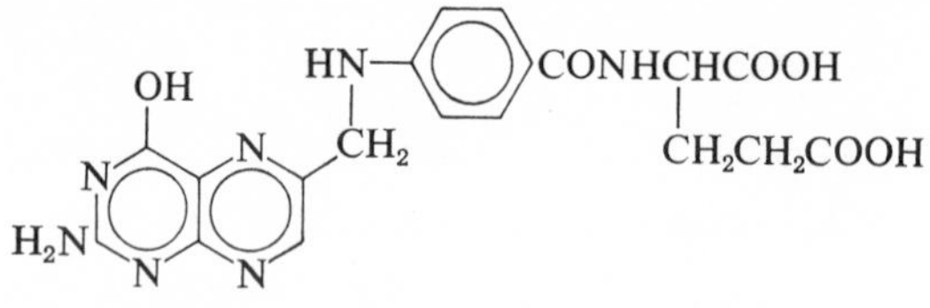

I

or is it elsewhere, such as near the region where the 4-oxo group of folic acid is complexed? If the hydrophobic region is not between these two moieties, then the anilino group of an inhibitor such as LXXIII would probably not be complexed with the *p*-aminobenzoyl locus. If the anilino

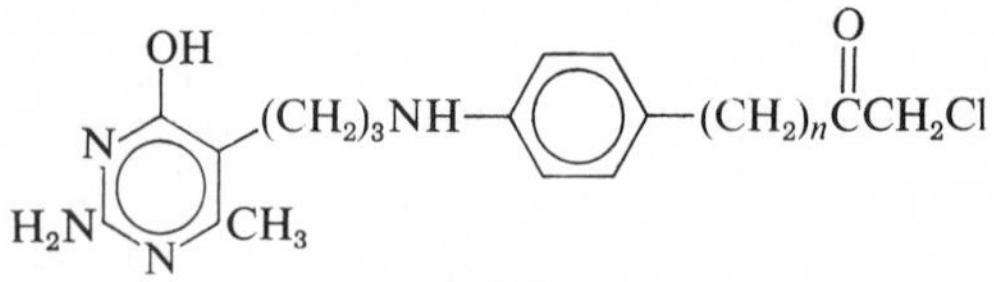

LXXIII

group of LXXIII is complexed with a different locus, then an inhibitor of this type would not have its alkylating function sufficiently close to the glutamate binding points of folic acid (I) to alkylate irreversibly such a binding point by the endo mechanism; furthermore, if the anilino group of

LXXIII is complexed to a hydrophobic region, then by definition there is not likely to be a nucleophilic group in this region of the enzyme. To obtain such an answer unequivocally is difficult; therefore several lines of evidence were accumulated that supported the concept that the hydrophobic region was *not* between the binding loci for the pyrimidyl and *p*-aminobenzoyl moieties of folic acid (I). One such line of evidence was the following[40]:

p-Aminobenzoyl-L-glutamic acid (LXXIV) was measured as an inhibitor of dihydrofolic reductase. With the consideration that LXXIV did not have

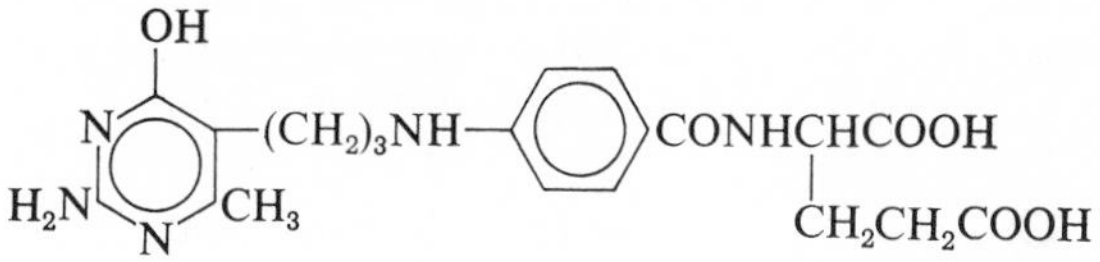

XIII

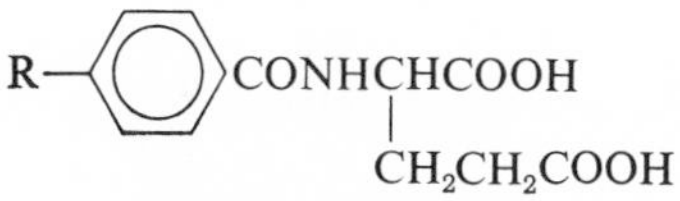

LXXIV, R = NH$_2$
LXXV, R = H

the pyrimidyl moiety of the prototype inhibitor, XIII, the 12 mM concentration of LXXIV needed for 50 per cent inhibition (Table 10–8) compared favorably with XIII, where 0.10 mM was needed for 50 per cent inhibition (Table 10–2). The 120-fold difference in binding between XIII and LXXIV is a difference of 2.9 kcal/mole. Because it can be calculated from the data in Table 10–5 that 2-amino-6-methyl-4-pyrimidinol (XLV in Series B) has a free energy of binding to dihydrofolic reductase of 3.0 kcal/mole, the agreement is fairly reasonable for the amount of inhibition that can be expected when the pyrimidyl moiety is removed from XIII to give LXXIV; these results support the suggestion that *p*-aminobenzoyl-L-glutamate (LXXIV) binds to the same region of dihydrofolic reductase that complexes this moiety of XIII and folic acid (I).

With the now-reasonable assumption that *p*-aminobenzoyl-L-glutamic acid (LXXIV) binds at the same locus as the *p*-aminobenzoyl-L-glutamate moiety of folic acid (I) then hydrophobic bonding by alkyl, aryl, or aralkyl groups substituted at the *p*- position of benzoyl-L-glutamate (LXXV) should be observed if the hydrophobic bonding region were between the loci that complex the pyrimidyl and *p*-amino-benzoyl-L-glutamate moieties of folic acid (I). Note that the *p*-amino group of LXXIV contributed little to inhibition since benzoyl-L-glutamic acid (LXXV) was about as good an

[40] B. R. Baker, T. J. Schwan, J. Novotny, and B.-T. Ho, *J. Pharm. Sci.*, **55**, 295 (1966).

Table 10–8. Inhibition of Dihydrofolic Reductase by

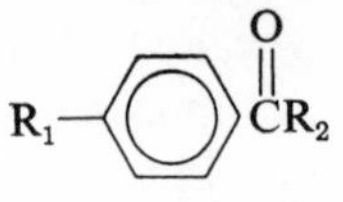

$$R_1 - \underset{}{\bigcirc} - \overset{\overset{O}{\|}}{C}R_2$$

No.	R_1	$R_2{}^a$	mM concen- tration	Per cent inhibition	Estimated mM concentration for 50 per cent inhibition
LXXIV	NH$_2$	GL	12	50	12
LXXV	H	GL	16	50	16
LXXVI	H	OH	75	0	> 300^b
LXXVII	Br(CH$_2$)$_3$—	OH	17	50	17
LXXVIII	Br(CH$_2$)$_3$—	GL	4.5	50	4.5
LXXIX	n-C$_8$H$_{17}$—	OH	1.0^c	15	5.6
LXXX	n-C$_8$H$_{17}$—	GL	0.17	50	0.17
LXXXI	C$_6$H$_5$—	OH	6.7	50	6.7
LXXXII	C$_6$H$_5$—	GL	6.5	50	6.5
LXXXIII	C$_6$H$_5$CH$_2$—	OH	10	50	10
LXXXIV	Br(CH$_2$)$_4$—	OH	6.2	50	6.2
LXXXV	Cl(CH$_2$)$_5$—	OH	6.0	50	6.0
LXXXVI	C$_6$H$_5$CO—	OH	13	50	13
LXXXVII	CONHC$_6$H$_4$— | (CH$_2$)$_2$CH(CH$_3$)$_2$-p	OH	0.20^c	0	> 0.80^b
LXXXVIII	CONHC$_6$H$_4$CH$_2$— | (CH$_2$)$_2$CH(CH$_3$)$_2$-p	OH	0.60^c	0	> 2.4^b
LXXXIX	m-NH$_2$C$_6$H$_4$CH$_2$NH—	OH	0.76	50	0.76
XC	m-NO$_2$C$_6$H$_4$CH$_2$NH—	OH	1.8	50	1.8

Dihydrofolic reductase from pigeon liver was assayed with 6 μM dihydrofolate; data from B. R. Baker, T. J. Schwan, J. Novotny, and B.-T. Ho, *J. Pharm. Sci.*, **55**, 295 (1966).

^{a} GL is L-glutamate.
^{b} Because 20 per cent inhibition is readily detectable, the concentration for 50 per cent inhibition is greater than four times the concentration measured.
^{c} Maximum solubility under assay conditions.

inhibitor (Table 10–8). Little, if any, hydrophobic bonding took place when a 3-bromopropyl (LXXVIII) or phenyl group (LXXXII) was introduced into the p- position. However, when the p- substituent was lengthened to n-octyl (LXXX), about a 90-fold increase in binding occurred (Table 10–8). These data clearly show that the hydrophobic region begins at least three atoms away from the *p*- position of benzoyl-L-glutamic acid (LXXV). Because the distance between the pyrimidyl and benzoyl-L-glutamate moieties of folic acid (I) consists of a four-atom chain, it is clear that the hydrophobic region lies elsewhere than between the binding loci for these two moieties. It should again be emphasized that this interpretation contains the assumption that LXXV and the *p*-amino-benzoyl-L-glutamate moiety of folic acid (I) are complexed to the same region on the enzyme; although this interpretation is quite reasonable, it is not unequivocal.

A particularly plaguing inconsistency has been the fact that pteroic acid (VIII) was 80-fold less effective than folic acid (I) (Table 10–1) as an inhibitor of dihydrofolic reductase, whereas XIII was as good or better an inhibitor than its pteroic acid analog, XIV (Table 10–2). Although XIII is probably complexed in the same manner as folic acid (I) to dihydrofolic reductase, the possibility existed that the less polar relative XIV was complexed with the hydrophobic region rather than the *p*-aminobenzoyl-L-glutamate region.

Note that benzoic acid (LXXVI) showed no inhibition at a concentration of 75 mM but that *p*- substitution of a bromopropyl gave a compound (LXXVII) that showed a 50 per cent inhibition at 17 mM. Lengthening the chain to bromobutyl (LXXXIV) or chloropentyl (LXXXV) gave still better inhibitors with 50 per cent inhibition at about 6 mM. Furthermore, *p*-phenyl- (LXXXI), *p*-benzyl- (LXXXIII), and *p*-benzoylbenzoic (LXXXVI) acids showed 50 per cent inhibition in the 6–13 mM range. Thus, these hydrophobic groups could give as much as a greater than 50-fold increase in binding compared to benzoic acid (LXXVI). Whether or not there were limitations on the length of this *p*- group for hydrophobic bonding could not be shown using LXXIX, LXXXVII, or LXXXVIII, due to their insolubility; however it was apparent that longer groups in LXXIX and LXXXVIII could not have increased hydrophobic bonding much more. Thus the hydrophobic region begins soon after the first atom in the *p*- position of benzoic acid when these benzoic acids are complexed to dihydrofolic reductase; in contrast, the *p*- position of benzoyl-L-glutamate must have greater than a four-atom chain before hydrophobic bonding is detected.

That hydrophobic bonding can also occur with *N*- substituents on *p*-aminobenzoic acid is demonstrated with the *m*-aminobenzoyl and the *m*-nitrobenzyl derivatives LXXXIX and XC; LXXXIX is actually the best of the benzoate-type inhibitors given in Table 10–8.

Regardless of the mode of binding of benzoyl-L-glutamic acid (LXXV) and the substituted benzoic acids (in Table 10–8) it is clear that the benzoyl group of the two classes of inhibitors are complexed to different regions on the enzyme. As a working hypothesis to this point, it can be proposed that the benzoyl-L-glutamates are complexed to the normal region for this moiety of folic acid, but the benzoic acids are complexed in the hydrophobic region.

A second line of evidence also supported the concept that the hydrophobic region on the enzyme was not between the binding loci for the pyrimidyl and *p*-aminobenzoyl moieties of folic acid (I). Note that *p*-phenylbenzoyl-L-glutamic acid (LXXXII) is a slightly better inhibitor of

LXXXII

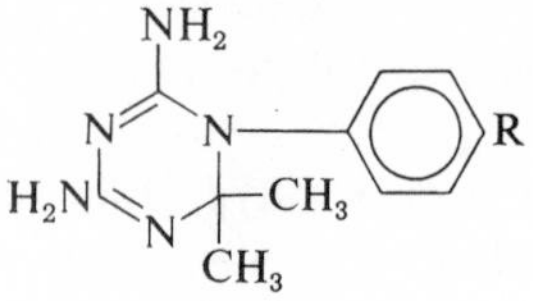

XXV, R = H
XL, R = C₆H₅

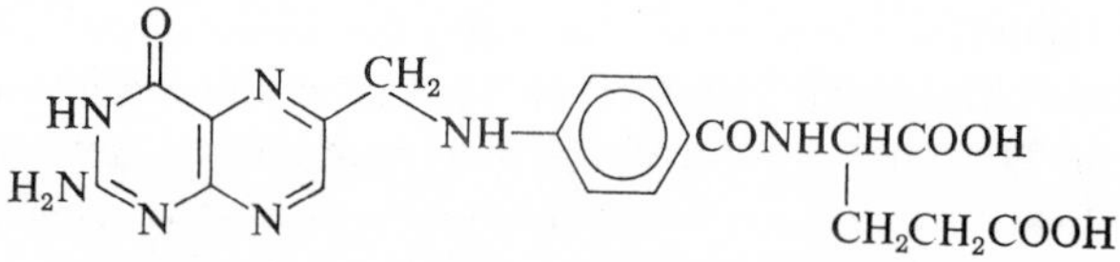

I

dihydrofolic reductase than benzoyl-L-glutamic acid (LXXV) (Table 10–8). In contrast, 1500-fold loss in binding occurs when the *p*-phenyl substituent (XL) is introduced onto the 1-phenyl-*s*-triazine (XXV) (Table 10–4). If the dihydro-*s*-triazine (XL) were complexed in the same manner as the pyrimidyl moiety of folic acid (I), then the outside phenyl group would overlap the position occupied by the outside phenyl group of the glutamate (LXXXII). Therefore, XXV cannot have the conformation indicated if it is complexed to the locus that complexes the pyrimidyl moiety of folic acid; stated another way, the *p*- position of XXV has no bulk tolerance for an in-plane group, but the *p*- position of LXXXII does. The results can be rationalized if the hydrophobic bonding region is elsewhere than between the binding loci for the pyrimidyl and *p*-aminobenzoyl moieties of folic acid (I). For example, a rotomer such as XXV*B* or XXV*C* could be complexed to the enzyme, the preferred rotomer for binding being primarily determined by the strong hydrophobic bonding of the phenyl to the enzyme; such rotomers have been evoked in order to explain the binding to chymotrypsin (Chapter 3) and the binding of isoadenosine and its derivatives to various enzymes.[41]

Fairly good evidence for support of rotomer XXV*B* or XXV*C* can be

[41] N. J. Leonard and R. A. Laursen, *Biochemistry*, **4**, 354, 365 (1965).

gleaned by comparing the prototype inhibitor (XIII) with its 6-phenyl analog (XCI).[42] When assayed with folic acid at pH 6.1 as a substrate,[42] XCI was complexed about 20 times tighter than XIII; with dihydrofolate at pH 7.4 as a substrate, XCI was complexed about 12 times stronger than

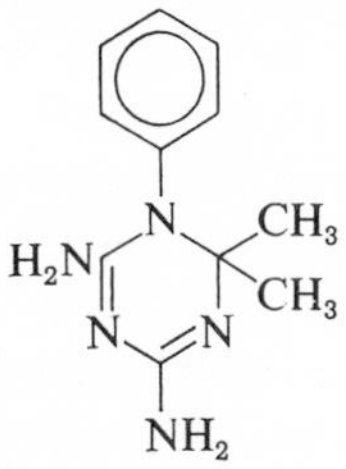

XXVB   XXVC

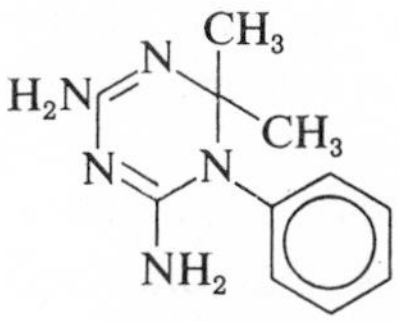

XIII. Note (a) the probability that the *p*-aminobenzoyl-L-glutamate moiety of XIII and XCI is complexed to the normal locus for this moiety of folic acid (I), (b) the probability that the pyrimidyl moiety of XIII and XCI is also complexed at the normal locus for the pyrimidyl moiety of

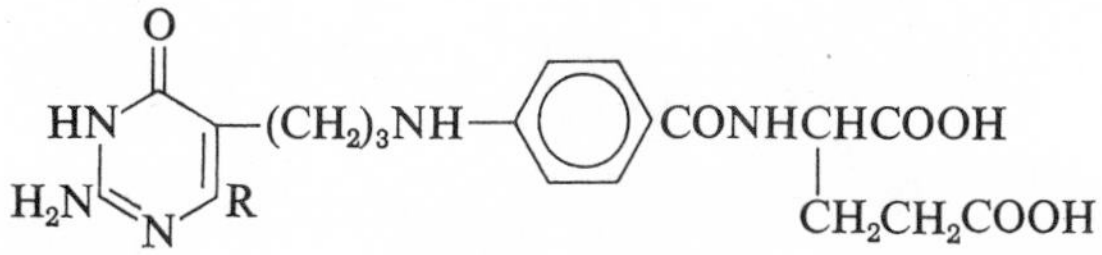

XIII, R = CH₃ (100 μM)
XCI4, R = C₆H₅ (8 μM)

XCIB

folic acid, and (c) the probability that the 6-phenyl moiety is complexed by hydrophobic bonding.[43] Therefore, XCI should have rotomer XCI in Series A or XCI in Series B when complexed to the enzyme; it follows that the hydrophobic region starts either near the 4-oxo group (XCI in Series B) or the N⁸- group (XCI in Series A) of folic acid (I) when the latter is complexed to the enzyme. So far no experimental approach to delineate

[42] B. R. Baker and H. S. Shapiro, *J. Med. Chem.*, **6**, 664 (1963).
[43] See Chapter 10, p. 205 for evidence on the hydrophobic bonding by phenylpyrimidines.

whether the hydrophobic region is in the region of the phenyl group in conformation XCI in Series A or XCI in Series B has as yet been found.

A third line of evidence can also be explained relying on the concept that the hydrophobic region does not lie between the binding loci for the pyrimidyl and *p*-aminobenzoyl moieties of folic acid (I); because some of the data are obtained in different systems, the comparisons are indirect and hence quite equivocal. 2,4-Diamino-6-methylquinazoline (XCII) is a 22-fold better inhibitor of the dihydrofolic reductase from pigeon liver than the corresponding pteridine, XX[44]; thus the benzo group of XCII can give hydrophobic bonding. In contrast, the tetrahydroquinazoline analog (XCIV) of aminopterin (IV) does not show hydrophobic bonding, XCIV being less than one one-hundredth as effective at IV as an inhibitor of the folic reductase from rat liver.[45] Thus the tetrahydrobenzo moiety of XCIV does not show hydrophobic bonding. Furthermore, this moiety of XCIV is located between the pyrimidine and *p*-aminobenzoyl-L-glutamate moieties. This interpretation suffers from two objections, namely, (a) the conformation of the 9-methylene group of aminopterin (IV) is in plane with

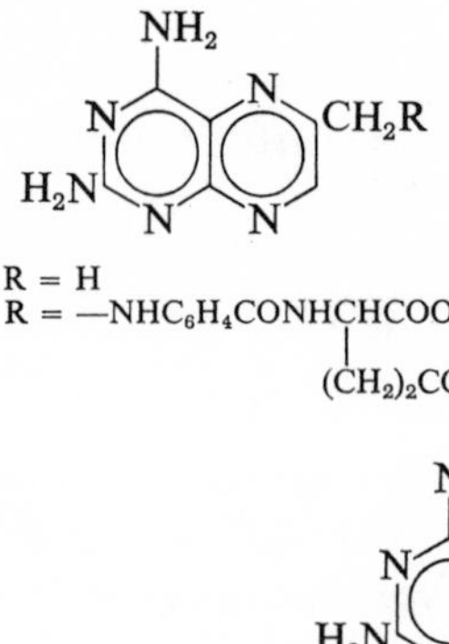

XX, R = H
IV, R = —NHC$_6$H$_4$CONHCHCOOH
                                    |
                                (CH$_2$)$_2$COOH

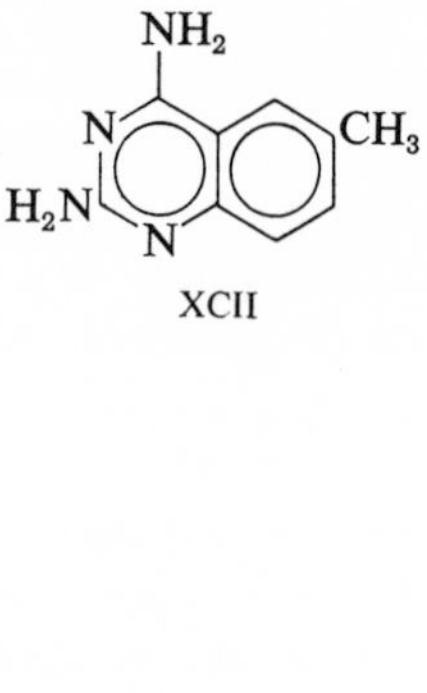

XCII

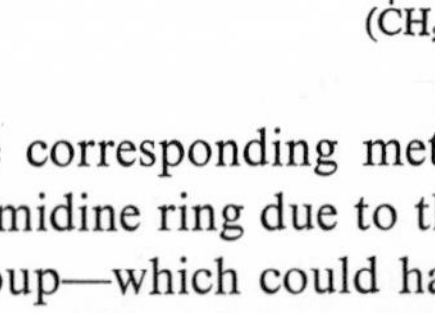

XCIII, R = CH$_3$
XCIV, R = CH$_2$NHC$_6$H$_4$CONHCHCOOH
                                              |
                                          (CH$_2$)$_2$COOH

the pteridine ring, but the corresponding methylene group of XCIV is above the plane of the pyrimidine ring due to the half-chair conformation of the tetrahydrobenzo group—which could have a detrimental effect on the binding of XCIV; (b) it cannot necessarily be assumed that the methyl-tetrahydrobenzo moiety of XCIII would give as good hydrophobic bond-

[44] B. R. Baker and J. K. Coward, unpublished.
[45] B. R. Baker, Preprint E-I, Symposia Papers, Scientific Section of the American Pharmaceutical Association, Las Vegas Meeting, 1962.

ing as the methylbenzo moiety of XCII, even though it is likely.[46] For a more realistic comparison one would need to evaluate the fully aromatic quinazoline analog of aminopterin on the dihydrofolic reductase from pigeon liver, then make a comparison with the results already available with aminopterin (IV), XX and XCII on this enzyme.

Mode of Binding Pyrimidines; pH Profiles of Inhibitors

The results of the studies on hydrophobic bonding discussed in the previous section could not be explained by a single rotomer of pyrimidine binding in the pyrimidyl locus for dihydrofolate. At least three rotomers were needed, depending upon the presence or absence of a group that gives hydrophobic bonding and upon the position of the hydrophobic group on the pyrimidine. Therefore studies on the mode of binding of pyrimidines to dihydrofolic reductase were initiated[47,48]; such studies must also be correlated with the fact that strongly basic 2,4-diaminoheterocycles that are partially protonated at physiological pH are 1500–3000-fold better inhibitors than the corresponding 2-amino-4-hydroxy-heterocycles (Tables 10–1 and 10–2).

Two schools of thought have arisen to rationalize the high ability of aminopterin (IV) and amethopterin (V), compared to folic acid (I) (Table 10–1), to bind to dihydrofolic reductase. Because a 2,4-diamino heterocycle such as IV is a stronger base than a 2-amino-4-hydroxy heterocycle, such as folic acid (I), Baker [49] proposed that the increase in binding of II was due to a protonated species of aminopterin complexing with a donor site on the enzyme; this proposal was amplified further by Perault and Pullman[50] on a mathematical basis.

A second rationalization by Zakrzewski[51] was based on thermodynamic studies of the binding of amethopterin (V) to folic reductase. As a result of these experiments, Zakrzewski proposed that four hydrogen bonds between the enzyme and the four nitrogen functions (XCV) of the 2,4-diaminopyrimidine moiety of amethopterin (V) could account for the strong binding of V; folic acid (I) would then have to isomerize from the more stable 4-oxo form with a resultant loss of energy. These thermodynamic studies were based on several tenuous assumptions and admittedly were difficult to perform because of the small change in K_i or K_m with temperature. Furthermore, on the basis of an analysis of the relationship

---

[46] See in this chapter the section on aryl and alkyl binding.
[47] See Reference 33, p. 212.
[48] B. R. Baker and J. H. Jordaan, *J. Pharm. Sci.*, **54**, 1740 (1965).
[49] B. R. Baker, *Cancer Chemotherapy Reports*, **4**, 1 (1959).
[50] A. M. Perault and B. Pullman, *Biochim. Biophys. Acta*, **52**, 266 (1961).
[51] S. F. Zakrzewski, *J. Biol. Chem.*, **238**, 1485 (1963).

to basicity of ten purines, pyrimidines, and pteridines to binding to folic reductase, Zakrzewski[52] concluded that "it appears that the ionic binding between folate reductase and its substrates or inhibitors is unlikely." His data suffer from the difficulty that proper compounds were not available for a realistic comparison to eliminate such factors as (a) the use of control compounds that would be fully protonated or fully unprotonated in the narrow pH range studied to show what changes may have taken

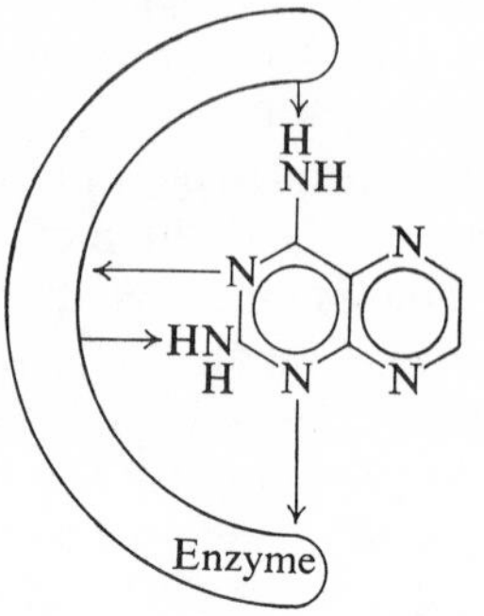

XCV

place on the enzyme, such as protonation, that could either be favorable or detrimental to binding, or (b) possible binding by N_5 or N_8 of a pteridine compared to the lack of such binding by some pyrimidines. Of even a more serious nature, he was unable to do the pH profile studies much above pH 6 with the use of folic acid as a substrate because folic acid shows about one quarter the velocity at pH 6.5 and one tenth the velocity at pH 7.0 that it shows at pH 5.[53]

Huennekens and Scrimgeour[54] have proposed that an additional hydrogen bond between the H of the 4-amino group of amethopterin (V) and the enzyme—a bond that cannot exist between the energetically favored 4-oxo form of dihydrofolate and the enzyme—could account for the observed difference in free energy of 3.7 kcal/mole between amethopterin and dihydrofolate.

In neither case[54,55] was there any direct evidence given for the number of bonds to the enzyme in XCV that must be present; if four bonds in XCV are invoked, then no possibility exists for the rotomers believed to be involved in the binding of substituted pyrimidines to dihydrofolic reductase.

[52] S. F. Zakrzewski, *J. Biol. Chem.*, **238**, 4002 (1963).

[53] See Reference 14, p. 199.

[54] F. M. Huennekens and K. G. Scrimgeour, in *Pterdine Chemistry*, W. Pfleiderer and E. C. Taylor, eds., The Macmillan Co., New York, 1964, p. 360.

[55] See Reference 51, p. 229, and Reference 52, p. 230.

Two more recent studies shed further light on these two different rationalizations. Bertino et al.[56] performed a pH profile study on dihydrofolic reductase with folic acid (I) and amethopterin (V) as inhibitors; they noted that the relative inhibition by amethopterin (V) was more pH dependent than folic acid but preferred not to draw any conclusion about the protonation of amethopterin (V) because "the ionization of the active center of the enzyme or the enzyme-inhibitor complex may be of importance."

Baker and Jordaan[57] noted that conversion of the 6-methyl group of 5-(*p*-chlorophenyl)-2,4-diamino-6-methylpyrimidine (XXII) to a trifluoromethyl group (XCVI) caused a 250-fold reduction in the binding of

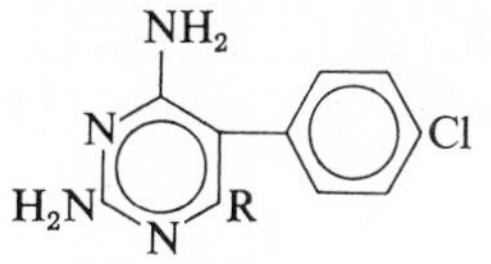

XXII, R = CH$_3$
XCVI, R = CF$_3$

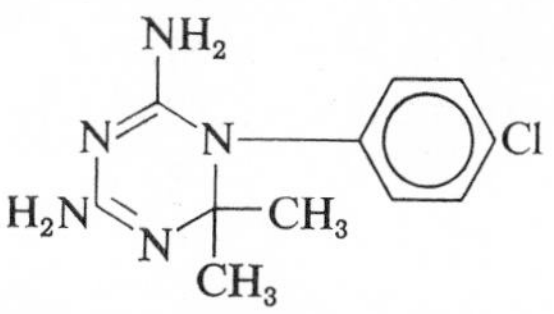

XXIII

XCVI to dihydrofolic reductase compared to XXII; furthermore, due to the electron-withdrawing properties of the trifluoromethyl group, XCVI was a weak base (pK$_a$ 2.8) unprotonated at pH 7.4, whereas XXII was mainly protonated (pK$_a$ 7.7), which presumably accounts for XXII being a better inhibitor than XCVI. They proposed[57] that one of the binding points of the pyrimidines, XXII and XCVI, to dihydrofolic reductase involved complexing to a weakly acidic group on the enzyme that is only partially ionized at pH 7.4. This group on the enzyme (E) was represented by RH. If Py is a nonprotonated pyrimidine and HPy$^+$ is a protonated pyrimidine, then two types of complexes, XCVII and XCVIII, respectively, could be formed. The only difference between XCVII and XCVIII lies in the property of whether or not the proton in question is firmly associated with the enzymic acidic group as in XCVII, or is firmly associated with the

$$ \text{E—R—H} \underset{\text{H}^+}{\overset{\text{OH}^-}{\rightleftharpoons}} \text{E—R}^- $$

$$ \downarrow \text{Py} \qquad\qquad \downarrow \text{HPy}^+ $$

$$ \text{E—R—H}\cdots\text{Py} \qquad \text{ER}^-\cdots\text{HPy}^+ $$

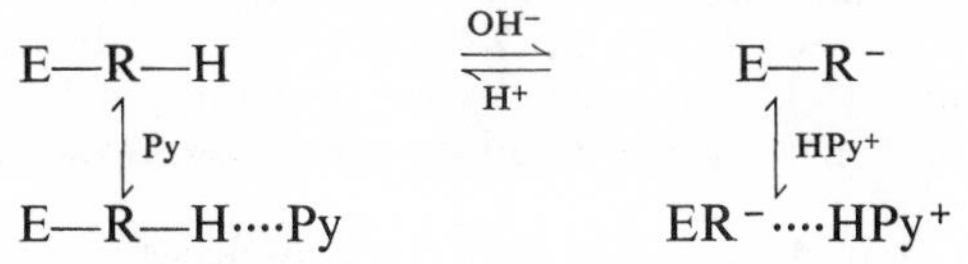

XCVII   XCVIII

strongly basic pyrimidine as in XCVIII, or is in between. The more associated the proton is with the pyrimidine, the more saltlike would be the

[56] See Reference 14, p. 199.
[57] See Reference 33, p. 212.

bond and the more energy might be involved in the bonding. Conversely, the weaker Py is as a base, the weaker could be the bonding energy which could approach that of a hydrogen bond, or even weaker than a hydrogen bond.

To gain evidence for or against the binding mechanism depicted using XCVII and XCVIII, inhibition pH profiles with the three structurally related heterocycles (XXII, XXIII and XCVI) were performed[58]; these three compounds were selected, furthermore, because XCVI is unprotonated through the pH range of 5–9, XXIII is fully protonated, and XXII varies from 99.8 per cent protonated at pH 5 to 4.8 per cent protonated at pH 9 (Table 10–9).

The effect on inhibition of dihydrofolic reductase by the various inhibitors is shown in Figs. 10–1 to 5; this inhibition is recorded as the ratio of velocity without inhibitor (V_0) to the velocity with inhibitor (V_I).

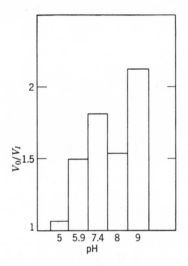

Fig. 10–1. The effect of pH on the inhibition of reduction of 6 μM dihydrofolate with 12 μM TPNH in the presence of 0.05 μM 1-(*p*-chlorophenyl)-4,6-diamino-2,2-dimethyl-1,2-dihydro-*s*-triazine (XXIII); pH 7.4–9 in 0.05 *M* Tris buffer and pH 5–5.9 in 0.05 *M* citrate buffer. V_0 is the velocity without inhibitor, and V_I is the velocity with inhibitor. From B. R. Baker and J. H. Jordaan, *J. Pharm. Sci.*, **54**, 1740 (1965).

The first compound examined was the dihydro-*s*-triazine (XXIII) that has pK_a 11.2 and is therefore greater than 99 per cent protonated over the pH range of 5–9 (Table 10–9). Therefore, this heterocycle most probably has to bind to the enzyme as a protonated species; if an unprotonated species were essential for binding, then XXIII should have been a poorer

[58] See Reference 48, p. 229.

Table 10–9. Effect of pH on Protonation of Inhibitors and Their Inhibition of Dihydrofolic Reductase

No.	pK_a of heterocyclic ring	μM concentration for 50 per cent inhibition at pH 7.4	Per cent of protonation at pH					V_0/V_I at pH[a]			V_0/V_I at pH[a]		
			5	5.9	7.4	8	9	μM concentration	5	5.9	μM concentration	8	9
XXIII	11.2	0.050	99.9+	99.9+	99.9+	99.9	99.4	0.050	1.05	1.76	0.10	2.13	3.21
XXII	7.7	0.20	99.8	98.0	66.6	33.4	4.8	0.20	1.30	2.00	1.0	2.22	1.52
XCVI	2.8	50	0.63	0.079	0.001	0.000	0.000	50	3.80	2.95	300	2.00	1.54
Folic acid I	~2.5	3.0	0.31	0.031	0.001	0.000	0.000	3.0	2.04	2.02	3.0	1.60	1.04
Amino-pterin IV	~5.5	0.001	76	24	1.2	0.32	0.032	0.002	1.56	2.86	0.001	1.90	1.00

[a] V_0 is the velocity without inhibitor and V_I is the velocity with inhibitor. With no inhibition, $V_0/V_I = 1$; with 50 per cent inhibition, $V_0/V_I = 2$. The enzyme from pigeon liver was assayed with 6 μM dihydrofolate. Data from B. R. Baker and J. H. Jordaan, *J. Pharm. Sci.*, **54**, 1740 (1965).

inhibitor than the unprotonated 6-trifluoromethyl pyrimidine (XCVI) rather than a better inhibitor (Table 10–9). The proposal of two possible enzyme-inhibitor species, XCVII and XCVIII, for binding a 2,4-diamino heterocycle predicts that at pH 5 where the enzyme binding site is more

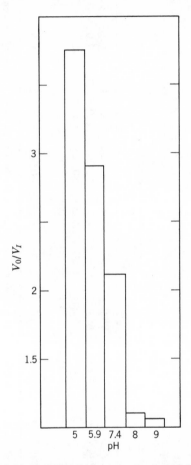

Fig. 10–2. The effect of pH on the inhibition of reduction of 6 μM dihydrofolate with 12 μM TPNH in the presence of 50 μM 5-(p-chlorophenyl)-2,4-diamino-6-(trifluoro-methyl)-pyrimidine (XCVI); pH 7.4–9 in 0.05 M Tris buffer and pH 5–5.9 in 0.05 M citrate buffer. V_0 is the velocity without inhibitor, and V_I is the velocity with inhibition. From B. R. Baker and J. H. Jordaan, *J. Pharm. Sci.*, **54**, 1740 (1965).

protonated, XXIII should be a poorer inhibitor than at higher pH's. Due to both the enzyme binding site and the inhibitor being protonated, a repulsion should be noted. Furthermore because XXIII is still protonated at pH 9 and the enzymic binding site is at the pH of least protonation in the range studied, the system predicts that XXIII should bind best at pH 9 as species XCVIII. That this was the case is shown in Fig. 10–1 and Table 10–9. The drop in inhibition between pH 7.4 and 8 is probably due to other ionizations of the enzyme or substrate, for all of the compounds (Figs. 10–1 through 10–5) except aminopterin show this drop.

The 6-trifluoromethyl pyrimidine (XCVI) is unprotonated throughout the pH range 5–9 (Table 10–9) and should therefore complex best with a more protonated binding site of the enzyme at pH 5, as in species XCVII, and poorest to the less protonated enzymic binding site at pH 9. That such is the case is seen clearly in Fig. 10–2.

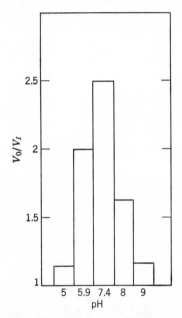

Fig. 10–3. The effect of pH on the inhibition of reduction of 6 μM dihydrofolate with 12 μM TPNH in the presence of 0.40 μM 5-(*p*-chlorophenyl)-2,4-diamino-6-methyl-pyrimidine (XXII); pH 7.4–9 in 0.05 *M* Tris buffer and pH 5–5.9 in 0.5 *M* citrate buffer. V_0 is the velocity without inhibitor, and V_I is the velocity with inhibitor. From B. R. Baker and J. H. Jordaan, *J. Pharm. Sci.*, **54**, 1740 (1965).

The 6-methyl pyrimidine (XXII) is intermediate between XCVI and XXIII in basicity, being 99 per cent protonated at pH 5 and 5 per cent protonated at pH 9 (Table 10–9). Therefore, XXII should bind poorly at pH 5 with a protonated form of enzyme binding site (XCVII) and poorly with the ionized form of the enzyme binding site at pH 9 (XCVIII) for the same reasons cited for XCVI and XXIII; XXII should bind best at intermediate pH. These predictions were borne out as shown in Fig. 10–3, the maximum inhibitor effect being observed at pH 7.4 with poorer binding at the pH extremes.

It should be noted (Table 10–9) that the dihydro-*s*-triazine (XXIII) was a fourfold better inhibitor than the 6-methylpyrimidine (XXII) at pH 7.4, and XXII was in turn a 250-fold better inhibitor than the 6-trifluoro-methyl pyrimidine (XCVI). Corrected for the per cent of protonation at pH 7.4, XXII and XXIII have the same magnitude of binding their pro-tonated species, whereas XCVI is a much poorer inhibitor, presumably because it is unprotonated. It should also be noted that because XXII and XCVI had almost identical bands in the NH, NH_2, and double-bond regions, the difference in their activity was unlikely to be due to some unusual tautomeric form of XCVI.

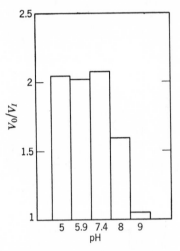

Fig. 10–4. The effect of pH on the inhibition of reduction of 6 μM dihydrofolate with 12 μM TPNH in the presence of 3 μM folic acid (I); pH 7.4–9 in 0.05 M Tris Buffer and pH 5–5.9 in 0.05 M citrate buffer. V_0 is the velocity without inhibitor and V_I is the velocity with inhibitor. From B. R. Baker and J. H. Jordaan, *J. Pharm. Sci.*, **54**, 1740 (1965).

Due to the complexity of their titration curves, the pK_a's for the pteridine ring of aminopterin (IV) and folic acid (I) are difficult to deter-mine; however, it can be estimated[59,60] that the basicity of the pteridine of folic acid should be about the same as 2-amino-6-methyl-4-pteridinol (pK_a 2.5) and aminopterin about the same as 2,4-diaminopteridine (pK_a 5.5). On this basis, aminopterin (IV) should have an inhibition pH

[59] See Reference 51, p. 229.
[60] See Reference 52, p. 230.

profile similar to the 6-methyl pyrimidine (XXII), that is, maximum inhibition at pH 5.9–7.4 and minimum inhibition at pH 5 and 9; such a profile was observed experimentally, as is shown in Fig. 10–5. Note that aminopterin has a lower pH maximum than the diaminopyrimidine (XXII) because the latter is a 100-fold stronger base.

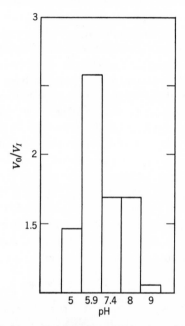

Fig. 10–5. The effect of pH on the inhibition of reduction of 6 μM dihydrofolate with 12 μM TPNH in the presence of 0.001 μM aminopterin (IV); pH 7.4–9 in 0.05 M Tris buffer and pH 5–5.9 in 0.05 M citrate buffer. V_0 is the velocity without inhibitor and V_I is the velocity with inhibitor. From B. R. Baker and J. H. Jordaan, *J. Pharm. Sci.*, **54**, 1740 (1965).

In contrast with aminopterin, folic acid (I) should have a pH profile resembling the nonprotonated 6-trifluoromethyl pyrimidine (XCVI); in Fig. 10–4 it can be seen that folic acid has best inhibition at pH 5–7.4, then drops off rapidly at pH 8 and 9. From these results we can infer that the substrate, dihydrofolate, is a stronger base than folate, perhaps being intermediate between the more basic pyrimidine and the less basic pteridine.[61,62]

With the not too unlikely assumption that these inhibitors are complexed with the active-site, the results in Figs. 10–1 to 10–5 and Table 10–9 support

[61] See Reference 50, p. 229.
[62] R. Collin and B. B. Pullman, *Biochim. Biophys. Acta*, **89**, 232 (1964).

the concept that there are two possible species for the complex between dihydrofolic reductase and a 2,4-diamino heterocycle, as depicted in structures XCVII and XCVIII; that is, a protonated combining site of the enzyme can complex the free base (as in XCVII) and the unprotonated combining site of the enzyme can complex with the protonated base (as in XCVIII). This concept still fully agrees with the data obtained by Zakrzewski.[63]

Based on the relative inhibition of dihydrofolic reductase by 2,4-diamino-6-methylpyrimidine versus 2-amino-6-methyl-4-pyrimidinol and XXII versus XCVI it was proposed[64] that a two-point attachment of a 2,4-diamino heterocycle is sufficient to account for both the magnitude and specificity of binding of this type of heterocycle; the current pH profile study lends further support to this concept. Although Perault and Pullman[65] have performed calculations to determine which is the most basic nitrogen of a 2,4-diaminopteridine, it is not necessarily the most basic nitrogen that will protonate when complexed to the enzyme.

There is not sufficient information available to determine with any certainty which functional group on a pyrimidine is complexing with the enzymic group depicted by XCVII and XCVIII. Among the possibilities are the π cloud of the pyrimidine, which is attractive because it would not be position sensitive on the pyrimidine ring; for example, a 2-amino-4-hydroxypyrimidine could complex as a π donor to the protonated enzymic

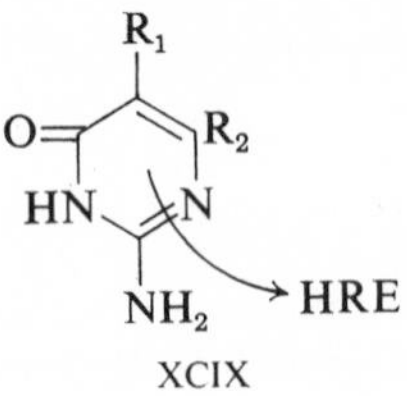

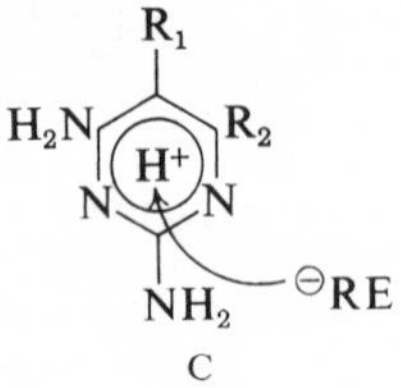

group, as depicted in XCIX, or a protonated 2,4-diaminopyrimidine could complex with the ionized enzymic group by coulombic attraction, as depicted in C.[66] However, the 2-amino group of XCIX or a partially protonated 2-amino group of C could also complex in the same way.

Serious attempts have been made to correlate binding points of 2,4-diamino-5-phenyl-6-methylpyrimidine,[67]   2,4-diamino-5-i-amyl-6-methyl-

[63] See Reference 52, p. 230.
[64] See Reference 33, p. 212.
[65] See Reference 50, p. 229.
[66] See Reference 33, p. 212, and Reference 48, p. 229.
[67] B. R. Baker, G. J. Lourens, and J. H. Jordaan, *J. Heterocyclic Chem.*, **4**, in press (1967).

pyrimidine,[68] 2,4-diamino-5-phenylbutyl-6-phenylpyrimidine,[69] 2,4-diamino-5-(anilinopropyl)-6-phenylpyrimidine,[69] and 2,4-diamino-5-(anilinopropyl)-6-methylpyrimidine[70,71] by replacing, in turn, each of the amino groups by hydroxyl (oxo), thio, or hydrogen; apparently the mode of complex formation is not a straightforward one and no satisfactory binding mechanism could explain all the data. The difficulties encountered when we try to correlate the data further amplify the probability that a number of rotomers for the pyrimidine ring are possible.

Fortunately, it is not necessary to know the exact mode of binding of the pyrimidines for the design of active-site-directed irreversible inhibitors other than the fact that the hydrophobic bonding locus of dihydrofolic reductase is not between the loci for binding the pyrimidine and *p*-aminobenzoyl moieties of dihydrofolate. It is only necessary to know whether or not a side chain at the 5- or 6- position is complexed in the hydrophobic region; if the covalent forming group is placed on a side chain that complexes in the hydrophobic region, then irreversible inhibition is not likely to occur.[72] Another, more certain, approach is to place hydrocarbon groups at both the 5- and 6- positions. If one of the R groups at the 6-position of the pyrimidine is a phenyl or phenylbutyl, this group will complex in the hydrophobic region; when another group, bearing the covalent forming group, is then placed at the 5- position, the 5- substituent should project into the hydrophilic area where covalent bond formation is likely to take place. The same approach can be used by placing a hydrophobic group such as phenyl or phenylbutyl at the 5- position and the covalent forming group off the 6- position.

Examples of the first class that have only one large side chain are CI[73] and CII[74]; these side chains are complexed in the hydrophobic region and are not irreversible inhibitors. Examples of the second class are CIII–CIV[75] and CV[76]; in this case one side chain is hydrophobically bonded and the other is projected into a hydrophilic area, resulting in active-site-directed irreversible inhibition.

Studies[77,78] on modification of the bridge between the phenyl and

[68] See Reference 67, p. 238.
[69] B. R. Baker and H. S. Shapiro, *J. Pharm. Sci.*, **55**, 308 (1966).
[70] B. R. Baker, B.-T. Ho, and T. Neilson, *J. Heterocyclic Chem.*, **1**, 79 (1964).
[71] B. R. Baker and B.-T. Ho, *J. Pharm. Sci.*, **53**, 1457 (1964).
[72] See Reference 12, p. 197.
[73] B. R. Baker and J. H. Jordaan, *J. Med. Chem.*, **8**, 35 (1965).
[74] B. R. Baker and D. V. Santi, *J. Pharm. Sci.*, **56**, in press (1967).
[75] B. R. Baker and J. H. Jordaan, *J. Pharm. Sci.*, **55**, 1417 (1966).
[76] B. R. Baker and H. S. Shapiro, *J. Pharm. Sci.*, **55**, 1422 (1966).
[77] B. R. Baker and B.-T. Ho, *J. Pharm. Sci.*, **54**, 1187 (1965).
[78] B. R. Baker and J. K. Coward, *J. Pharm. Sci.*, **54**, 714 (1965).

pyrimidyl moieties of the anilinopropyl-pyrimidine XV were made prior to the discovery of the strong hydrophobic bonding to dihydrofolic reductase; therefore the conclusions are now clouded by the possibility of two

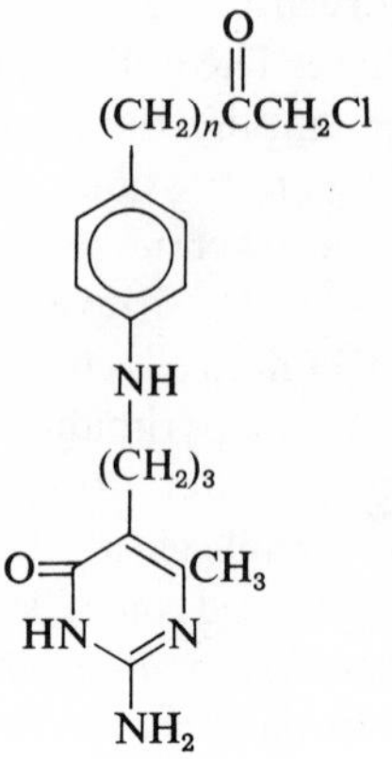

CI

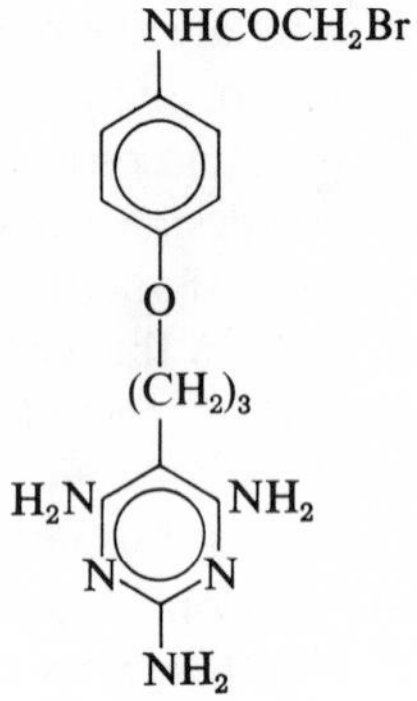

CII

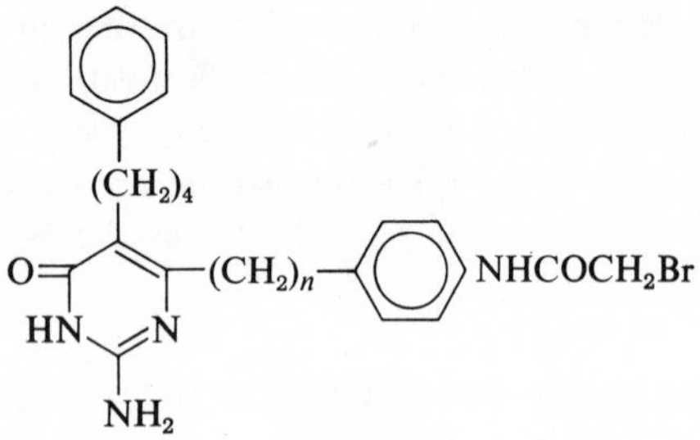

CIII, n = 2
CIV, n = 4

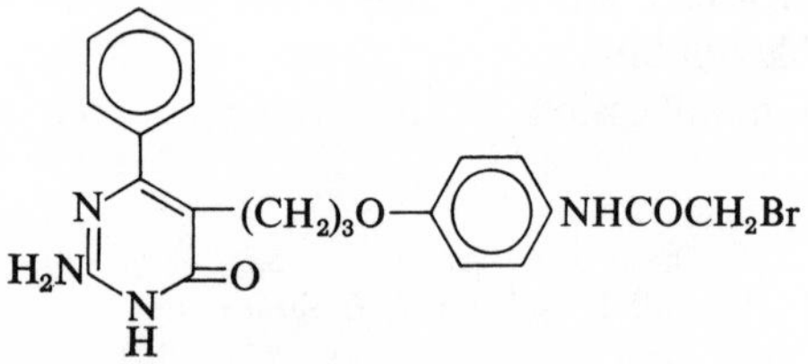

CV

or more conformations, one where the phenyl group is complexed in the *p*-aminobenzoyl locus—as depicted in XV*A*—and another where the phenyl group is complexed to the hydrophobic region—as depicted in XV*B*, depending upon the relative hydrophobic character of the 5- side chain. Similarly, studies on the mode of binding of the anilino moiety[79,80] are complicated by two or more rotomer possibilities depending upon the relative hydrophobic character of the group replacing the anilino moiety.

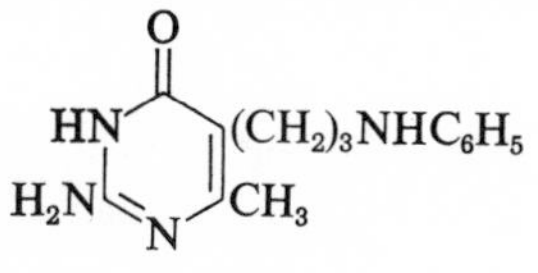

XVA   XVB

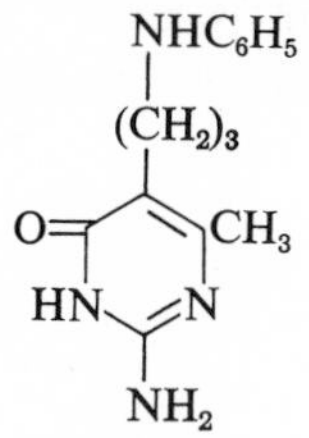

ACTIVE-SITE-DIRECTED IRREVERSIBLE INHIBITORS

General Considerations

A variety of potential irreversible inhibitors were synthesized for evaluation before the strong hydrophobic bonding by dihydrofolic reductase, with its conformational implications, was discovered. Thus, when the anilinomethylpteridine moiety of folic acid (I) is complexed

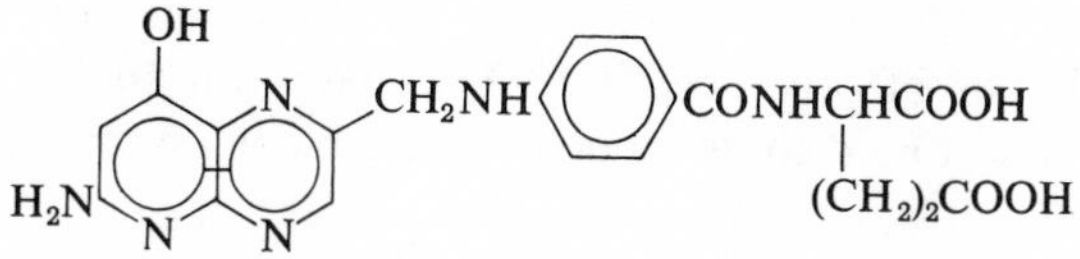

I

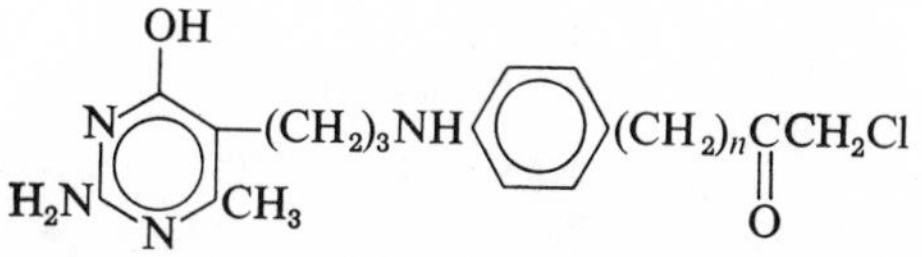

CIA, $n = 0,2,4,6$

"normally" it would be theoretically possible to modify folic acid with a chloromethyl ketone group in place of one of the carboxyls in order to obtain an active-site-directed irreversible inhibitor by the endo mechanism. The synthesis of such a pteridine is fraught with monumental incompatibilities of functional groups. The anilinopropylpyrimidines of type CI should be much easier to synthesize, as has been described.[81] These four inhibitors and a related inhibitor with a —CH=CHCOCH$_2$Cl side chain

[79] B. R. Baker, B.-T. Ho, and G. B. Chheda, *J. Heterocyclic Chem.*, **1**, 88 (1964).
[80] B. R. Baker and J. Novotny, *J. Heterocyclic Chem.*, **4**, in press (1967).
[81] See Reference 73, p. 239.

were evaluated; although they were good reversible inhibitors of dihydrofolic reductase, they failed to show irreversible inhibition. In retrospect, these failures were most probably due to the possibility that the anilinopropyl group is complexed with the hydrophobic region in a "twist" conformation such as CI*B*; such a conformation (CI*B*) would destroy the

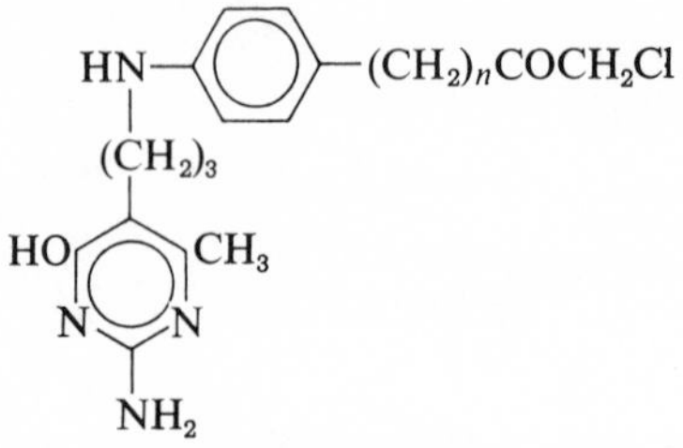

CI*B*

juxtaposing of the nucleophilic groups on the enzyme that complex the glutamate carboxyls with the alkylating function of CI in the "normal" conformation (as depicted in CI*A* and I).

Another type of potential endo alkylating irreversible inhibitor was constructed on the proposition that there might well be an enzymic proton donor, such as imidazole, that aids in the TPNH reduction of the 5,6- and 7,8- double bonds of folic acid (I).[82] The Daraprim analog, CVI*A*, was synthesized[83] and found to be a potent reversible inhibitor, but ineffective

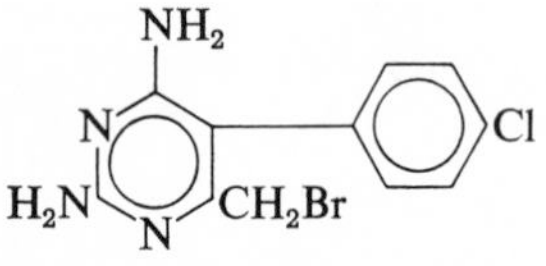

CVI*A* 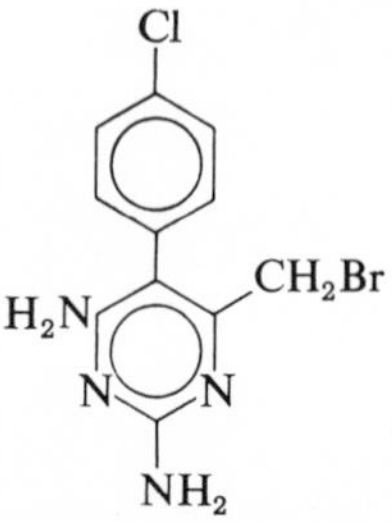   CVI*B* 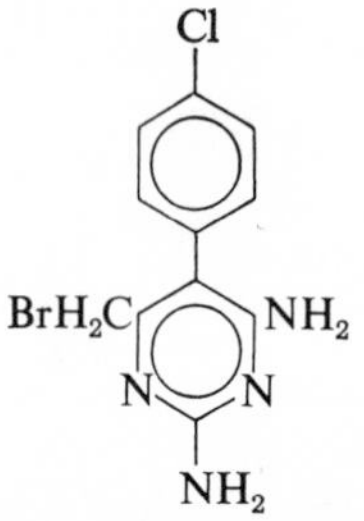   CVI*C*

irreversibly. Again in retrospect, it is possible that the 5-phenylpyrimidine binds to the hydrophobic region in a "twist" conformation, such as CVI*B*, and therefore does not have its bromomethyl group in close enough proximity to the enzymic proton donor; it is also possible that the bromomethyl group is not long enough to bridge to the proton donor, and there-

[82] See Reference 77, p. 239.
[83] B. R. Baker and J. H. Jordaan, *J. Heterocyclic Chem.*, **2**, 21 (1965).

fore a two-carbon bridge may be needed. Similar conclusions can be drawn if the analog complexes in a "twist-flip" conformation (*CVIC*).

Several chloromethyl ketones of type *CVIIB* were synthesized and found to be good reversible inhibitors but not irreversible inhibitors.[84] Again, if

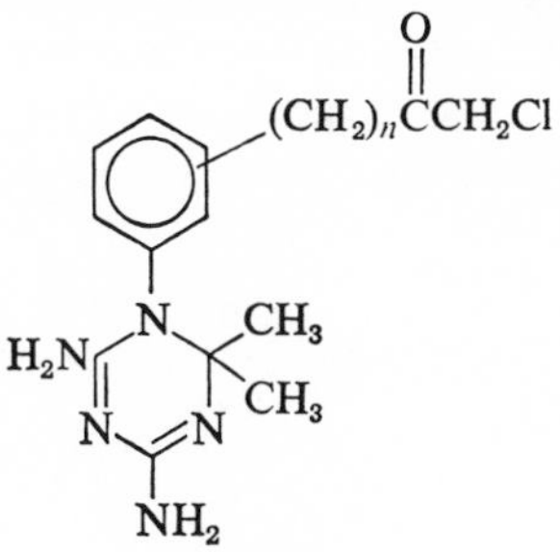

CVII*B*
$n = 0, 2$ (*p*- series)
$n = 0$, (*m*- series)

the dihydro-*s*-triazines are complexed to the hydrophobic region in a "twist" conformation such as is depicted in structure *CVIIB*, it is unlikely that an enzymic nucleophilic group would be in the hydrophobic region.

Similarly, some 5- substituted derivatives (CII, CVIII, CIX) of 2,4,6-triaminopyrimidines were good reversible inhibitors, but not irreversible inhibitors.[85]

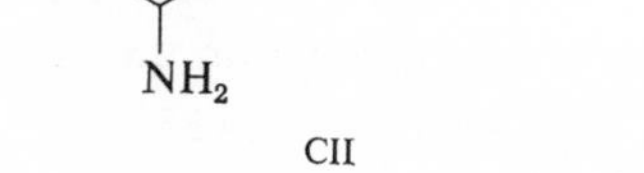

CII

CVIII, R = —$(CH_2)_2$
CIX, R = —$(CH_2)_3$—

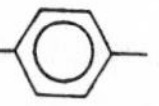

After the establishment of a hydrophobic bonding region on dihydrofolic reductase, it was possible to design active-site-directed irreversible inhibitors by having one group on a pyrimidine that complexed with the hydrophobic region and a second group that projected into a hydrophilic region. Several 5,6- disubstituted 2-amino-4-pyrimidinols were found to operate by this mechanism, as will be described in the section that follows.

[84] B. R. Baker and B.-T. Ho, *J. Pharm. Sci.*, **56**, 28 (1967).
[85] B. R. Baker and D. V. Santi, *J. Pharm. Sci.*, **56**, in press (1967).

2-Amino-4-Pyrimidinol Type

Evidence that the hydrophobic bonding region of dihydrofolic reductase was not between the binding loci for the pyrimidyl and *p*-aminobenzoyl moieties of folic acid (I) was presented in the section on hydrophobic bonding. It was proposed that a molecule such as XVI had conformation XVI*A* with respect to folic acid with its conformation I. Such a conformation for XVI*A* suggests that lengthening of the R group should project it into a hydrophilic region. That this was the case was supported by the

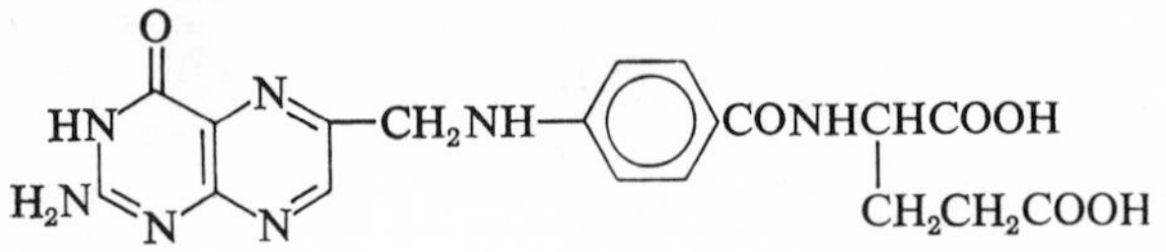

I

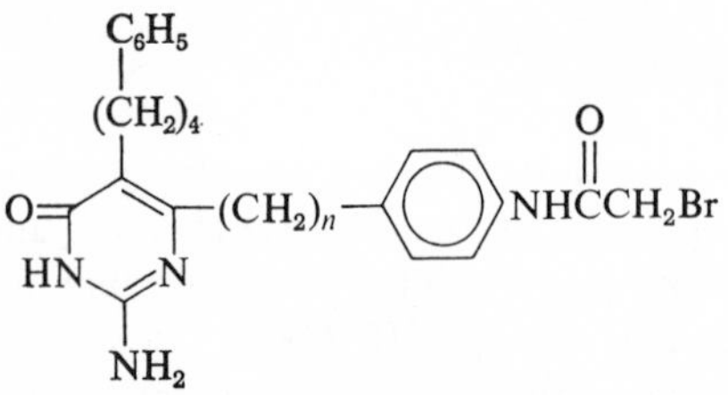

CIII, *n* = 4
CIV, *n* = 2

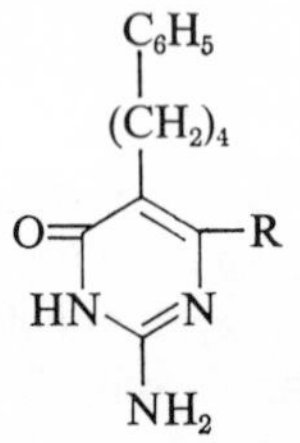

XVI*A*, R = CH₃
CX, R = *n*-C₃H₇
CXI, R = C₆H₅(CH₂)₄

observation that *n*-propyl group caused CX to be a 30-fold less effective inhibitor[86] than XVI*A* with a methyl group; such poorer inhibition could result from the repulsion of the hydrophobic propyl group from a hydrophilic area on the enzyme or by steric interaction with the enzyme. That steric interaction was unlikely was demonstrated by a further increase in group size to phenylbutyl as in CXI; this compound was a fivefold better inhibitor than CX indicating that not only was steric interaction unlikely to be the cause of the poor inhibition by CX, but that the phenyl group on the 6- position of CX was complexing to the enzyme.

When a *p*-bromoacetamido group was placed on CXI to give CIII, the long-sought first active-site-directed irreversible inhibitor of dihydrofolic reductase was found.[87] CIII had $K_i = 4 \times 10^{-5}$ *M*; when 40 μM CIII was incubated at 37° with dihydrofolic reductase in the absence of TPNH, inactivation occurred with a half-life of about 20 minutes. When CIII, iodoacetamide, and *p*-bromoacetamido phenylbutyric acid—all at 40 μM— were simultaneously incubated with the enzyme at 37° for 25 minutes, CIII

[86] See Reference 69, p. 239.
[87] See Reference 75, p. 239.

gave 65 per cent inactivation, but the other two compounds gave 2–3 per cent inactivation; thus, the bimolecular inactivation by CIII was ruled out.

Protection experiments are summarized in Table 10–10. As expected the

Table 10–10. Inactivation of Dihydrofolic Reductase by

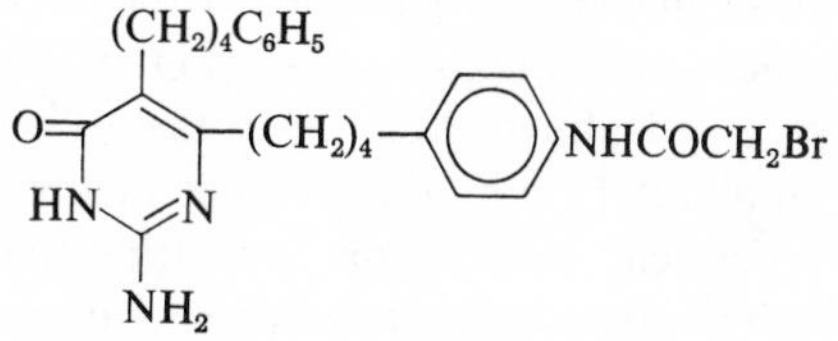

(CIII)

Experiment	Incubation mixture	Time	Per cent inactivation
A	40 μM CIII		65
	40 μM Iodoacetamide	25	3
	40 μM p-BrCH$_2$CONHC$_6$H$_4$(CH$_2$)$_3$COOH		2
B	40 μM CIII	25	73
	40 μM CIII + 15 μM folic acid		50
C	40 μM CIII	25	68
	40 μM CIII + 0.15 μM of 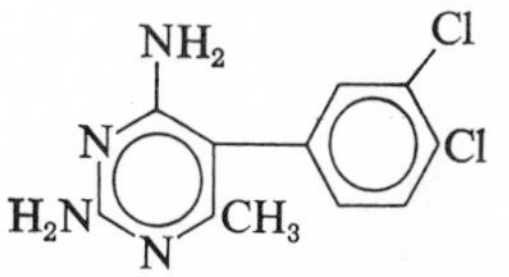		32
D	40 μM CIII		62
	40 μM CIII + 12 μM TPNH	25	23
	40 μM CIII + 60 μM TPNH		0

Data from B. R. Baker and J. H. Jordaan, *J. Pharm. Sci.*, **55**, 1417 (1966). Dihydrofolic reductase from pigeon liver in 0.05 *M* Tris buffer (pH 7.4) was incubated with the additions indicated; in each case, little or no inactivation took place in an enzyme control with no additions. Each experiment was a simultaneous run.

reversible inhibitors, folic acid[88] and 2,4-diamino-5-(3,4-dichlorophenyl)-6-methylpyrimidine[89] slowed the rate of inactivation. Surprisingly, TPNH also protected against inactivation; this result suggested that either (a) the phenyl group on the 6- position of CIII was complexed in the TPNH region, (b) alkylation of a binding point for TPNH occurred, or (c) TPNH caused a conformational change which no longer allowed the alkylatable

[88] See Reference 33, p. 212.
[89] See Reference 27, p. 206.

nucleophilic group on the enzyme to be properly juxtaposed for covalent-bond formation. The reversible inhibition of dihydrofolic reductase by CIII was found to be independent to TPNH concentration and therefore proposition (a) was ruled out. Evidence to choose between (b) and (c) is not yet available.

CIV, with its shorter phenethyl side chain at the 6- position, had $K_i = 3 \times 10^{-5}$ M. At a concentration of 40 μM—where CIV forms 63 per cent EI reversible complex with dihydrofolic reductase—the enzyme was half inactivated at 37° in about 12 minutes. Further incubation time led to a maximum of 80–90 per cent inactivation, indicating the type of modified enzyme noted with chymotrypsin where some activity is still present after complete reaction.[90] The inactivation of dihydrofolic reductase by CIV was slowed by the presence of either folic acid, 2,4-diamino-5-(3,4-dichlorophenyl)-6-methylpyrimidine, or TPNH similar to what is shown for CIII in Table 10–10.

A related inhibitor, CV, also showed active-site-directed irreversible

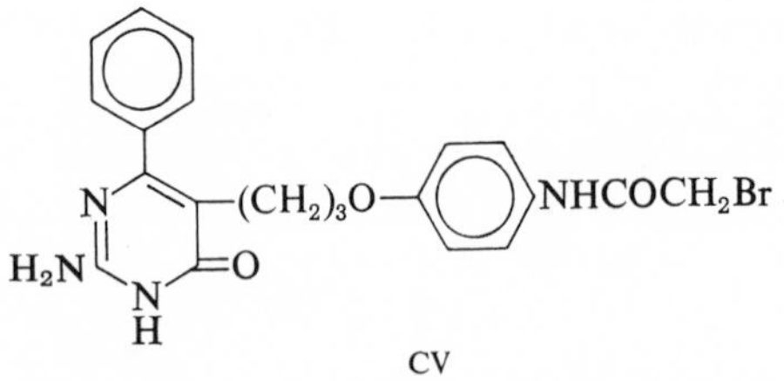

CV

inhibition of dihydrofolic reductase with parameters similar to those for CIII in Table 10–10, except that the time for 50 per cent inactivation was about 45 minutes in the presence of 40 μM CV.[91] Note that CV has the hydrophobic group on the 6- position and the covalent forming group on the 5- position, just the reverse of CIII and CIV.

At this stage it should be possible to synthesize tissue-specific irreversible inhibitors related to CIII–CV by use of the concepts developed with lactic dehydrogenase.[92] Even though such a study might be successful with isolated enzyme systems, an intracellular concentration of $5–40 \times 10^{-6}$ M would be needed, which is on the edge of attainable intracellular concentration in a whole animal. Because 2,4-diaminopyrimidines with a hydrophobic group are 300–1000 times more potent reversibly, the same amount of reversible EI complex should be attainable with a $10^{-7}–10^{-9}$ M intracellular concentration. Therefore attention has been turned to the search

[90] See Chapter 8, p. 136.
[91] B. R. Baker and H. S. Shapiro, *J. Pharm. Sci.*, **55**, 1422 (1966).
[92] See Chapter 9, Bridge Principle of Specificity.

for irreversible inhibitors of the 2,4-diaminopyrimidine type on which tissue specificity studies can be done.

2,4-Diaminopyrimidine Type

As was indicated in the section on pyrimidine binding to dihydrofolic reductase, it is quite possible that 2,4-diaminopyrimidines do not complex exactly the same way as 2-amino-4-pyrimidinols[93]; such a difference could then sufficiently change the position on a juxtaposed alkylating function in a successful 2-amino-4-pyrimidinol type of irreversible inhibitor that inactivation with an identical side chain may not occur.

Because of the relative ease with which it can be synthesized, CXII was

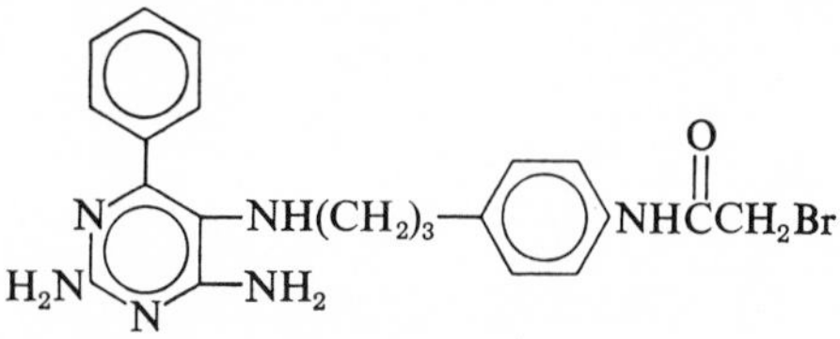

CXII

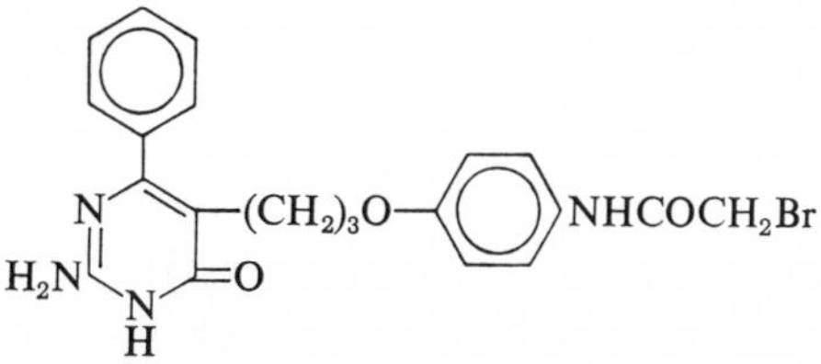

CV

selected as a candidate irreversible inhibitor related to the successful CV; although CXII was an excellent reversible inhibitor with $K_i = 5 \times 10^{-8} M$, when CXII was incubated with pigeon liver dihydrofolic reductase at $3 \times 10^{-7} M$, it showed no irreversible inhibition.[94] This negative result on irreversible inhibition by CXII could be due either to a difference in the mode of pyrimidine binding of CXII and CV or to a difference in the freedom of rotation of the CH_2—O—C_6H_4 bonds of CV compared to the lesser rotational possibilities of the CH_2—CH_2—C_6H_4 group of CXII; to resolve this question, the diamino analog of CV with an identical 5- side chain should be synthesized and evaluated.

In a later study[95] CXIII was synthesized for enzymic evaluation since it

[93] See Mode of Pyrimidine Binding, p. 229.

[94] B. R. Baker, G. D. F. Jackson, and R. B. Meyer, Jr., *J. Pharm. Sci.*, **56**, in press (1967).

[95] B. R. Baker and J. H. Jordaan, *J. Heterocyclic Chem.*, **4**, in press (1967).

is an exact 2,4-diamino analog of the active-site-directed irreversible inhibitor CIV; CXIII was an excellent reversible inhibitor with $K_i = 7 \times 10^{-9} M$ but did not inactivate pigeon liver dihydrofolic reductase when incubated at $1 \times 10^{-8} M$ in the presence or absence of TPNH, a concentration of CXIII sufficient to convert 60 per cent of the enzyme to a reversible complex. These results then supported the earlier hypothesis, derived

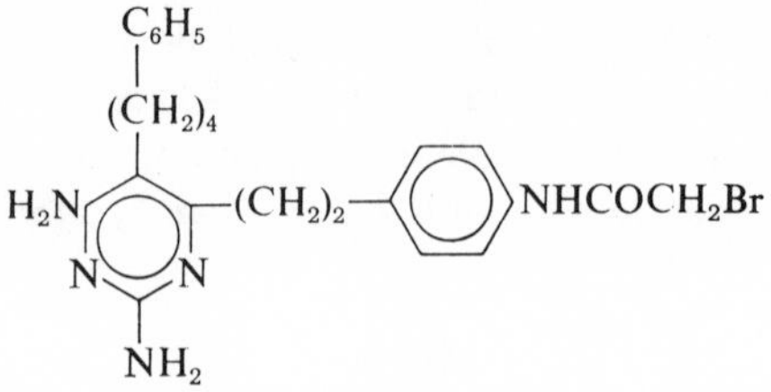

CXIII

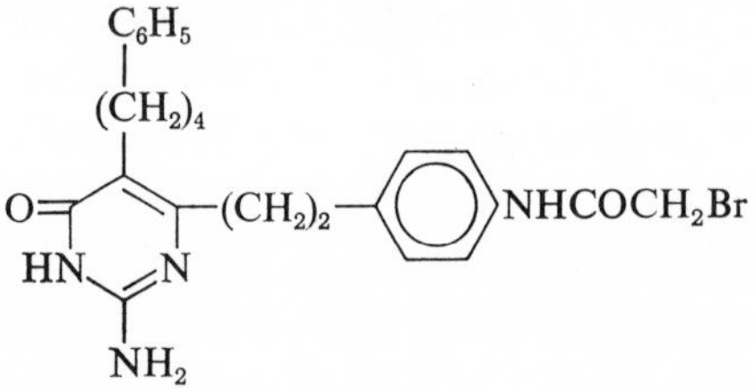

CIV

from reversible data, that 2,4-diaminopyrimidines and 2-amino-4-pyrimidinols do not have the same mode of binding to dihydrofolic reductase. Since the mode of binding of CXIII is different, further studies on bridging distance in CXIII should be pursued to find a structure of type CXIII that will show active-site-directed irreversible inhibition.

Other Types

In the next section the species differences in hydrophobic bonding to dihydrofolic reductase will be presented. Because this hydrophobic region is most probably just adjacent to the active-site, but not part of the active-site, then the hydrophobic region is nonfunctional with respect to the binding of substrate. In an area outside the active-site a successful mutational change of an amino acid may be expected to take place without effect on the substrate activity. Therefore, probably the greatest difference in irreversible inhibition of dihydrofolic reductase from different tissues and species would arise if the group on the inhibitor complexing to the hydrophobic region can be branched back towards a hydrophilic area; if a covalent forming group is then attached to this branch, its ability to form a covalent bond is also dependent upon the effect of the hydrophobic bonding region on the bridging to the nucleophilic site. Schematically, this can be represented by Fig. 10–6; note its relationship to the more general schematic for the bridge principle of specificity in Fig. 10–7 that was presented previously in Chapter 1.

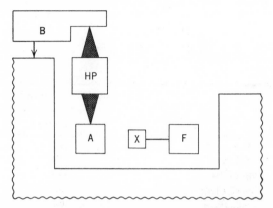

Fig. 10–6. A schematic representation of the bridge principle of spcificity with dependence on the mode of hydrophobic bonding. A is the pyrimidine binding area, HP is the hydrophobic bonding area, B is a group in a noncontact area bearing a covalent forming group represented by the arrow, and X–F is the coenzyme or co-substrate.

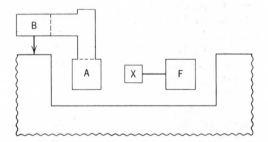

Fig. 10–7. A schematic representation of the bridge principle of specificity in which A is the binding region of the inhibitor, B is a noncontact area between the enzyme and the inhibitor, and the arrow is a covalent-forming group that can attack a nucleophilic site on the enzyme.

In order to reduce this concept to practice, the 1-phenyl-1,2-dihydro-*s*-triazine system was selected and is represented schematically by CXIV. A number of types of side chains on the *m*- position were first investigated for reversible binding and the results are recorded in Table 10–11.

The baseline 1-phenyl-*s*-triazine (XXV) showed 50 per cent inhibition at 110 mµ *M*. About a threefold gain in binding occurred by introducing an *n*-butyl group on the *m*- position (CXVI); thus hydrophobic bonding occurring with this *m*-butyl group was minimal. However, when the *n*-butyl group was substituted on the terminal carbon by phenyl to give the

Table 10–11. Inhibition of Dihydrofolic Reductase by

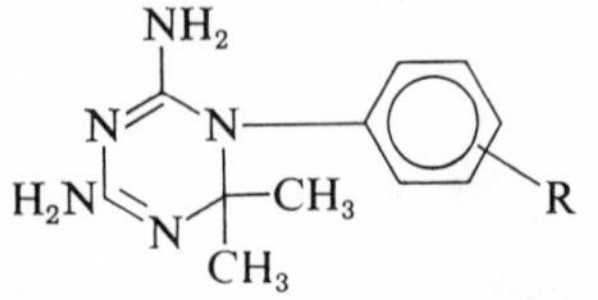

No.	R	mμ M concentration for 50 per cent inhibition	Reference
XXV	H	110	[a]
XXXVIII	m-CH$_3$	78	[b]
CXV	m-OCH$_3$	540	[c]
CXVI	m-C$_4$H$_9$-n	30	[d]
XXXIX	p-C$_4$H$_9$-n	64	[b]
CXVII	m-CH$_2$C$_6$H$_5$	19	[d]
CXVIII	m-(CH$_2$)$_2$C$_6$H$_5$	24	[d]
CXIX	m-(CH$_2$)$_3$C$_6$H$_5$	5.9	[d]
CXX	m-(CH$_2$)$_4$C$_6$H$_5$	2.3	[d]
CXXI	m-(CH$_2$)$_5$C$_6$H$_5$	7.1	[d]
CXXII	m-(CH$_2$)$_4$C$_6$H$_3$Cl$_2$-2,4	8.0	[d]
CXXIII	p-(CH$_2$)$_4$C$_6$H$_3$Cl$_2$-2,4	5.3	[d]
XLIV	p-CH$_2$C$_6$H$_5$	40	[b]
CXXIV	p-(CH$_2$)$_2$C$_6$H$_5$	18	[d]
CXXV	m-O(CH$_2$)$_2$C$_6$H$_5$	280	[c]
CXXVI	m-O(CH$_2$)$_3$C$_6$H$_5$	88	[c]
CXXVII	m-O(CH$_2$)$_2$OC$_6$H$_5$	74	[c]
CXXVIII	m-O(CH$_2$)$_3$OC$_6$H$_5$	110	[c]
CXXIX	m-CH$_2$OC$_6$H$_5$	55	[c]
IV	Aminopterin	0.9	[e]

Assayed with dihydrofolic reductase from pigeon liver using 6 μM dihydrofolate at pH 7.4.

[a] B. R. Baker and B.-T. Ho, *J. Pharm. Sci.*, **53**, 1137 (1964).
[b] B. R. Baker and B.-T. Ho, *J. Heterocyclic Chem.*, **2**, 335 (1965).
[c] B. R. Baker and G. J. Lourens, *J. Pharm. Sci.*, **56**, in press (1967).
[d] B. R. Baker, B.-T. Ho and G. J. Lourens, *J. Pharm. Sci.*, **56**, in press (1967).
[e] B. R. Baker and J. H. Jordaan, *J. Heterocyclic Chem.*, **2**, 162 (1965).

m-phenylbutyl derivative (CXX), a 14-fold enhancement in binding was noted. That maximum bonding occurred in this series at phenylbutyl (CXX) was shown by the somewhat lesser bonding of phenylamyl (CXXI), phenylpropyl (CXIX), phenethyl (CXVIII), and benzyl (CXVII), although all showed at least a fivefold increment in binding over the parent phenyl-*s*-triazine (XXV). That additional binding could also occur with a phenyl-alkyl group at the *p*- position was noted by comparison of XLIV and

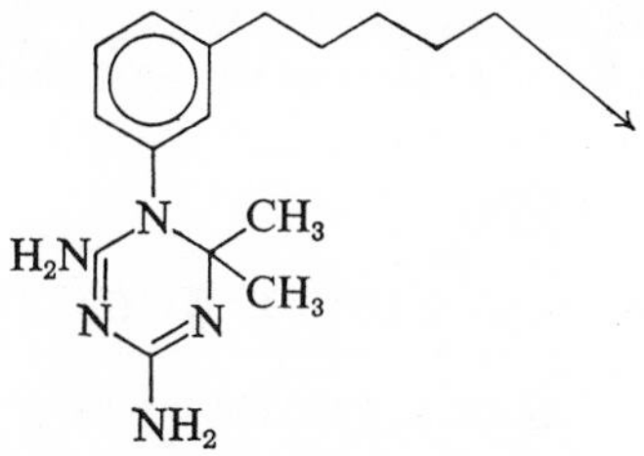

CXIV

CXXII through CXXIV. Whether the terminal aryl group in these inhibitors is complexed by hydrophobic bonding or with a more polar type of donor-acceptor binding was then investigated.

A second class of compounds investigated was the aralkyloxy series represented by CXXVI. The *m*-methoxy derivative (CXV) was taken as a baseline; note that CXV is only one fifth as effective as the parent phenyl derivative (XXV), probably because of repulsion of the polar ether oxygen from a hydrophobic region. Compared to the *m*-methoxy derivative (CXV), the phenethyloxy derivatives (CXXV) gave about a twofold increment in binding and the phenylpropyloxy derivatives (CXXVI) about a sixfold increment. Similar increments were obtained with the more polar phenoxyethyloxy (CXXVII) and phenoxypropyloxy (CXXVIII) side chains, indicating that the terminal phenyl is not complexed to a completely hydrophobic region; otherwise, the terminal phenylmethyl should bind better than terminal phenoxy.

Future studies will involve the conversion of a variety of derivatives such as CXXVIII or CXX in Table 10–11 to potential active-site-directed irreversible inhibitors by placement of a bromoacetamido group on the

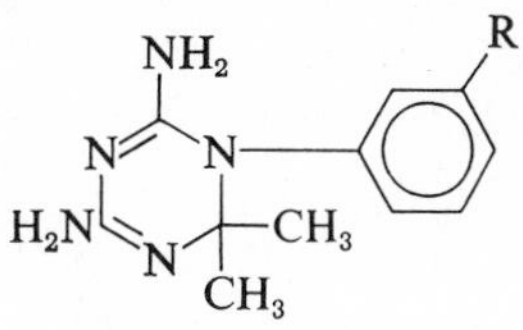

XXV, R = H
XLII, R = Cl

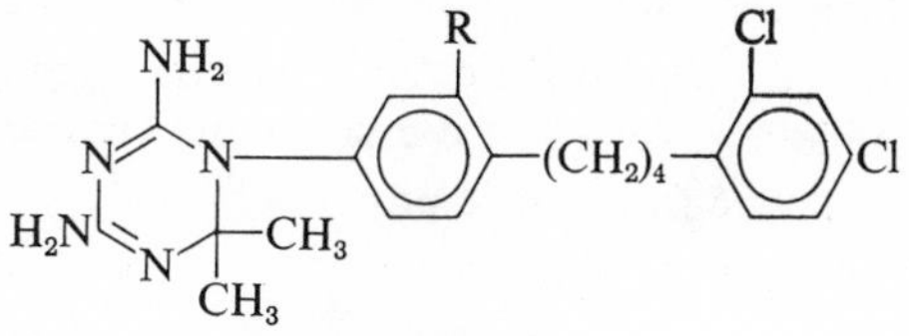

CXIII, R = H
CXIII*B*, R = Cl

o-, *m*-, or *p*- position of the terminal aryl group. An ancillary study that would be useful might be made to search for even more potent reversible inhibitors of the type in Table 10–11, for the *n*-phenylbutylphenyl triazine (CXX) is nearly as potent as aminopterin (IV); for example, the 13-fold increment in binding that is obtained with the *m*-chloro group (XLII) is placed on the 1-phenyl triazine (XXV) (Table 10–4) suggests that an *m*-chloro group should be introduced on CXIII; if the resultant CXIII*B* had even half the increment in binding observed between XXV and XLII, it would be as effective as aminopterin (IV) (Table 10–11). Such a compound could be useful for treatment of cancer cells that have an impaired active-transport system for folic acid.[96]

SPECIES DIFFERENCES IN DIHYDROFOLIC REDUCTASES

General Considerations

As we pointed out at the beginning of Chapter 10, when *E. coli* is infected with T_2 phage, a rapid 20–50-fold rise in the level of dihydrofolic reductase and thymidylate synthetase takes place. Based on kinetic parameters the new enzymes are different from the original enzymes present in the *E. coli*; furthermore, the new dihydrofolic reductase and thymidylate synthetase is genetically controlled by the virus and is not merely an induction of more *E. coli* enzyme.[97] The two thymidylate synthetases are even sufficiently different in charge that they are readily separated with a DEAE-cellulose column.[98]

In the case of invasion of a normal cell by a tumorigenic virus, the viral coding information becomes an integral part of the original cell, thus producing a cancer cell that contains the genetic information of both the virus and the original cell. In order for the cell to reproduce more rapidly, DNA must be synthesized more rapidly; this requires more dTMP per unit time, which, in turn, requires more thymidylate synthetase and more dihydrofolic reductase. The new enzymes are presumably coded by the nucleic acid originally present in the virus and therefore could be anticipated to be subtly different in structure than these two enzymes in the uninvaded cell.

That the dihydrofolic reductases from different species can have readily detectable differences has been shown in numerous cases; for example, the effect of the sulfhydryl reagent, *p*-chloromercuri benzoate. The enzyme from rat liver is unaffected by this reagent[99]; in contrast, the enzyme from S-180 cells in tissue culture,[100] calf thymus,[101] or *S. faecalis*[102]

---

[96] See Chapter 10, p. 263.
[97] See Reference 4, p. 195.
[98] See Reference 5, p. 195.
[99] B. T. Kaufman, *J. Biol. Chem.*, **239**, PC 669 (1964).
[100] M. Hakala, *Fed. Proc.*, 1965.
[101] R. Nath and D. M. Greenberg, *Biochem.*, **1**, 435 (1962).
[102] R. L. Blakely and B. M. McDougall, *J. Biol. Chem.*, **236**, 1163 (1961).

are inhibited. A third type of effect with chloromercuribenzoate was observed with the dihydrofolic reductase from Ehrlich ascites cells,[103] L-1210 leukemic cells,[104] and chicken liver,[99] namely a stimulation in rate. Iodoacetamide had no effect on the chicken liver enzyme,[105] but inactivated the enzyme from S-180 cells[100]; DPNH at pH 7.5 is as effective a cofactor as TPNH for the purified calf thymus enzyme,[101] but DPNH is ineffective at pH 7.5 on the chicken liver enzyme and about one third as effective at pH 5; pH profiles for FAH_2 can be radically different in different species.[99,102]

Hydrophobic Bonding Differences

Alkyl or aryl groups attached to the 5- position of pyrimidines or the 1-position of 1,2-dihydro-*s*-triazines can give strong hydrophobic bonding to dihydrofolic reductase, as was described in an earlier section of this chapter (p. 205); also evidence that the aryl groups also are bonded hydrophobically rather than by a donor-acceptor complex with the enzyme was presented. Some of the conformational aspects of hydrophobic bonding to the dihydrofolic reductase from pigeon liver were discussed. The hydrophobic bonding region is most probably not in the area where dihydrofolate is complexed; if it is adjacent to the 4- position or 8- position of dihydrofolate when the latter is complexed with dihydrofolic reductase, this hydrophobic region would therefore be in a nonfunctional part of the enzyme just adjacent to the active-site. Furthermore, it might be expected that outside of the active-site, one hydrophobic amino acid could be replaced by another hydrophobic amino acid without affecting the function of the active-site, whereas amino acid replacement within the active-site could be expected to be much more sensitive with respect to enzyme activity.[106,107] *Ergo*, it can be anticipated that there should be species differences in the nonfunctional hydrophobic area presumed to be adjacent to the active-site of dihydrofolic reductase. Some aspects of hydrophobic bonding to the dihydrofolic reductase from *E. coli* B and their relationship to the dihydrofolic reductase from pigeon liver were investigated.[108]

Four discrete series of dihydro-*s*-triazines with variants at either the 1- position or 2- position were compared as inhibitors of the dihydrofolic reductase from pigeon liver and from *E. coli* B; the results are tabulated in Table 10–12.

[103] J. Perkins and J. R. Bertino, *Biochem. Biophys. Res. Commun.*, **15**, 121 (1964).
[104] E. R. Kashket, E. J. Crawford, M. Friedkin, S. R. Humphreys, and A. Goldin, *Biochem.*, **3**, 1928 (1964).
[105] C. K. Mathews and F. M. Huennekens, *J. Biol. Chem.*, **238**, 3436 (1963).
[106] J. G. Joshi and P. Handler, *J. Biol. Chem.*, **239**, 2741 (1964).
[107] See Chapter 9, Enzyme Evolution.
[108] B. R. Baker and B.-T. Ho, *J. Pharm. Sci.*, **55**, 470 (1966).

Table 10–12. Inhibition of Dihydrofolic Reductases by

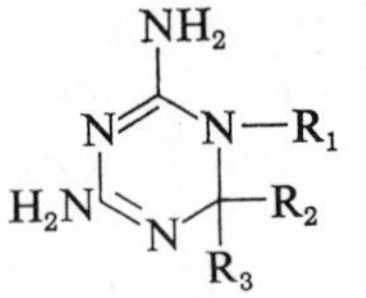

$$\text{structure: 2-amino-1,6-dihydro-1,3,5-triazine with } N-R_1, \; R_2, \; R_3 \text{ substituents; } NH_2 \text{ and } H_2N \text{ groups}$$

No.	R_1	R_2	R_3	Pigeon liver[b]	E. coli B[c]	Ratio of Pigeon liver to E. coli B
				μM concentration for 50 per cent inhibition[a]		
XXV	$-C_6H_5$	CH_3	CH_3	0.11	3.0	$\frac{1}{27}$
CXXX	$-CH_2C_6H_5$	CH_3	CH_3	3.3	34	$\frac{1}{10}$
CXXXI	$-(CH_2)_2C_6H_5$	CH_3	CH_3	0.71	3.8	$\frac{1}{5.3}$
LXX-E	$-(CH_2)_3C_6H_5$	CH_3	CH_3	0.028	0.063	$\frac{1}{2.2}$
LXXI-E	$-(CH_2)_4C_6H_5$	CH_3	CH_3	0.041	0.21	$\frac{1}{5.1}$
XXVI	$-CH_3$	CH_3	CH_3	74	48	1.5
XLVII-E	$-C_2H_5$	CH_3	CH_3	200	62	3.5
XLVIII-E	$-C_3H_7$-n	CH_3	CH_3	11	4.7	2.3
XXVIII	$-C_4H_9$-n	CH_3	CH_3	0.36	2.1	$\frac{1}{5.8}$
LV-E	$-C_5H_{11}$-i	CH_3	CH_3	0.058	0.69	$\frac{1}{12}$
LI-E	$-C_6H_{13}$-n	CH_3	CH_3	0.32	0.92	$\frac{1}{2.9}$
LII-E	$-C_8H_{17}$-n	CH_3	CH_3	0.14	0.27	$\frac{1}{1.9}$
XL	$-C_6H_4$-C_6H_5-p	CH_3	CH_3	160	5.8	28
XLI	$-C_6H_4$-C_6H_5-m	CH_3	CH_3	1.3	1.0	1.3
XXXIX	$-C_6H_4$-$(C_4H_9$-$n)$-p	CH_3	CH_3	0.064	7.2	$\frac{1}{110}$
CXXXII	9-fluorenone-2-yl	CH_3	CH_3	85	1.5	57
CXXXIII	$-C_6H_4\overset{\text{O}}{\overset{\|}{C}}C_6H_5$-$m$	CH_3	CH_3	1.1	0.61	1.8
XLII	$-C_6H_4Cl$-m	CH_3	CH_3	0.0085	0.60	$\frac{1}{71}$
XLIV	$-C_6H_4CH_2C_6H_5$-p	CH_3	CH_3	0.062	4.8	$\frac{1}{77}$
CXVII	$-C_6H_4CH_2C_6H_5$-m	CH_3	CH_3	0.019	0.28	$\frac{1}{15}$

254

No.	R_1	R_2	R_3	μM concentration for 50 per cent inhibition[a]		Ratio of Pigeon liver to *E. coli* B
				Pigeon liver[b]	*E. coli* B[c]	
CXVIII	—$C_6H_4CH_2CH_2C_6H_5$-*m*	CH_3	CH_3	0.024	0.092	$\frac{1}{3.5}$
CXXXIV	—$(CH_2)_4C_6H_5$	*p*-$AcNHC_6H_4$	H	0.62	0.41	1.5
CXXXV	—C_6H_4Cl-*m*	*p*-$AcNHC_6H_4$	H	190	180	1.0
CXXXVI	—C_2H_5	—C_6H_5	H	15,000	310	50

[a] Data from B. R. Baker and B.-T. Ho, *J. Pharm. Sci.*, **55**, 470 (1966).
[b] A 45–90 per cent saturated ammonium sulfate fraction from pigeon liver acetone powder was assayed with 6 μM dihydrofolate and 12 μM TPNH at pH 7.4 in Tris buffer.
[c] A 45–90 per cent saturated ammonium sulfate fraction from *E. coli* B was assayed with 6 μM dihydrofolate and 30 μM TPNH at pH 7.4 in Tris buffer.

Series A consisted of 1-$C_6H_5(CH_2)_n$ variants. Insertion of one methylene group (CXXX) between the 1-aryl group and the *s*-triazine of XXV was detrimental to the binding of both the *E. coli* B enzyme and the pigeon liver enzyme, being 10-fold with the *E. coli* B enzyme and 30-fold with the pigeon liver enzyme; thus when the aryl group is out of the plane of the triazine, a loss in binding occurs in both enzymes. By comparing 1-benzyl-*s*-triazine (CXXX) with 1-methyl-*s*-triazine (XXVI), we can see that the phenyl group of CXXX gives little binding to the *E. coli* enzyme, but a 22-fold increment in binding to the pigeon liver enzyme—presumably due to the phenyl group—still remains. The next higher homolog, phenylethyl (CXXXI), can have the phenyl ring nearly coplanar with the *s*-triazine ring; as a result activity is better than benzyl (CXXX) with both enzymes. On the *E. coli* B enzyme, the phenethyl (CXXXI) side chain is just as effective as the phenyl side chain (XXV); in contrast, phenethyl (CXXXI) is 6.5-fold less effective than phenyl (XXV) with the pigeon liver enzyme.

Maximum effectiveness against both the *E. coli* B and pigeon liver enzymes is shown with the phenylpropyl side chain (LXX*E*) with phenyl-butyl (LXXI*E*) being 1.5–3 times less effective. However, the increment between phenyl (XXV) and phenylpropyl (LXX*E*) is much larger (48-fold) with the *E. coli* enzyme than with the pigeon liver enzyme (fourfold); most of this difference is due to the fact that the 1-phenyl (XXV) binds to the pigeon liver enzyme 27-fold better than does the *E. coli* B enzyme, for possible reasons that are discussed later. Furthermore, the greatest specificity towards the pigeon liver enzyme (27-fold) is shown by the 1-phenyl side chain (XXV), but none of the compounds in this series are more effective on the *E. coli* B enzyme than the pigeon liver enzyme.

The second series consisted of 1-alkyl variants. With straight-chain alkyl substituents maximum hydrophobic bonding with the pigeon liver enzyme occurred at *n*-butyl (XXVIII) with *n*-hexyl (LI*E*) being equal and *n*-octyl (LII*E*) perhaps twofold better; in contrast, with the *E. coli* B enzyme *n*-hexyl (LI*E*) was 2.3-fold better than *n*-butyl (XXVIII), and *n*-octyl (LII*E*) was 3.4-fold better than *n*-hexyl (LI*E*). Extension of the series was not made in order to reveal whether or not maximum straight-chain hydrophobic bonding to the *E. coli* B enzyme had occurred at *n*-octyl.

Branching of the *n*-butyl group (XXVIII) to isoamyl (LV*E*) gave a six-fold increment in binding on the pigeon liver enzyme and LV*E* was the most effective alkyl group found for the enzyme from this source; the isoamyl group (LV*E*) gave a threefold increment in binding over the *n*-butyl group (XXVIII) with the *E. coli* enzyme, but—in contrast to the pigeon liver enzyme—the isoamyl group (LV*E*) was still less effective than *n*-octyl group (LII*E*). Whether chain-branching farther out on the chain than the C-3 branch of isoamyl (LV*E*) would result in a still better inhibitor of the *E. coli* B enzyme is as yet unknown.

It was previously noted (p. 211) that the increment in binding between methyl (XXVI) and *n*-butyl (XXVIII) to the pigeon liver enzyme was 200-fold; that is well within the 1000-fold increment (10-fold per methylene) that is theoretically possible. However, it was pointed out that there was a 20-fold increment in binding in proceeding from ethyl (XLVII*E*) to *n*-propyl (XLVIII*E*), and a 30-fold increment in *n*-propyl (XLVIII*E*) to *n*-butyl (XXVIII), both of which are above the 10-fold increments theoretically possible. The fact that the range from methyl to butyl gave only a 200-fold increment, which is within the theoretical 1000-fold increment in binding for three methylene groups, was rationalized by assuming a conformational change in the enzyme; if this conformational change in the enzyme required no more than 900 cal/mole, then this 900 cal/mole could be supplied by the fivefold difference between the 200-fold increment observed in proceeding from methyl to butyl and the 1000-fold increment theoretically possible. Thus, the greater than 10-fold increment in binding between *n*-propyl and ethyl or *n*-butyl and *n*-propyl is still energetically possible including the energy required for a conformational change in the pigeon liver enzyme. With the *E. coli* B enzyme only the change between ethyl and *n*-propyl gave greater than a 10-fold increment (13-fold), which indicates that little or no conformational change in this enzyme need take place for maximum hydrophobic bonding; it should be further noted that the maximum increment in hydrophobic bonding by straight-chain alkyl groups with the *E. coli* enzyme is only 180-fold (between methyl and *n*-octyl), whereas the pigeon liver enzyme has a maximum increment of 530-fold between methyl and *n*-octyl groups.

In this series, the isoamyl-*s*-triazine (LV*E*) shows the most specificity towards the pigeon liver enzyme, being 12-fold more effective than on the *E. coli* B enzyme; the most specific compound towards the *E. coli* B enzyme is the ethyl-*s*-triazine (XLVII*E*), which is 3.5 times more effective than on the pigeon liver enzyme.

The third series investigated was 1-phenyl dihydro-*s*-triazines with *m*- and *p*- substituents. In this series is seen the largest spread in specificity between the two enzymes in both directions. The *E. coli* B enzyme is relatively insensitive to *m*- or *p*- substituents, the maximum variation being between 7.2 μM for the *p*- (*n*-butyl) substituent (XXXIX) to 0.092 μM for the *m*-phenethyl-*s*-triazine (CXVIII), an 80-fold spread; in contrast, the pigeon liver enzyme is extremely sensitive to substitution, varying from 0.0085 μM for the *m*-chlorophenyl group (XLII) to 160 μM for the *p*-biphenyl group (XL) at the 1- position of the *s*-triazine, a 19,000-fold spread. As a result the *p*-(*n*-butyl)-phenyl-*s*-triazine (XXXIX) is 110-fold more effective on the pigeon liver enzyme than the *E. coli* B enzyme; similarly, the *m*-chlorophenyl-*s*-triazine (XLII) and the *p*-(benzyl)-phenyl-*s*-triazine (XLIV) are 71- and 77-fold, respectively, more effective on the pigeon liver enzyme. In contrast the *p*-biphenyl-*s*-triazine (XL) and the 9-fluorenon-2-yl-*s*-triazine (CXXXII) are 28- and 57-fold more effective, respectively, on the *E. coli* B enzyme. Note that the benzoyl group of CXXXIII causes a 10-fold loss in binding to the pigeon liver enzyme, but a fivefold gain in binding to the *E. coli* B enzyme. When the *m*-benzoylphenyl group of CXXXIII is cyclized to the 9-fluorenon-2-yl group as in CXXXII, only a 2.5-fold loss in binding occurs in the *E. coli* B enzyme, but a further 77-fold loss in binding to the pigeon liver enzyme occurs; thus the pigeon liver enzyme cannot tolerate a large flat substituent at the 1- position,

CXXXII   CXXXIII

but the *E. coli* B enzyme can. Reduction of the ketone of CXXXIII to give the *m*-benzyl derivative (CXVII) causes little change with the *E. coli* B enzyme, but 46-fold better inhibition is seen with the pigeon liver enzyme.

The most active and one of the most specific compounds for the pigeon liver enzyme in this series is *m*-chlorophenyl-*s*-triazine (XLII) at 0.0085 μM. The most active compound in this series for the *E. coli* B enzyme is the *m*-phenethylphenyl-*s*-triazine (CXVIII) at 0.092 μM, but this compound has no specificity towards the *E. coli* B enzyme because CXVIII is even more effective on the pigeon liver enzyme.

The fourth series investigated was variation at the 2- position of the *s*-triazine structure. Introduction of larger groups has a much more detrimental effect on binding to the pigeon liver enzyme than the *E. coli* B enzyme. Note that replacement of the 2,2-dimethyl group of the 1-phenylbutyl-*s*-triazine (LXXI*E*) by 2- (*p*-acetamidophenyl) (CXXXIV) reduces binding to the pigeon liver enzyme by a factor of 15-fold, but reduces binding to the *E. coli* enzyme by only a factor of 2. Similarly, the same 2- substituent exchanged on the 1-(*m*-chlorophenyl)-*s*-triazine (XLII) to give CXXXV causes a 19,000-fold loss in binding to the pigeon liver enzyme, but only an 850-fold loss to the *E. coli* B enzyme; it should be noted that this structural change giving a 1,2-diaryl-*s*-triazine reduces coplanarity of at least one phenyl and possibly both phenyls with the *s*-triazine ring.[109] When the 2,2-dimethyl group of the 1-ethyl-*s*-triazine (XLVII*E*) is replaced by phenyl to give CXXXVI, it results in only a fivefold reduction in binding to the *E. coli* B enzyme, but a 68-fold reduction in binding to the pigeon liver enzyme results. A study of other 2-substituents could well reveal their higher affinity for the *E. coli* B enzyme than the pigeon liver enzyme, for the latter is more sensitive to structural change at this 2- position; note that CXXXVI, although it is a poor inhibitor, is 50-fold more effective on the *E. coli* B enzyme than the pigeon liver enzyme and that no compound in this series shows the converse order of affinity.

Relative Topography of Hydrophobic Bonding to the Two Enzymes

The difference in binding to the two enzymes of *E. coli* B and pigeon liver can give considerable insight into the differences in topography of their hydrophobic regions. It is well established that the phenyl group of XXV must be nearly coplanar with the triazine ring for maximum binding[110] to the enzyme because introduction of an *o*-chloro group causes a great reduction in the affinity of the inhibitor to both enzymes due to the restricted rotation of the 1-phenyl-*s*-triazine system imposed by the *o*-chloro group.[111,112] Because there is strong experimental support for the 1-phenyl group being hydrophobically bonded to the enzyme (see p. 211), it is a reasonable assumption that the 1-phenyl group of XXV and a 1-alkyl group of CXXXVII*A* are bonded in the same region. The alkyl

[109] E. J. Modest, *J. Org. Chem.*, **21**, 1 (1956).
[110] See Reference 109, p. 258.
[111] See Reference 27, p. 206.
[112] B. R. Baker and B.-T. Ho, *J. Heterocyclic Chem.*, **2**, 72 (1965).

group can then be staggered in the plane of the triazine either away from the 2- position, as in CXXXVII*A*, or towards the 2- position, as in CXXXVII*B*. Because CXXXIV and CXXXVI (Table 10–12) can still bind reasonably well to both enzymes, a downward-stagger of the CXXXVII*B* type is not possible due to the 2-phenyl group of CXXXIV occupying the same space as the C_2-methylene group of the side chain. With the upward-staggered *A* conformation, there is no steric interaction between the

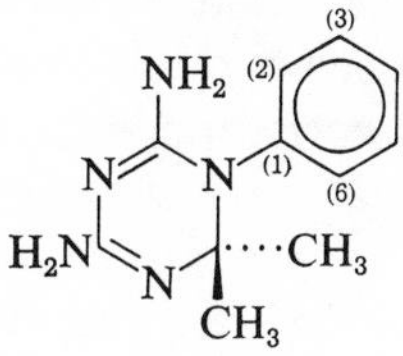

XXV*A*

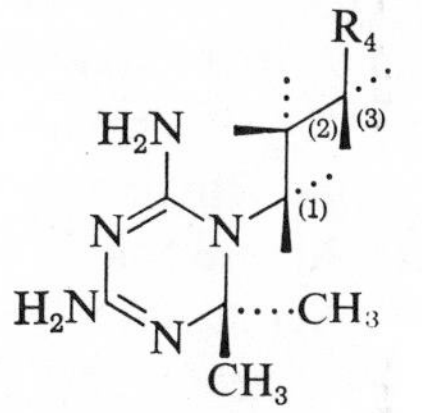

CXXXVII*A*, R = H
CXXXVIII*A*, R = $C_6H_5CH_2$
CXXXIX*A*, R = CH_3

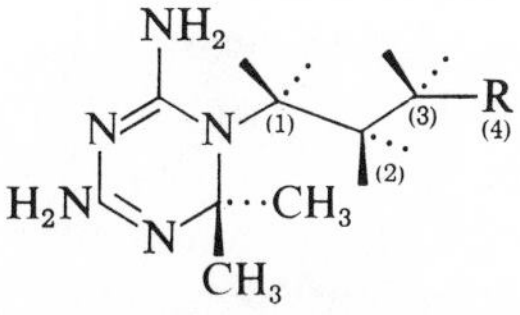

CXXXVII*B*, R = H
CXXXVIII*B*, R = $C_6H_5CH_2$
CXXXIX*B*, R = CH_3

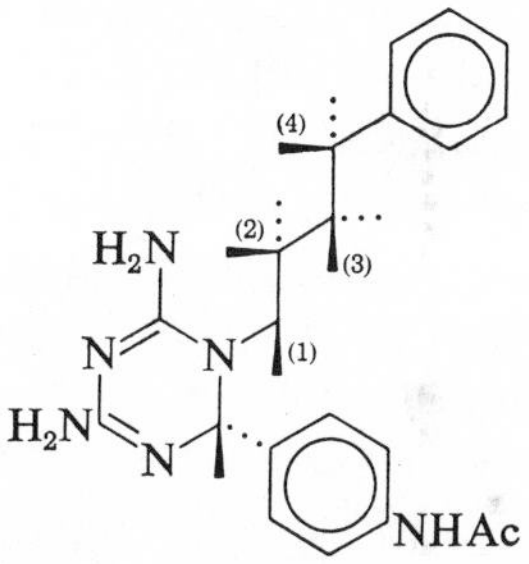

CXXXIV *A*

C_2-methylene group and the 2-phenyl, but there is now a possible steric interaction between the C_1-methylene group and the 2-phenyl group; this C_1-methylene steric interaction does not occur if the 2-phenyl group is in a plane perpendicular to the triazine, but it is strong if the plane of the phenyl group is moved 90°. It follows that the *E. coli* B enzyme has more tolerance for the 2-phenyl group approaching a plane perpendicular to the triazine than the pigeon liver enzyme, for little activity is lost in the *E. coli* B enzyme when the 2-phenyl group is inserted; the large reduction in affinity to the pigeon liver enzyme indicates that this enzyme cannot tolerate the 2-phenyl group approaching a plane perpendicular to the *s*-triazine ring.

Note that the *n*-propyl-*s*-triazine (XLVIII*E*) (Table 10–12) is nearly as effective as the 1-phenyl-*s*-triazine (XXV) on the *E. coli* B enzyme, but

XXV is 100-fold more effective than XLVIIIE on the pigeon liver enzyme. Models clearly indicate that C_1, C_2, and C_3 of the phenyl group exactly overlap the C_1, C_2, and C_3 groups of an alkyl side chain when they have conformation XXVA and CXXXVIIA, respectively. Because the 1-propyl-s-triazine (CXXXVIIA) binds almost as well as the 1-phenyl-s-triazine (XXVA) to the *E. coli* enzyme, it is reasonable to propose that most of the phenyl bonding of XXVA occurs through the C_1, C_2, and C_3 carbons; the remaining 1.6-fold difference between XXVA and CXXXVIIA might be due to slight additional bonding by the C_4 or C_6 carbons of the phenyl, or the C_1, C_2, and C_3 carbons of the phenyl of XXVA may hydrophobically bond slightly better than the corresponding carbons of CXXXVIIA; this 1.6-fold difference with the *E. coli* enzyme is, however, practically negligible.

The 100-fold better binding of the 1-phenyl of XXVA than the 1-propyl of CXXXVIIA to the pigeon liver enzyme suggests that at least two more carbons of the benzene ring—in addition to C_1, C_2, and C_3—are complexed hydrophobically to this enzyme; one of these carbons is most probably C_4 because the isoamyl group with its skewed C_4 and C_4' carbons has been shown to have both of these carbons hydrophobically bonded (see p. 215).

Both the *n*-octyl (LIIE) and the phenylbutyl-s-triazine (LXXIE) (Table 10–12) are better—and about equally effective—inhibitors of the *E. coli* B enzyme than the 1-phenyl-s-triazine (XXV) by a factor of 11- to 14-fold. Furthermore, LIIE and LXXIE are about 10-fold better inhibitors than the *n*-butyl-s-triazine (CXXXIXA); because the terminal four carbons of LIIE can only increase affinity to the enzyme by hydrophobic bonding of one or more of these terminal carbons, it follows that the phenyl group of CXXXVIIIA does likewise. In contrast, the pigeon liver enzyme has only a twofold greater affinity for the octyl group than the butyl group, but the phenylbutyl group is complexed eightfold better than the butyl group; it follows that the additional hydrophobic bonding to the pigeon liver enzyme past the *n*-butyl group requires the relatively flat interaction that can occur with a benzene ring, but the *E. coli* B enzyme can bind either a flat or staggered group in this area. The greater tolerance to the type of group that is attached to the 1-phenyl substituent by the *E. coli* B enzyme has already been pointed out.

Of further interest is the fact that there is less than a twofold difference in binding to the two enzymes with the 1-methyl-s-triazine (XXVI) (Table 10–12), but there is a 12-fold difference with the *i*-amyl-s-triazine (LVE) and even larger differences in both directions with XXXIX and CXXXII. Since it is highly probable that the 4,6-diamino-s-triazine moiety binds within the normal complexing region for the pteridine ring of the substrate, dihydrofolate, and since the active-site of an enzyme has a considerable limitation on the extent of the structural change allowed that will still enable the enzyme to be effective little difference should be seen in binding of the 4,6-diamino-*s*-triazine moiety to the enzyme. In contrast, large differences in hydrophobic bonding were anticipated and found, for this is supposedly a nonspecific part of the enzyme that could readily vary from species to species and still leave an effective enzyme.

Further examples of differences in the ability of dihydrofolic reductase to bind 2,4-diamino-heterocycles with varying hydrophobic groups that are due to differences in species have been collated by Hitchings and Burchall.[113] They also noted that the biggest difference due to species existed when substituents on the 1-phenyl group or 2- position of the 2,4-diamino-heterocycles were varied. Although they proposed that the hydrophobic groups were complexed to dihydrofolic reductase at a locus between the pyrimidyl and *p*-aminobenzoyl loci without evidence, they had no *a priori* reason to believe otherwise, nor did they consider the binding from the hydrophobic standpoint. Their schematic representation of species differences is given in Fig. 10–8; this same figure, if rotated 60° would also agree with the results in Table 10–12.[114]

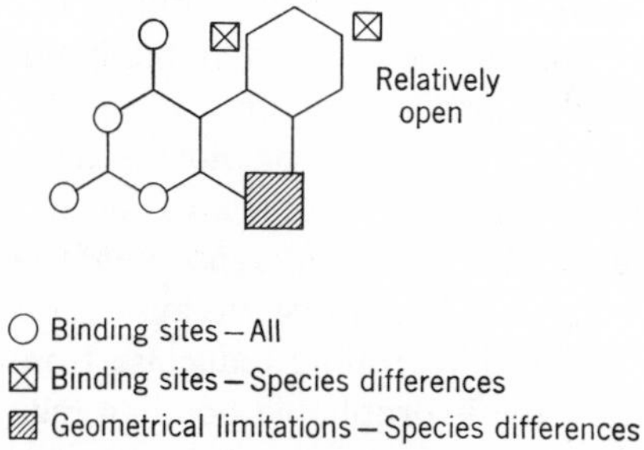

○ Binding sites — All
⊠ Binding sites — Species differences
▨ Geometrical limitations — Species differences

Fig. 10–8. Representation of the dimensions of inhibitors for binding to various dihydrofolic reductases. From G. H. Hitchings and J. J. Burchall, *Adv. Enzymology*, **27**, 417 (1965).

The two extremes on inhibition of the dihydrofolic reductases from mammalian livers and from bacteria that they observed[113] were with *p*-*n*-butylphenyl-*s*-triazine, XXXIX, and 2,4-diamino-5-(3,4,5-trimethoxy-benzyl)-pyrimidine (CXL). With *E. coli*, *S. aureus* and *P. vulgaris* the average K_i with the pyrimidine (CXL) was 5×10^{-8} *M*, and with the triazine (XXXIX) the average was 7×10^{-4} *M*, a spread of 14,000; in

[113] G. H. Hitchings and J. J. Burchall, *Adv. Enzymol.*, **27**, 417 (1965).
[114] See Reference 108, p. 253.

contrast, the average with human, rat, and rabbit liver for the pyrimidine (CXL) was $K_i = 3 \times 10^{-4}$ M, and for the triazine (XXXIX) the average was 1.5×10^{-7} M, a spread of 2000 in the opposite direction. Thus, CXL—the antibacterial agent known as trimethoprim—is on the average

XXXIX   CXL (trimethoprim)

6000 times more potent on bacterial dihydrofolic reductase than mammalian liver dihydrofolic reductase; in contrast, XXXIX is 4000 times more potent on the mammalian liver enzyme.

Although differences in hydrophobic bonding between invading organisms such as bacteria and protozoa on the one hand and mammalian enzymes on the other hand are sufficiently large to permit chemotherapeutic application of reversible inhibitors in vivo,[115] such differences between a cancer cell and the host are most probably too small to allow any chemotherapeutic application of reversible inhibitors of the 2,4-diaminoheterocycle type. By utilizing both hydrophobic bonding to dihydrofolic reductase and the bridge principle of specificity with active-site-directed irreversible inhibitors,[116] it should be possible to magnify immensely any small difference between the hydrophobic areas of the malignant and host dihydrofolic reductases; this small difference might be unusable or even undetectable with reversible inhibitors. Because active-site-directed irreversible inhibitors of the dihydrofolic reductase from pigeon liver have been found that utilize the hydrophobic bonding region,[117] only a small difference in the hydrophobic region of a malignant dihydrofolic reductase would be sufficient for high specificity—such as a change of a valine for a leucine or a slightly different conformation in the hydrophobic region caused by a single amino acid exchange in another region. Such a small difference could be exploited by attaching a bridging moiety to the hydrophobic bonding moiety of an inhibitor, so that the subsequent attack by the bridging group to form a covalent bond to a nucleophilic site on the enzyme is subject to proper juxtapositioning by the hydrophobic area on the enzyme. This is indicated schematically in Fig. 10–6.

[115] See Reference 113, p. 261.
[116] See Chapter 9, p. 172.
[117] See Chapter 10, p. 244.

MEMBRANE PERMEABILITY OF INHIBITORS

Monomer-sized molecules enter cells through the cell membrane in one of two ways. Relatively neutral molecules such as the antimalarials, pyrimethamine (VI), and the related XXIII, can diffuse through a cell membrane by a passive mechanism requiring no energy or particular specificity of structure.[118,119] In contrast, folic acid (I) and its classical-type antagonist, aminopterin (IV), enter several types of bacterial cells—and presum-

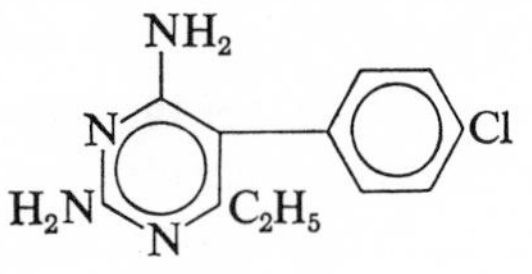

VI

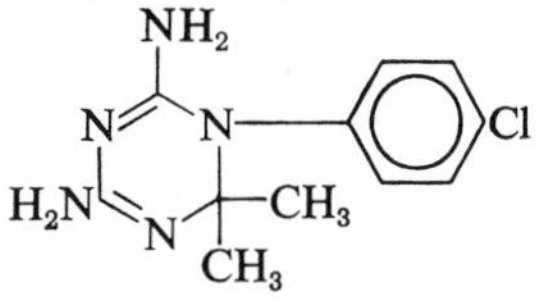

XXIII

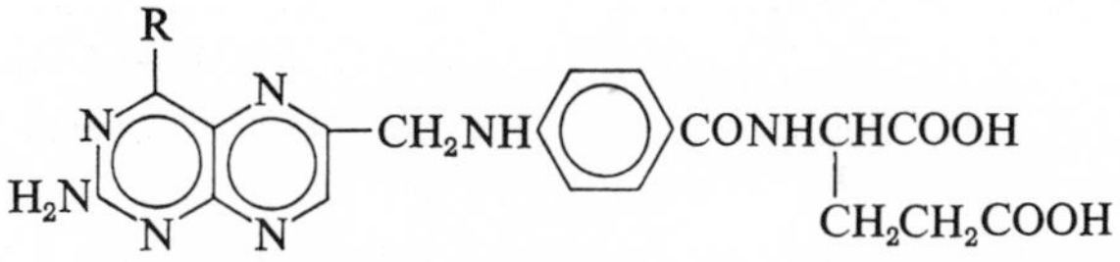

I, R = OH
IV, R = NH$_2$

ably mammalian cells[120]—by active transport,[118,119] a process that requires energy. This suggests that the *p*-aminobenzoyl-L-glutamate of I and IV, which has one completely ionized carboxyl and a second almost completely ionized, is involved in the active-transport mechanism[121]; furthermore, this ionization probably accounts for the inability of folic acid (I) and aminopterin (IV) to enter a cell by passive diffusion.

Those cells which synthesize dihydrofolate by the *de novo* pathway do not appear to have an active-transport mechanism for folic acid; hence such bacterial and protozoan cells are not inhibited by aminopterin[122] at normal levels even though the dihydrofolic reductase of a broken-cell system is just as sensitive to aminopterin (IV) or aomethopterin.[113] The mechanism of selectivity of pyrimethamine (VI) on the malaria parasite is probably due to a combination of (a) better hydrophobic bonding to the malarial enzyme than the mammalian enzyme and (b) the inability of the malaria parasite to transport actively folic acid through its cell wall from

[118] R. C. Wood and G. H. Hitchings, *J. Biol. Chem.*, **234**, 2381 (1959).
[119] R. C. Wood and G. H. Hitchings, *J. Biol. Chem.*, **234**, 2377 (1959).
[120] See Reference 10, p. 196.
[121] See Reference 7, p. 196.
[122] J. K. Frenkel and G. H. Hitchings, *Antibiot. Chemotherapy*, **7**, 630 (1957).

the host blood stream, in contrast to most mammalian tissues which can actively transport folic acid or 5-formyl-tetrahydrofolate[122] thus affording some protection to the host from the effect of VI.

Some tumor lines such as the rat Walker 256 are naturally resistant to aminopterin (IV), apparently because of the failure of the cell line to take up enough of the drug by active transport[123]; other cell lines have become resistant to aminopterin (IV) by loss of the active-transport system.[124,125,126] Furthermore, the ability of amethopterin (V) to inhibit a tumor line has been directly related to the ability of the tumor to take up the drug, presumably by active transport. In a beautiful experiment,[127] rats transplanted with both the susceptible Murphy-Sturm tumor and the insensitive Walker 256 tumor were investigated for the level of folic reductase remaining after drug treatment—an indirect method for measuring relative drug transport; the order of uptake observed was Murphy-Sturm > intestinal mucosa (the most susceptible normal tissue) > liver > Walker 256.

The Walker 256 tumor line is quite sensitive to a dietary folic acid deficiency in the rat; a "resistant" line could be developed which was then sensitive to amethopterin,[128] presumably because the "resistant" line now had a sufficiently good active-transport system for folic acid to compete with the host cells for the uptake of both folic acid and amethopterin (V).

In 11 clinical cases of leukemia, the susceptibility of the leukemia to amethopterin (V) was related to the relative ability of the leukemic cells to take up tritiated amethopterin (V). In two cases where the response was excellent, uptake was excellent, but in seven cases with no response, the uptake was near zero; two cases showing a partial response had an uptake of amethopterin in between the two extremes.[129]

Based on the information on transport mechanism given above, a useful clinical experiment that should be performed is the following:

Tumor lines with practically no uptake of tritiated amethopterin presumably have an impaired active-transport mechanism. If such cases were treated with a potent dihydrofolate reversible inhibitor such as CXLI and CXX—which can enter cells by passive diffusion—by simultaneous administration of citrovorum factor (5-formyl-tetrahydrofolate), the nor-

[123] W. C. Werkheiser, *Proc. Am. Assoc. Cancer Res.*, **3**, 371 (1962).

[124] M. J. Pine, *J. Bact.*, **79**, 827, 835 (1960).

[125] G. A. Fischer, *Biochem. Pharmacol.*, **11**, 1233 (1962).

[126] W. C. Werkheiser, L. W. Law, R. A. Roosa, and C. A. Nichol, *Proc. Am. Assoc. Cancer Res.*, **4**, 71 (1963).

[127] W. C. Werkheiser, *Proc. Am. Assoc. Cancer Res.*, **3**, 371 (1962).

[128] F. Rosen, H. Sotobayashi, and C. A. Nichol, *Proc. Am. Assoc. Cancer Research* (1964).

[129] J. R. Bertino and G. A. Fischer, unpublished.

mal cells having good active-transport mechanisms should be protected[130]; thus, of seven of the 11 clinical cases having an impaired active-transport system and therefore not responding to amethopterin, some might have responded to the reverse treatment with CXLI or CXX with simultaneous administration of the protecting agent.

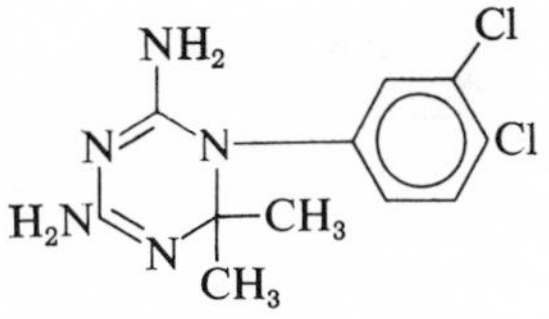

CXLI 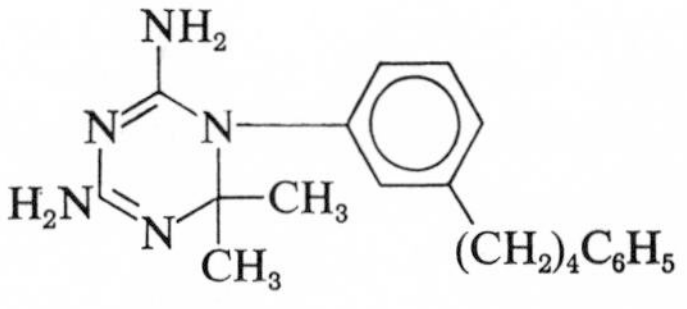   CXX

The problem of transport through cell membranes is an important one with any potential drug. What are the factors with active-site-directed irreversible inhibitors?

Inherent in the design of an active-site-directed irreversible inhibitor is the need for a nonclassical type of antimetabolite which has an oversized—but properly placed—group that can bridge back to a nucleophilic site adjacent to the enzymic active site for formation of a covalent bond with anchimeric assistance (Fig. 10–7). Because active-transport mechanisms can have as much specificity as an enzyme reaction, it should be anticipated that even though the target enzyme may tolerate a large, properly placed group, this same large group would probably not be tolerated by the active-transport mechanism; no such operational disadvantage exists with passive diffusion entry into a cell, for almost any monomeric-sized substrate with no more than one charge should be able to diffuse through a cell wall.

That the oversized 6-phenyl group on XCI could stop transport into S-180 cells in tissue culture was indicated by the fact that the 6-phenyl-pyrimidine without the carboxy-L-glutamate side chain (CXLII) and the 4-mercaptopyrimidine analog with the intact carboxy-L-glutamate moiety (CXLIII) were equally effective at inhibiting growth of these cells, whether or not they were resistant to amethopterin. In contrast, the 6-phenyl-pyrimidine analog with the intact carboxy-L-glutamate moiety (XCI) was devoid of growth inhibitory properties at considerably higher concentrations than were used for CXLII and CXLIII.[131] These results agreed with the concept that CXLIII could enter the cell by active transport because only a small structural change had been made, compared to folic acid (I),

[130] See Reference 11, p. 197.
[131] Private communication from Dr. M. Hakala.

CXLII entered by passive diffusion, and XCI could not enter by either mechanism.

It can therefore be anticipated that active-site-directed irreversible inhibitors such as type CIII should be able to penetrate cell membranes

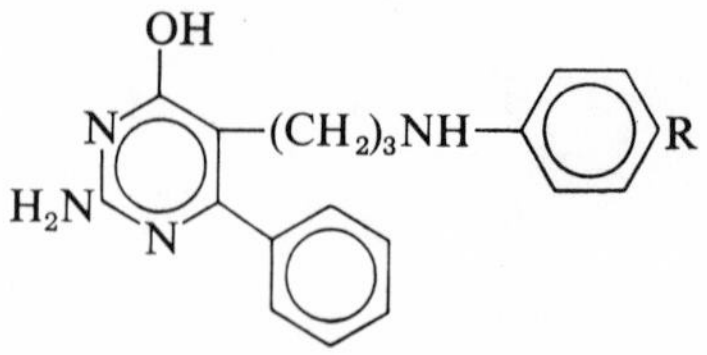

$$OH$$

$$\text{H}_2\text{N} \quad \text{N} \quad \text{N} \quad (\text{CH}_2)_3\text{NH} \quad \text{---} \quad R$$

CXLII, R = H
XCI, R = —CONHCHCOOH
$$\quad\quad\quad\quad\quad\quad\quad\quad \text{CH}_2\text{CH}_2\text{COOH}$$

SH

$$\text{H}_2\text{N} \quad \text{N} \quad \text{N} \quad \text{CH}_3 \quad (\text{CH}_2)_3\text{NH} \quad \text{---} \quad \text{CONHCHCOOH}$$
$$\quad\quad\quad\quad\quad\quad\quad\quad\quad\quad\quad\quad\quad \text{CH}_2\text{CH}_2\text{COOH}$$

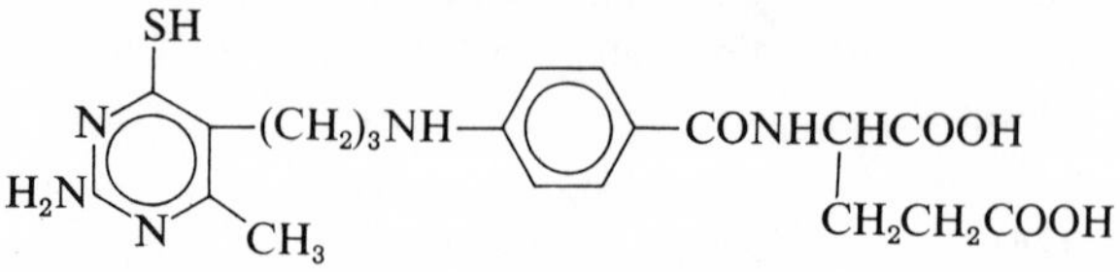

CXLIII

$$\text{C}_6\text{H}_5$$
$$(\text{CH}_2)_4$$

$$\text{O} \quad \text{HN} \quad \text{N} \quad \text{CH}_2\text{CH}_2 \quad \text{---} \quad \text{NHCOCH}_2\text{Br}$$
$$\quad\quad\quad \text{NH}_2$$

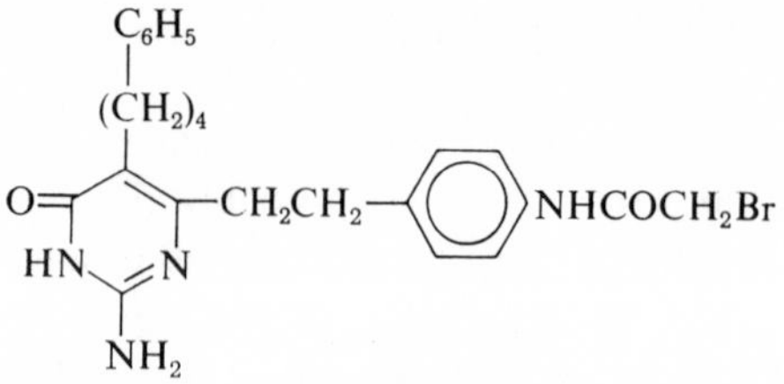

CIII

by passive diffusion, the tissue specificity being built into these neutral molecules by the bridge principle of specificity.[132]

[132] See Chapter 9, p. 172.

11 | Modus Operandi. III. Other Folate Cofactor Area Enzymes

Once folic acid is reduced to the cofactor form, tetrahydrofolate, a myriad of some 15 enzymes utilize various one-carbon derivatives of tetrahydrofolate for one-carbon transfer reactions[1]; among these enzymes are those which insert the 2- and 8- carbons of purines and the 5-methyl of thymidylate. Insertion of the 5-methyl of thymidylate catalyzed by thymidylate synthetase uses 5,10-methylene-*l*-tetrahydrofolate (I) as a cosubstrate.[2] Insertion of the eventual 8-carbon of purines utilizes the transformylation of 5,10-methenyl-*l*-tetrahydrofolate (II) to glycineamide ribotide.[3] I and II are interconvertible, being catalyzed by the enzyme 5,10-methylene-*l*-tetrahydrofolate dehydrogenase, where TPN or TPNH is the cofactor.[4] Although little work on the mode of binding of substrates and inhibitors to these enzymes has been done, some studies have been made on 5,10-methylene-*l*-tetrahydrofolate dehydrogenase and thymidylate synthetase.

5,10-METHYLENE-*l*-TETRAHYDROFOLATE DEHYDROGENASE

This reversible enzyme interconverts I and II. The reaction is readily followed because TPNH and II have a strong absorption at 340 mμ, but the products I and TPN have none[5] at this wavelength. The following studies were performed with the enzyme isolated from pigeon liver.

---

[1] For a review see T. H. Jukes and H. P. Broquist, in *Metabolic Inhibitors*, R. M. Hochster and J. H. Quastel, eds., Academic Press, New York, 1963, pp. 481–534.

[2] A. J. Wahba and M. Friedkin, *J. Biol. Chem.*, **237**, 3794 (1962).

[3] J. M. Buchanan and S. C. Hartman, *Advances in Enzymology*, **21**, 199 (1959).

[4] F. M. Huennekens, M. J. Osborn, and H. J. Whitely, *Science*, **128**, 120 (1960).

[5] See Reference 4.

The prototype inhibitor (III) for dihydrofolic reductase showed a 50 per cent inhibition of this enzyme at 30 times the concentration of *l*-substrate.[6] When the propylamino bridge was changed to amide (V), little difference in the inhibition was noted.[6,7] Replacement of the 4-hydroxyl of

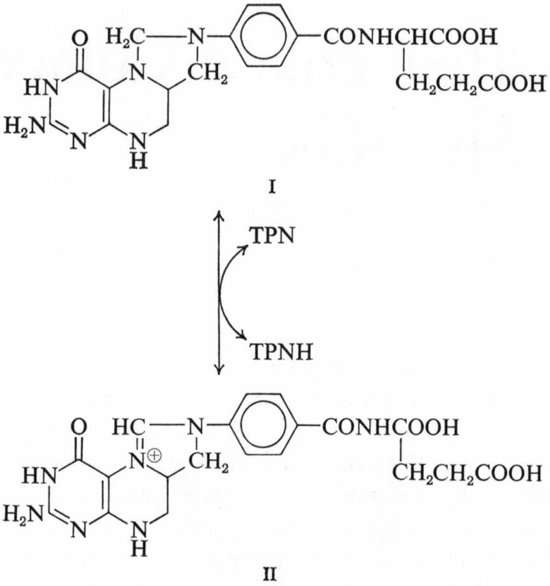

I

TPN

TPNH

II

III by 4-mercapto (IV) gave a 10-fold better inhibitor.[8] Similarly, replacement of the 6-methyl group of III by a 6-phenyl group[9] gave a better inhibitor.

The effect of changing substituents at the 2,4- and 6- positions of the pyrimidine was studied by modifying V.[10] Again VI and VII were 10-fold better inhibitors than V; however attempts to increase inhibitory properties by both changes (VIII) did not give a further increment in binding. It is noteworthy that replacement of the 2-amino group of V by 2-mercapto gave a compound (IX), that was a slightly better inhibitor.

Removal of the carboxy-L-glutamate moiety from I gave a compound that showed no inhibition at one half the concentration (the maximum solubility) used for I. In contrast, removal of the pyrimidine portion, as in

[6] B. R. Baker, D. V. Santi, P. I. Almaula, and W. C. Werkheiser, *J. Med. Chem.*, 7, 24 (1964).

[7] B. R. Baker and P. I. Almaula, *J. Heterocyclic Chem.*, 1, 263 (1964).

[8] B. R. Baker, C. E. Morreal, and B. T.-Ho, *J. Med. Chem.*, 6, 658 (1963).

[9] B. R. Baker and H. S. Shapiro, *J. Med. Chem.*, 6, 664 (1963).

[10] See Reference 7.

p-acetamidobenzoyl-L-glutamic acid, led to only a 25 per cent loss in binding energy. Because the carboxy-L-glutamate portion was necessary for good binding and because the carboxy-L-glutamate moiety of folic acid is probably necessary for active transport,[11] further studies on this

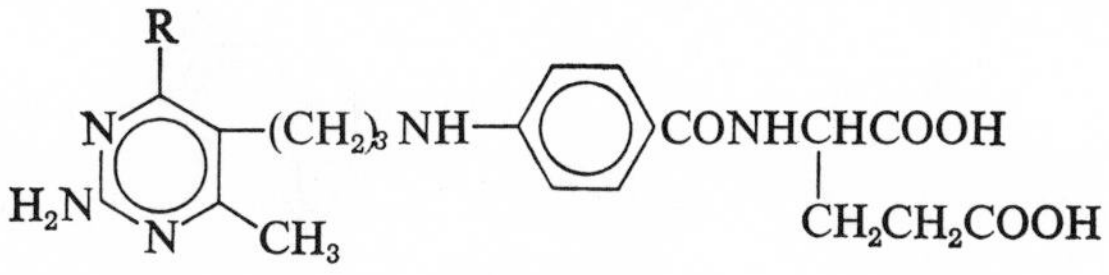

III, R = OH
IV, R = SH

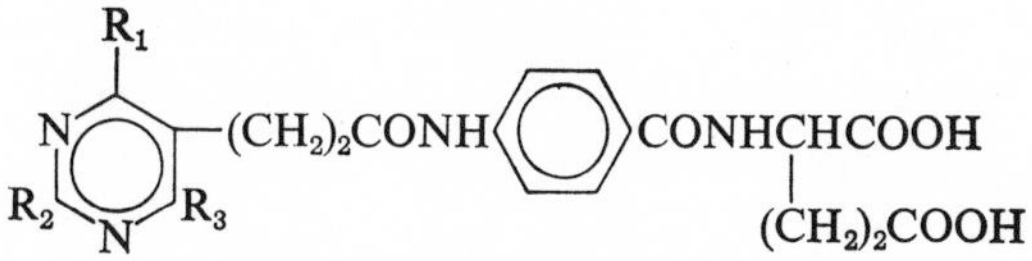

V, R_1 = OH, R_2 = NH_2, R_3 = CH_3
VI, R_1 = OH, R_2 = NH_2, R_3 = C_6H_5
VII, R_1 = SH, R_2 = NH_2, R_3 = CH_3
VIII, R_1 = SH, R_2 = NH_2, R_3 = C_6H_5
IX, R_1 = OH, R_2 = SH, R_3 = CH_3

enzyme were discontinued; it seemed unlikely that a "nonclassical" structure necessary for a candidate irreversible inhibitor would be able to pass through a cell wall by either active transport or passive diffusion.

As a calculated risk it might be worth studying (a) derivatives of benzoyl-L-glutamic acid as possible active-site-directed irreversible inhibitors, and (b) the mode of binding of the phenyl group of VI to determine if utilizable hydrophobic bonding might be observed so that the carboxy-L-glutamate moiety of V could be deleted successfully.

THYMIDYLATE SYNTHETASE

General Considerations

Thymidylate synthetase is one of the two anabolic enzymes for cellular synthesis of thymidylate (II), the other being thymidine kinase (Chapter 4). Thymidylate is then converted to DNA via thymidine triphosphate. 2'-Deoxyuridylate (I) is converted to thymidylate (II) by transfer of the methylene group of 5,10-methylene-l-tetrahydrofolate (III) to the 5-position, followed by a redox disproportionation that leads to dihydrofolate (IV)[12]; because IV has ultraviolet absorption at 338 mm, but III

[11] See Chapter 10, p. 263.
[12] S. J. Wahba and M. Friedkin, *J. Biol. Chem.*, 237, 3794 (1962).

does not, the enzyme can be assayed spectrophotometrically.[12] The strongest inhibitor of this enzyme known is 5-fluoro-2'-deoxyuridylate, which binds 1000 times more strongly to the enzyme than 2'-deoxyuridylate (I). Considerable study has been devoted to inhibitors of the enzyme which

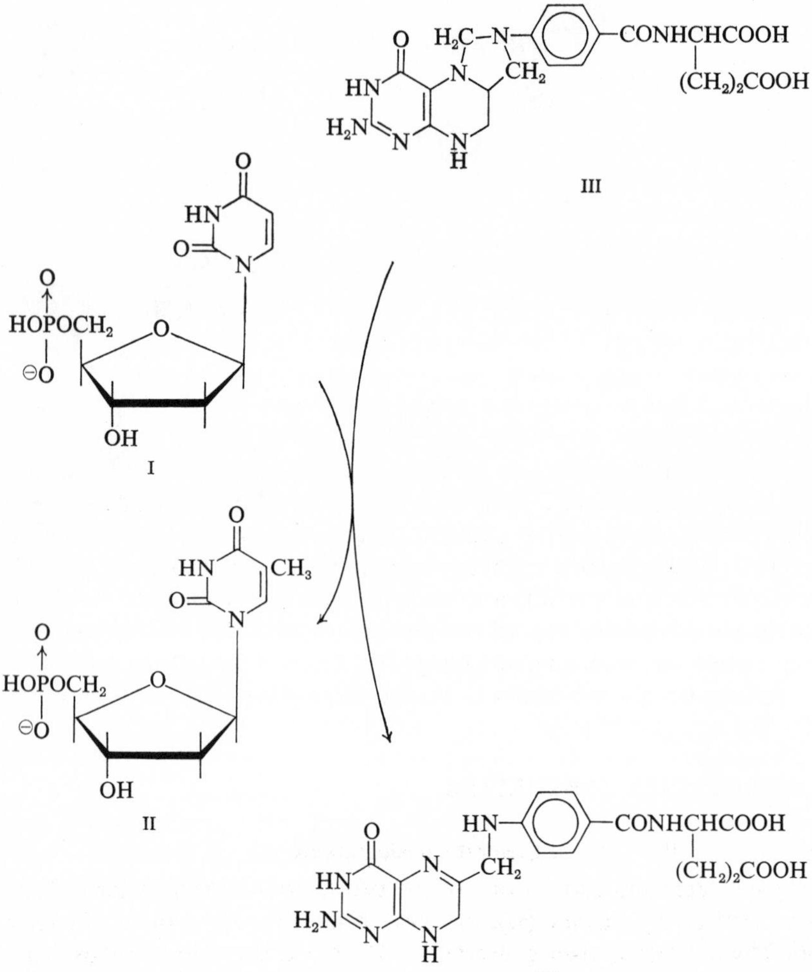

compete with 2'-deoxyuridylate (I), such as the 5-fluoro derivative. Discussion in this chapter will be limited to inhibitors competing with the cosubstrate, 5,10-methylene-*l*-tetrahydrofolate (III).

The strongest inhibitor competing with III known is tetrahydro-*dl*-

homofolic acid (V),[13] which gives a 50 per cent inhibition at one fortieth the concentration of 5,10-methylene-*l*-tetrahydrofolate; if only the *l*-isomer of V is considered to be active, then the ratio of inhibitor to

V

substrate for 50 per cent inhibition is one eightieth. Because V appears to give an N^5—N^{11} methylene bridge with formaldehyde,[13] its lack of substrate properties, combined with its higher affinity to the enzyme, is of interest. Since V, as its methylene derivative, complexes 80-fold better than the substrate (III), it follows that V has a more favorable ground-state conformation for complexing with the ground-state conformation of the enzyme. It follows further that the enzyme probably changes from the ground-state conformation when complexing with the substrate (III), for both III and the methylene derivative of V have rather rigid structures; such a conformational change could bring the catalytic site into alignment at the expense of the binding energy of the substrate. Because presumably the complexing between the enzyme and the methylene derivative of V is closer to the ground state, greater free energy of binding should be evolved, but the catalytic site is obviously not in proper alignment if the methylene derivative of V is not a substrate. Such an explanation for some of the relative binding constants and substrate properties for chymotrypsin and trypsin was discussed in Chapter 3.

Tetrahydro-*dl*-aminopterin (VI) and tetrahydro-*dl*-amethopterin (VII) showed strong inhibition at an inhibitor-substrate ratio near one[14] with the enzyme from *E. coli* B. Tetrahydro-*dl*-2-amino-6,7-dimethyl-4-pteridinol (VIII) showed a 50 per cent inhibition at an inhibitor to *l*-substrate ratio of 30 with enzyme from beef thymus[15]; since VIII had $K_i = 1.5 \times 10^{-5}$ M and 5,10-methylene-*dl*-tetrahydrofolate (III) had $K_m = 1.0 \times 10^{-6}$ M in this system, it can be estimated that only 20 per cent of the total free energy of binding of the substrate can be attributed to the *p*-aminobenzoyl-L-glutamate moiety.

The pyrimidine-type inhibitor (IX) of dihydrofolic reductase was also an inhibitor of the thymidylate synthetase from *E. coli* B, a ratio of

---

[13] L. Goodman et al., *J. Am. Chem. Soc.*, **86**, 308 (1964).

[14] See Reference 12, p. 269.

[15] D. M. Greenberg, L. I. Malkin, and R. Nath, *Biochem. Biophys. Res. Comm.*, **3**, 603 (1960).

inhibitor to *l*- substrate of 23 being required for 50 per cent inhibition.[16] When the 4-hydroxyl group of IX was replaced by 4-mercapto as in X, a ratio of only 2 was needed for 50 per cent inhibition.[17]

In contrast to dihydrofolic reductase,[18] the butylpyrimidine (XI) showed no hydrophobic bonding to thymidylate synthetase[18]; thus, it is likely that

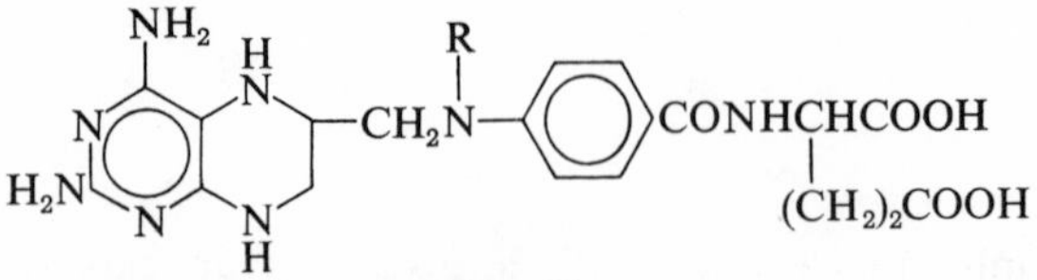

VI, R = H
VIII, R = CH$_3$

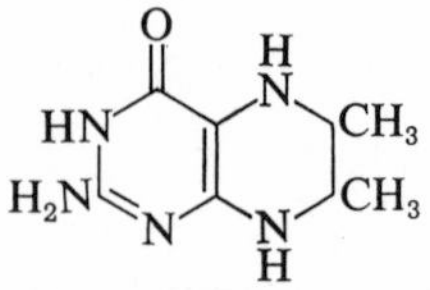

VIII

only a single rotomer of these pyrimidines is involved in complexing to thymidylate synthetase; that is, in the discussion of the pyrimidine binding to follow, it is probable that they have the "normal" pyrimidine binding in the same fashion as the pyrimidine moiety of the substrate (III). Also

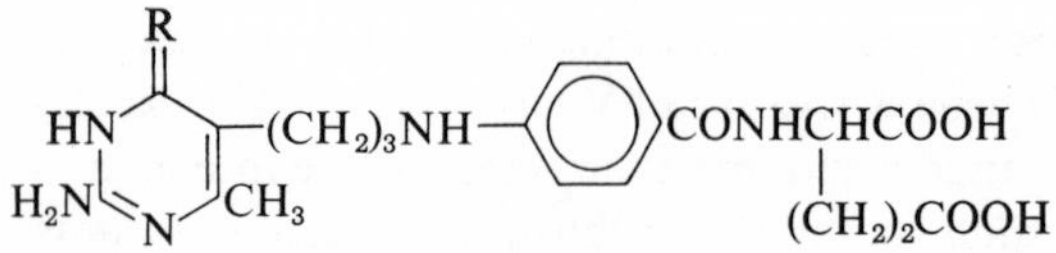

IX, R = 0
X, R = S

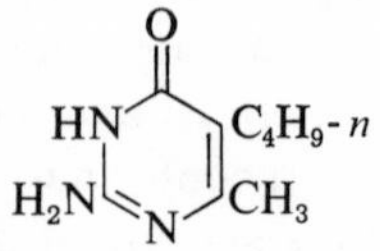

XI

note that no hydrophobic bonding could be found at the *p*- position of the anilino moiety (see XVI, Table 11–1).

Mode of Benzoyl-L-Glutamate Binding

Because the prototype pyrimidine inhibitor (IX) of dihydrofolic reductase was a reasonably good inhibitor and because variants of the benzoyl-L-glutamate were available from a study of the mode of binding to folic reductase,[19] these variants were investigated as inhibitors of thymidylate synthetase (Table 11–1).

Removal of the entire carboxy-L-glutamate moiety from IX to give XII resulted in a compound that was still a surprisingly good inhibitor compared to IX. This result could be interpreted to mean that there is little contribution to binding by the glutamate moiety. It should be noted that this is a net measured change, and therefore some binding lost from the carboxy-L-glutamate moiety may have been compensated for by increased binding of some other moiety such as the anilino; that this was indeed

[16] B. R. Baker, B. T.-Ho, and T. Neilson, *J. Heterocyclic Chem.*, 1, 79 (1964).
[17] See Reference 16.
[18] B. R. Baker, B. T.-Ho, and D. V. Santi, *J. Pharm. Sci.*, 54, 1415 (1965).
[19] See Reference 6, p. 268.

the case was shown by determining the inhibition by XIII, XIV, and XV. An actual decrease in binding by XIII compared to XII was observed; thus the *p*-carboxyl group has a detrimental effect on binding of the anilino moiety. This effect was partially overcome in both XIV and XV, but neither

Table 11–1. Inhibition of Thymidylate Synthetase by

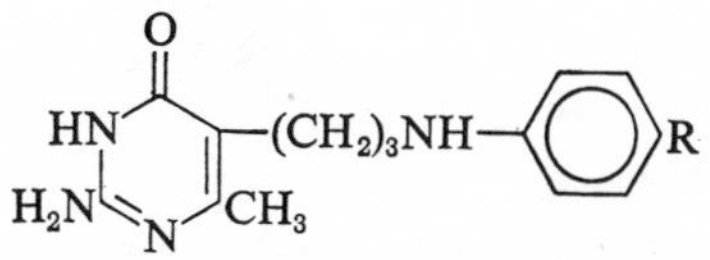

No.	R	$[I/S]_{0.5}{}^{a}$	Reference
IX	—CONHCHCOOH | $(CH_2)_2COOH$	23	b
XII	H	50	b
XIII	COOH	110	c
XIV	—CONHCH_2COOH	41	c
XV	—CONH(CH_2)_3COOH	62	c
XVI	—C_4H_9-*n*	85	d

Thymidylate synthetase from *E. coli* B was assayed with either 25.7 μM or 51.4 μM 5,10-methylene-*dl*-tetrahydrofolate (III) and 80 μM 2′-deoxyuridylate (I).

[a] Ratio of inhibitor to *l*- isomer of 5,10-methylene-tetrahydrofolate (III) giving 50 per cent inhibition.
[b] B. R. Baker, B. T.-Ho, and T. Neilson, *J. Heterocyclic Chem.*, **1**, 79 (1964).
[c] Unpublished data by B. R. Baker and D. V. Santi.
[d] Unpublished data by B. R. Baker and J. H. Jordaan.

was quite as good as the carboxy-L-glutamate analog (IX). Thus both glutamate carboxyl groups contribute weakly to binding. Whether or not the *p*-carbonyl group contributes to binding is difficult to evaluate, but it is probably minor if at all.

Mode of Pyrimidine Binding

In Table 11–2 are listed the inhibition results on variation of the 2- and 4- substituents of 2-amino-5-(3-anilinopropyl)-6-methyl-4-pyrimidinol (XII). The data are apparently best rationalized on the basis that (a) the 2-amino group is complexed to the enzyme, but whether as a donor or acceptor cannot be ascertained and (b) to an enzymic alcoholic group through the enzymic oxygen to a 3-NH pyrimidine (XXV) or through the enzymic hydroxylic hydrogen to the 3-N if the 4- substituent gives the fully aromatic pyrimidine (XXVI). The evidence for the 2-amino group being complexed to the enzyme is the following.

1. Removal of the 2-amino group from XII to give XVIII resulted in an eightfold loss in binding (Table 11–2); similarly removal of the 2-amino

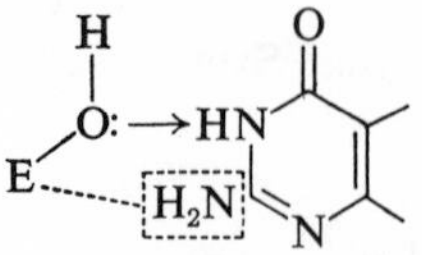

group from the 2-amino-4-mercaptopyrimidine (XIX) to give XX led to a ninefold loss in binding. Removal of the 2-amino group from the 2,4-diaminopyrimidine (XXI) to give XXII only leads to a twofold loss in binding; this may be due to a basicity effect because 4-aminopyrimidine is

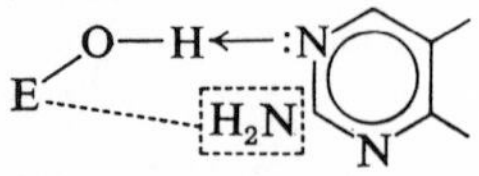

Table 11–2. Inhibition of Thymidylate Synthetase by

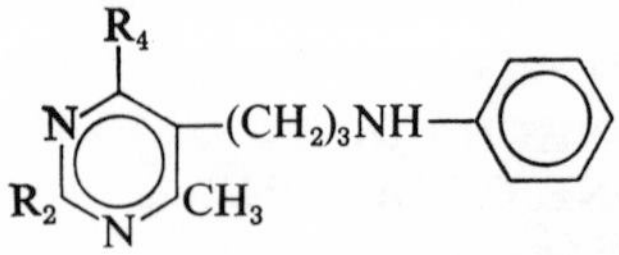

No.	R_2	R_4	$[I/S]_{0.5}$[a]	Reference
XII	NH_2	OH	50	b
XVII	NH_2	H	100	b
XVIII	H	OH	420	b
XIX	NH_2	SH	11	b
XX	H	SH	90	b
XXI	NH_2	NH_2	63	b
XXII	H	NH_2	210	c
XXIII	$(CH_3)_2N$	OH	>480	c
XXIV	NH_2	$(CH_3)_2N$	100	c

Thymidylate synthetase from *E. coli* B was assayed with either 25.7 or 51.4 μM 5,10-methylene-*dl*-tetrahydrofolate (III) and 80 μM 2′deoxyuridylate (I).

[a] Ratio of inhibitor to *l*- isomer of 5,10-methylene-tetrahydrofolate (III) giving 50 per cent inhibition.
[b] B. R. Baker, B. T.-Ho and T. Neilson, *J. Heterocyclic Chem.*, **1**, 79 (1964).
[c] B. R. Baker and B. T.-Ho, *J. Pharm. Sci.*, **53**, 1457 (1964).

a considerably stronger base than 2-aminopyrimidine and bonding may be stronger at N_3 than in the case of XVII.

2. Replacement of the 2-amino group of the 2-amino-4-hydroxypyrimidine (XII) by dimethylamino to give XXIII results in a greater than

ninefold loss in binding. The result indicates that the enzyme is close to the 2-amino group in the complex; whether the decrease in binding is due to a steric intolerance of the two N-methyl groups or whether a hydrogen on the 2-amino group is an acceptor in bonding to the enzyme cannot as yet be differentiated.

The evidence that the 3-NH as an acceptor or the 3-N as a donor can complex to the enzyme and that the 4-oxo group does not complex is the following.

1. Replacement of the 4-hydroxyl of the 2-amino-4-hydroxypyrimidine (XVII) by mercapto to give XIX results in a fourfold increase in bonding; similarly, the 4-mercaptopyrimidine (XX) is a four- to fivefold better inhibitor than the corresponding 4-hydroxypyrimidine (XVIII). If both the 3-NH and 4-oxo group were involved in bonding, a decrease in binding would be expected to occur, as was noted with 9-phenylguanine versus 9-phenyl-6-thioguanine binding to guanine deaminase.[20] Therefore the increased binding observed with the mercapto pyrimidines is best rationalized by the increased acidity of the 3-NH group, which results in the 3-NH being a better acceptor.

2. Replacement of the 4-hydroxyl group of the 2-amino-4-hydroxypyrimidine (XII) with amino to give XXI results in no change in binding. Because it is most likely that the 3-NH of the 4-oxopyrimidine (XII) and 4-thionopyrimidine (XIX) is complexing to the enzyme, the fact that XXI complexes as well as XII can be rationalized by the two modes of complexing to an enzymic hydroxyl group, as depicted in XXV and XXVI. Similarly, the replacement of the 4-hydroxyl of the 2-amino-4-hydroxypyrimidine (XII) by hydrogen to give XVII resulted in only a twofold loss in binding.

3. Bulk tolerance for the 4-dimethylamino group of the 2-amino-4-dimethylaminopyrimidine (XXIV) is indicated by the less than twofold loss in binding compared to the 2,4-diaminopyrimidine (XXI). This result suggests, but it is far from being unequivocal, that there is no binding at the 4- position of the pyrimidine; however unlikely, it is still possible that the 4-oxo, the 4-amino, and the 4-dimethylamino could bond as electron donors.

There is no evidence available on whether or not the 1-N is involved in binding to the enzyme. However, varying the 6- substituent can effect binding. Note in Table 11–3 that the 5-(phenylbutyl) pyrimidine (XXVII) is as good an inhibitor as the 5-(anilinopropyl) pyrimidine (XII); some structural modifications at the 6- position of 2-amino-6-methyl-5-(4-phenylbutyl)-4-pyrimidinol (XXVII) were then investigated. Replacement of the 6-methyl group of XXVII by a *n*-propyl to give XXXII resulted in

[20] See Chapter 5, p. 105.

little change in binding; similar results were obtained when the 6-methyl group of the prototype inhibitor (IX) was replaced by 6-phenyl.[21] Thus, there is bulk tolerance for in-plane or out-of-plane hydrocarbon substituents at the 6- position, and there is no apparent hydrophobic bonding in this region.

Table 11–3. Inhibition of Thymidylate Synthetase by

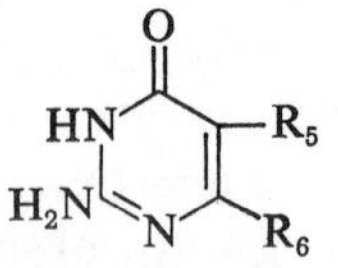

$$\begin{array}{c} O \\ \| \\ HN \diagup \diagdown R_5 \\ H_2N \diagdown_N \diagup R_6 \end{array}$$

No.	R_5	R_6	$[I/S]_{0.5}$[a]	Reference
XII	—$(CH_2)_3NHC_6H_5$	CH_3	50	[b]
XXVII	—$(CH_2)_4C_6H_5$	CH_3	35	[b]
XXVIII	—$NH(CH_2)_3C_6H_5$	CH_3	58	[b]
XXIX	—$(CH_2)_4C_6H_5$	NH_2	> 130	[b]
XXX	—$(CH_2)_4C_6H_5$	CF_3	> 160	[c]
XXXI	—$(CH_2)_4C_6H_5$	$COOH$	> 1200	[c]
XXXII	—$(CH_2)_4C_6H_5$	n-C_3H_7	37	[d]

Thymidylate synthetase from *E. coli* B was assayed with either 25.7 or 51.4 μM 5,10-methylene-*dl*-tetrahydrofolate (III) and 80 μM 2′-deoxyuridylate (I).

[a] Ratio of inhibitor to *l*- isomer of 5,10-methylene-tetrahydrofolate (III) giving a 50 per cent inhibition.
[b] B. R. Baker and D. V. Santi, *J. Pharm. Sci.*, **54**, 1252 (1965).
[c] B. R. Baker and J. H. Jordaan, *J. Heterocyclic Chem.*, **2**, 162 (1965).
[d] Unpublished data by B. R. Baker.

Surprisingly, replacement of the 6-methyl group of XVIII by either amino (XXIX), carboxylate (XXXI), or trifluoromethyl (XXX) was detrimental to binding. These results are difficult to reconcile with only a single effect, such as inductive effect, for the carboxylate group has a Hammett σ value near zero, the amino group is electron donating and the trifluoromethyl is electron withdrawing. Similarly, a single effect such as coulombic repulsion would not satisfy both the amine and carboxylate, being detrimental to binding. It should be noted that the substrate (III) has an NH group corresponding to the 6- position of the pyrimidine, XXIX; therefore, the detrimental effect of the 6- amino group is even more surprising.

Regardless of the exact mode of binding, replacement of the 4-oxo

[21] Unpublished data by B. R. Baker and H. S. Shapiro.

group of the 2-amino-4-oxopyrimidine (XII) by 4-thione (XIX) leads to the strongest pyrimidine binding. It is also of interest that replacement of the 4-hydroxy group of XII by 4-amino (XXI) gives little change in binding, whereas the same charge gives a 300-fold increment in binding to dihydrofolic reductase.

Mode of Anilino Binding

In Table 11–4 are listed the results on modification of the anilino moiety; comparisons were made in two series, the 4-mercaptopyrimidine

XII, R = OH
XIX, R = SH

series (XIX) and the 4-hydroxypyrimidine series (XII). That the NH group was not involved in binding was shown by replacing the NH group of XII with CH_2 to give the phenylbutyl pyrimidine (XXVII), which was a slightly better inhibitor than XII. It was further demonstrated by acetylating the anilino hydrogen of XIX to give XXXIV, which resulted in a threefold increment in binding.

That the benzene ring is involved in binding is indicated by comparison of *n*-butyl (XI) with phenylbutyl (XXVII). Furthermore, that a more electronegative benzene ring could complex better was indicated by *p*-substitution with electron-withdrawing groups; the *p*-Cl group of XXXV gave an eightfold increment, the *p*-F group of XXXVII gave a threefold increment, and the *p*-chloroacetyl group (XLI) gave a 3.5-fold increase in binding. However, electron-donating groups such as *p*-dimethylamino (XXXVI) and *p*-(*n*-butyl) (XVI) had little effect on binding. Furthermore, replacement of the benzene ring of XLII by more electronegative rings (XLIII–XLV) or a more electropositive ring (XLVI) led to a decrease in binding; one factor here is the greater hydrophilic character of the heterocyclic rings compared to the benzene ring. Thus the best binding of the benzene ring takes place if it remains hydrophobic but is substituted by electron-withdrawing substituents. Such a conclusion could be rationalized by hydrophobic bonding to a hydrophobic aromatic group on the enzyme that can also act as an electron donor in a charge-transfer complex. Another possibility is that hydrophobic bonding takes place by the benzene ring to the enzyme along with a separate electron donor interaction by the *p*-halogens (XXXV and XXXVII) and the *p*-ketone group (XLI).

Table 11–4. Inhibition of Thymidylate Synthetase by

No.	R_1	R_2	$[I/S]_{0.5}{}^a$	Binding increment	Reference
XII	OH	—NHC$_6$H$_5$	50	Baseline	f
XIX	SH	—NHC$_6$H$_5$	11	Baseline	f
XXVII	OH	—CH$_2$C$_6$H$_5$	35		f
XXXIII	OH	—OC$_6$H$_5$	> 140^b		f
XI	OH	—CH$_3$	> 100^b		g
XXXIV	SH	—N(Ac)C$_6$H$_5$	3.9	2.8^c	f
XXXV	SH	—NHC$_6$H$_4$Cl-p	1.4	8^c	f
XXXVI	SH	—NHC$_6$H$_4$N(CH$_3$)$_2$-p	8.6	1.2^c	f
XXXVII	OH	—NHC$_6$H$_4$F-p	19	2.6^d	h
XXXVIII	OH	—NHC$_6$H$_4$CF$_3$-m	> 8^b		h
XXXIX	OH	—NHC$_6$H$_4$—(CH=CHCOCH$_2$Cl)-p	> 100^b	< $\frac{1}{2}{}^d$	i
XL	OH	—NHC$_6$H$_4$—[(CH$_2$)$_4$COCH$_2$Cl]-p	> 100^b	< $\frac{1}{2}{}^d$	i
XLI	OH	—NHC$_6$H$_4$(COCH$_2$Cl)-p	14	3.5^d	i
XIII	OH	—NHC$_6$H$_4$COO$^-$-p	110	$\frac{1}{4}{}^d$	j
XVI	OH	—NHC$_6$H$_4$(C$_4$H$_9$-n)-p	85	0.6^d	i
XLII	OH	—N(Ac)CH$_2$C$_6$H$_5$	39	Baseline	h
XLIII	OH	—N(Ac)CH$_2$-pyridyl-4	200	$\frac{1}{5}{}^e$	h
XLIV	OH	—N(Ac)CH$_2$-pyridyl-3	190	$\frac{1}{5}{}^e$	h
XLV	OH	—N(Ac)CH$_2$-pyridyl-2	490	$\frac{1}{11}{}^e$	h
XLVI	OH	—N(Ac)CH$_2$-Furyl-2	170	$\frac{1}{4}{}^e$	h

Thymidylate synthetase from *E. coli* B was assayed with 25.7 or 51.4 μM 5,10-methylene-*dl*-tetrahydrofolate (III) and 80 μM 2′-deoxyuridylate (I).

^{a} The ratio of concentration of inhibitor to the *l*- isomer of 5,10-methylenetetrahydrofolate (III) giving 50 per cent inhibition.

^{b} Limit of solubility.

^{c} Compared to XIX.

^{d} Compared to XII.

^{e} Compared to XLII.

^{f} B. R. Baker, B.-T.-Ho, and G. B. Chheda, *J. Heterocyclic Chem.*, **1**, 88 (1964).

^{g} B. R. Baker, B.-T.-Ho, and D. V. Santi, *J. Pharm. Sci.*, **54**, 1415 (1965).

^{h} B. R. Baker and J. Novotny, *J. Heterocyclic Chem.*, **4**, in press (1967).

^{i} Unpublished data by B. R. Baker and J. H. Jordaan.

^{j} Unpublished data by B. R. Baker and D. V. Santi.

Bridge Variation Between Pyrimidyl and Phenyl Moieties

Because both the pyrimidyl and phenyl moieties of XII are complexed to thymidylate but the —(CH$_2$)$_3$NH— bridge apparently does not contribute to binding, studies on the variation of the bridge have been made. The results are tabulated in Table 11–5. Among the advantages such bridge variants could provide are (a) a greater variation in synthetic possibilities directed towards active-site-directed irreversible inhibitors and (b) other bridges that might allow better binding of the phenyl moiety perhaps by a more favorable ground-state conformation between the two binding moieties.

As was noted previously in an earlier section, the —$(CH_2)_3NH$— bridge of XII (Table 11–5) can be replaced by the butylene bridge (XXVII) with a

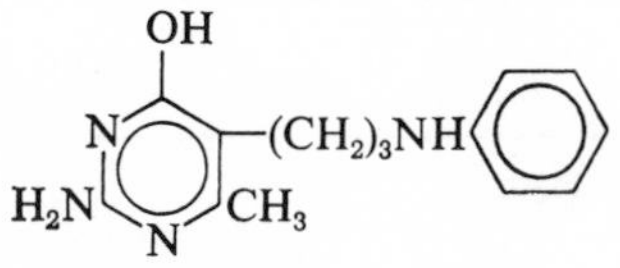

XII

slight increment in binding; the propylene bridge (XLVIII) was not as effective as the butylene bridge by a factor of about 3. Surprisingly, the —$(CH_2)_3O$— bridge of XXXIII was at least threefold less effective than XII at the highest concentration of XXXIII that could be measured. When the propylamino group of XII was reversed to give XXVIII, about the same binding was observed.

It is interesting to compare the 5-(cinnamylamino)-pyrimidine (XLIX) with the 5-(phenylpropylamino)-pyrimidine (XXVIII); the two compounds have nearly the same binding capacity to thymidylate synthetase. The *trans*-cinnamyl group of XLIX has a ground-state conformation that is staggered and has the benzene ring in the plane of the vinyl group due to the overlapping orbitals of the styryl system, as is indicated in structure XLIX*A*. Because XLIX and XXVIII have about equal binding it follows

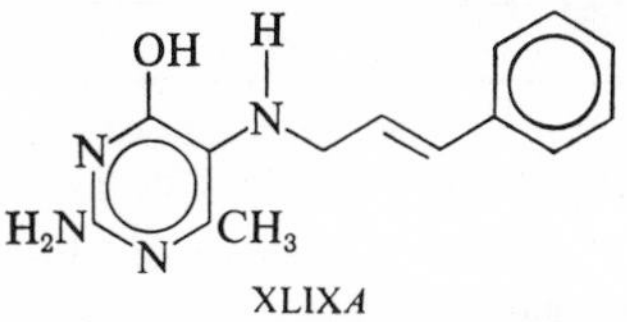

XLIX*A*

that both are complexed to the enzyme (as is indicated in XLIX*A*) except for the possible rotations of the bond between the pyrimidine and the bridge nitrogen and the adjacent bond.

Replacement of the —$(CH_2)_3NH$— bridge of XII by —$(CH_2)_3NHCH_2$— as in LI has an effect additional to lengthening the chain; that is, the aliphatic NH group in the bridge will be completely protonated at the pH 7.4 of the assay. Note that an eightfold loss in binding occurred, compared to XII, and that the benzyl group binds no better than the butyl group of L or the acetyl group of LII. This result suggests no binding occurs in the side chain of LI, but only binding by the pyrimidyl moiety. The acetamido group would be expected to contribute little to binding in

Table 11–5. Inhibition of Thymidylate Synthetase by

No.	R_5	$[I/S]_{0.5}{}^a$	Binding increment	Reference
XII	—$(CH_2)_3NHC_6H_5$	50		[b]
XXVII	—$(CH_2)_4C_6H_5$	35	1.4	[b]
XLVIII	—$(CH_2)_3C_6H_5$	110	$\frac{1}{2.2}$	[c]
XXXIII	—$(CH_2)_3OC_6H_5$	> 140	$<\frac{1}{3}$	[b]
XXVIII	—$NH(CH_2)_3C_6H_5$	58	1	[c]
XLIX	—$NHCH_2CH{=}CHC_6H_5$	80	$\frac{1}{1.6}$	[c]
L	—$(CH_2)_3\overset{+}{N}H_2C_4H_9\text{-}n$	350	$\frac{1}{7}$	[b]
LI	—$(CH_2)_3\overset{+}{N}H_2CH_2C_6H_5$	400	$\frac{1}{8}$	[d]
XLII	—$(CH_2)_3N(Ac)CH_2C_6H_5$	39	1.3	[d]
LII	—$(CH_2)_3NHCOCH_3$	500	$\frac{1}{10}$	[e]
LIII	—$(CH_2)_3NHCOC_6H_5$	> 230	$<\frac{1}{4}$	[e]
LIV	—$(CH_2)_3NHCOCH_2C_6H_5$	> 90	$<\frac{1}{2}$	[e]
LV	—$(CH_2)_3NHCOC_6H_4(CH_2OC_2H_5)\text{-}p$	66	$\frac{1}{1.3}$	[e]
LVI	—$(CH_2)_3NHCOC_6H_4NO_2\text{-}p$	> 170	$<\frac{1}{3}$	[e]
LVII	—$(CH_2)_3NHCOC_6H_4NH_2\text{-}p$	> 230	$<\frac{1}{5}$	[e]
LVIII	—$(CH_2)_3NHSO_2C_6H_4CH_3\text{-}p$	11	4.5	[e]
LIX	—$(CH_2)_3NHSO_2C_4H_9\text{-}n$	180	$\frac{1}{3.6}$	[e]

Thymidylate synthetase from *E. coli* was assayed with 25.7 or 51.4 µM 5,10-methylene-*dl*-tetrahydrofolate (III) and 80 µM 2′-deoxyuridylate (I).

[a] Ratio of concentration of inhibitor to *l*- isomer of 5,10-methylene-tetrahydrofolate (III) giving 50 per cent inhibition.

[b] B. R. Baker, B.-T. Ho, and G. B. Chheda, *J. Heterocyclic Chem.*, **1**, 88 (1964).

[c] B. R. Baker and D. V. Santi, *J. Pharm. Sci.*, **54**, 1252 (1965).

[d] B. R. Baker and J. Novotny, *J. Heterocyclic Chem.*, **4**, in press (1967).

[e] B. R. Baker and J. K. Coward, *J. Pharm. Sci.*, **54**, 714 (1965).

view of the comparison of the anilinopropyl-pyrimidine (XIX) (Table 11–4) and its *N*-acetyl derivative (XXXIV); it binds only about threefold better than XIX.[22] Therefore the lack of phenyl binding by the benzylammonium group of LI may be due to a repulsion of the cationic group on the bridge from the enzyme, which results in a different positioning of the phenyl. When the cationic group of LI is removed by *N*-acetylation, the

[22] B. R. Baker, B.-T. Ho, and G. B. Chheda, *J. Heterocyclic Chem.*, **1**, 88 (1964).

resultant XLII binds slightly better than the anilinopropyl-pyrimidine (XII) and 10 times better than the benzylammoniumpropyl-pyrimidine (LI); another factor is the coplanarity of the amide nitrogen bonds in the side chain of XLII.

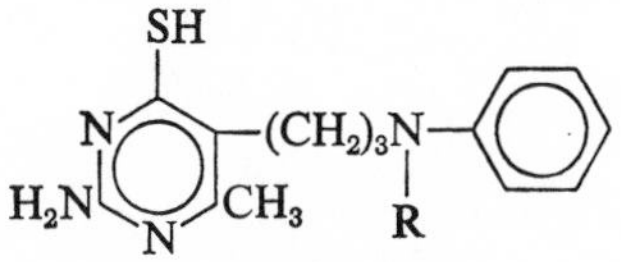

XIX, R = H
XXXIV, R = Ac

Increasing the bridge length of XII by replacing the phenyl by benzoyl (LIII) or phenylacetyl (LIV) gave a decrease in binding, the amount of which could not be ascertained because of its insolubility; however, replacement of the phenyl group of XII by *p*-ethoxymethylbenzoyl, as in LV, resulted in little change in binding. Because *p*- substitution on the benzoyl group of LIII by the electron-withdrawing nitro (LVI) or electron donating amino (LVII) groups did not give as good an inhibitor as the *p*-ethoxymethyl group (LV), the effect of the latter is not inductive on benzene binding. It may be direct binding by the ether oxygen to the enzyme.

The best inhibitor in Table 11–5 was found with the $-(CH_2)_3NHSO_2-$ bridge of LVIII. A fourfold increment in binding was observed compared to the $-(CH_2)_3NH-$ side chain of XII; it is unlikely that the *p*-methyl group had any influence on binding. Furthermore, that the phenyl of the sulfonamide (LVIII) and not the sulfonamide group was probably complexed to the enzyme was indicated by the 16-fold decrease in effectiveness of the *n*-butylsulfonamide (LIX). From the standpoint of the ease with which synthesis can be carried out, the excellent binding by the arylsulfonamidopropyl side chain of LVIII is most useful, for structural variants of the arylsulfonamide moiety are readily synthesized.

Bulk Tolerance

Tolerance for bulky groups on inhibitors such as XII, after complexing with thymidylate synthetase, can be divided into three areas of study, namely, (a) the pyrimidine area, (b) the bridge, and (c) the benzene ring.

It was previously noted that the 6-methyl group of XXVII could be substituted with *n*-propyl (XXXII) without loss of binding[23] (Table 11–3). Furthermore, the 6-methyl group (IX) could be replaced by 6-phenyl (LXI) with no change in binding.[23] Therefore, there is bulk tolerance at the 6-

[23] Unpublished data by B. R. Baker and H. J. Shapiro.

position of the pyrimidine for either an in-plane phenyl group or the three-dimensional more bulky, n-propyl group.

Substitution of the 2-amino group of XII by dimethylamino (XXIII) gave a large loss in binding (Table 11–2), indicating there is no bulk toler-

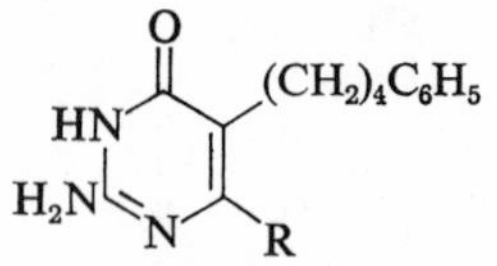

XXVII, R = CH_3
XXXII, R = n-C_3H_7

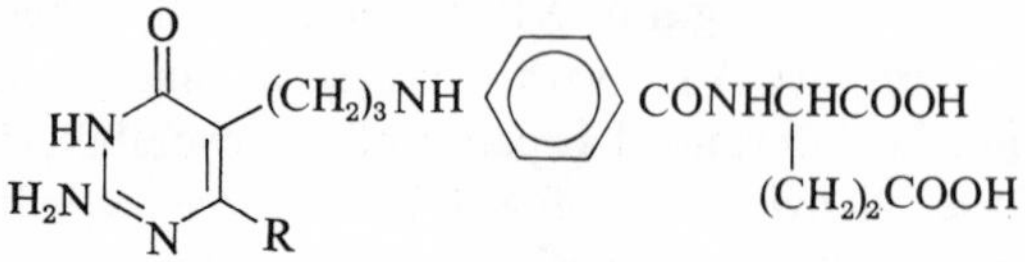

IX, R = CH_3
LXI, R = C_6H_5

ance at this position. In contrast, substitution of the 4-amino group of XXI by dimethylamino (XXIV) gave no loss in binding, indicating a bulk tolerance. Whether larger groups could be substituted on N^4 of XXI or

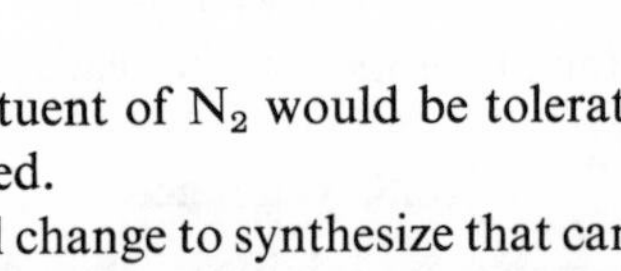

XII, R_1 = NH_2, R_2 = OH
XXI, R_1 = NH_2, R_2 = NH_2
XXIII, R_1 = $(CH_2)_2N$, R_2 = OH
XXIV, R_1 = NH_2, R_2 = $N(CH_3)_2$

whether a single substituent of N_2 would be tolerated within the complex has not been determined.

The easiest structural change to synthesize that can be made in the bridge between the pyrimidyl and benzene moiety is to substitute on a bridge NH group (Table 11–6). Note that acylation of the bridge NH group of XIX with acetyl (XXXIV), benzoyl (LX), or carbophenoxy (LXI) gives up to a threefold increase in binding, but no decrease; therefore there is bulk tolerance for these acyl groups within the enzyme-inhibitor complex. Similarly, there is bulk tolerance for an acetyl group on XLII (higher acyl groups have not been investigated). The N-succinyl group of LXII is not tolerated as much, for a fourfold loss in binding occurs compared to XII;

this may be due to repulsion of the terminal anionic carboxylate group, which is fully ionized at the pH 7.4 of the assay.

Substitution on the bridge nitrogen of the sulfonamide (LVIII) was also enlightening; little change in binding occurred on *N*-butylation to give LXIII. Substitution of aryl or aralkyl groups on the bridge nitrogen

Table 11–6. Inhibition of Thymidylate Synthetase by

No.	R_1	R_2	R_3	$[I/S]_{0.5}$[a]	Reference
XII	OH	H	$C_6H_5—$	50	b
XIX	SH	H	$C_6H_5—$	11	b
XXXIV	SH	$CH_3CO—$	$C_6H_5—$	3.9	b
LX	SH	$C_6H_5CO—$	$C_6H_5—$	7.0	c
LIII	OH	$C_6H_5CO—$	H	>230	d
LXI	SH	$C_6H_5OOC—$	$C_6H_5—$	5.1	c
LXII	OH	$HOOCCH_2CH_2CO—$	$C_6H_5—$	220	e
LI	OH	H	$C_6H_5CH_2—$	400	f
XLII	OH	CH_3CO	$C_6H_5CH_2—$	39	f
LVIII	OH	H	$p\text{-}CH_3C_6H_4SO_2—$	11	d
LXIII	OH	$n\text{-}C_4H_9—$	$p\text{-}CH_3C_6H_4SO_2—$	16	c
LXIV	OH	$C_6H_5—$	$p\text{-}NH_2C_6H_4SO_2—$	3.5	g
LXV	OH	$C_6H_5—$	$p\text{-}NO_2C_6H_4SO_2—$	12	g
LXVI	OH	$m\text{-}NO_2C_6H_4CH_2—$	$p\text{-}CH_3C_6H_4SO_2$	3.9	g

Thymidylate synthetase from *E. coli* B was assayed with 25.7 or 51.4 μM 5,10-methylene-*dl*-terahydrofolate (III) and 80 μM 2′-deoxyuridylate.

[a] Ratio of concentration of inhibitor to *l*- isomer of 5,10-methylenetetrahydrofolate giving 50 per cent inhibition.

[b] B. R. Baker, B.-T. Ho, and T. Neilson, *J. Heterocyclic Chem.*, **1**, 88 (1964).

[c] B. R. Baker and B.-T. Ho, *J. Pharm. Sci.*, **54**, 1187 (1965).

[e] B. R. Baker and D. V. Santi, unpublished.

[f] B. R. Baker and J. Novotny, *J. Heterocyclic Chem.*, **4**, in press (1967).

[g] B. R. Baker and J. K. Coward, *J. Heterocyclic Chem.*, **4**, in press (1967).

(LXIV–LXVI) of the sulfonamide also showed bulk tolerance because the compounds were as good or better inhibitors than the parent toluenesulfonamide (LVIII). In the case of LXIV–LXVI it is difficult at this stage to decide which aryl group is complexed to the enzyme without additional information. In the case of the *N*-benzoyl derivative (LX) it is clear that the *N*-benzoyl is not complexing, for removal of the *N*-phenyl causes a loss in binding (compare XII and LIII in Table 11–6). It is clear that further positioning of a covalent forming group on R_2 or R_3 of XXXIV, LX, XLII, LVIII, and LXIII–LXVI would give potential active-site directed irreversible inhibitors; such studies are being pursued.

Evidence for bulk tolerance on the phenyl group of XII is as yet fragmentary, but appears to be likely. Note in Table 11–4 that the *p-n*-butyl (XVI), *p*-chloro (XXXV), *p*-dimethylamino (XXXVI), and *p*-chloroacetyl (XLI) substituents are tolerated. Also note in Table 11–5 that the *p*-ethoxymethyl (LV) and *p*-methyl (LVIII) substituents are tolerated, but a good baseline for either compound is not yet available.

Hydrophobic Bonding

No hydrophobic bonding to thymidylate synthetase has yet been found, but there are a number of areas where it is not present in a molecule such as XII. There is no apparent hydrophobic bonding between the phenyl and

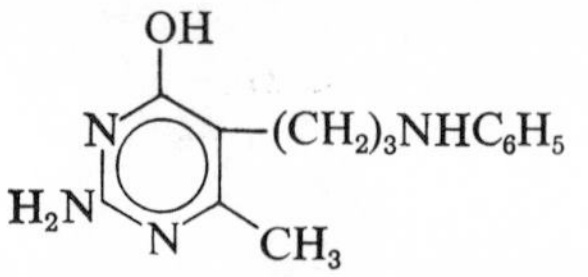

XII

pyrimidyl moieties because replacement of the anilino of XII by benzyl (XXVII, Table 11–4) gives only a slight increment in binding and replacement of the anilino group of XII by methyl (XI), (Table 11–4) gives a loss in binding.

There is apparently no hydrophobic bonding at the *p-* position of the phenyl group because introduction of the *n*-butyl group at this position to give XVI (Table 11–4) results in a slight decrease in binding. Similarly there does not appear to be hydrophobic bonding near the bridge nitrogen of XII because introduction of an *N*-butyl group (LXIII) on the sulfonamide (LVIII) (Table 11–6) gives practically no change in binding. Whether the *o* or *m* positions of the phenyl, or the methylenes of the bridge of XII, can be a point of entry to a hydrophobic region has not been determined.

On the pyrimidine ring the 6- position is apparently not near a hydrophobic region because replacement of the 6-methyl group of XXVII by *n*-propyl (XXXII) (Table 11–3) gives no change in binding; similarly replacement of the 6-methyl group of the prototype inhibitor IX by 6-phenyl (XXIII) (p. 276) makes no change in binding. Whether or not the 4-position of the pyrimidine of XII could be an entry to a hydrophobic region remains to be determined. Because bulk tolerance at the 2- position seems minimal, the chances of detecting hydrophobic bonding in this region are probably small.

I 2 | Modus Operandi.
IV. Adenosine Deaminase

GENERAL CONSIDERATIONS

Adenosine deaminase catalyzes the conversion of adenosine (I) to inosine (II), has no cofactor requirements, and is apparently irreversible[1]; the "deamination" probably proceeds by an enzyme-catalyzed addition of water to the N_1=C_6 double bond followed by elimination of ammonia. The enzyme, partially purified from calf intestine, is commercially avail-

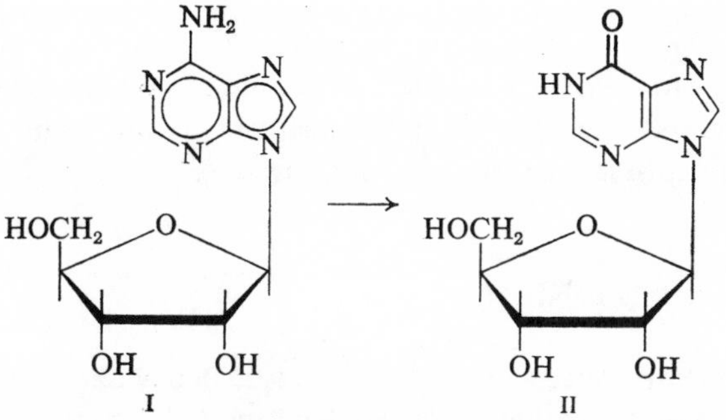

I   II

able. It is readily assayed by the change in optical density at 265 mμ where a 40 per cent decrease in ultraviolet absorption occurs when adenosine (I) is converted to inosine (II).[1]

    Adenosine can be incorporated into nucleic acids, via conversion to its 5′-phosphate, adenylic acid, with adenosine kinase,[2] but no enzyme is known that phosphorylates inosine.[2] In contrast, both adenosine and inosine can be enzymatically cleaved to the free bases. Because inosinic

[1] H. M. Kalckar, *J. Biol. Chem.*, **167**, 445 (1947).
[2] See Chapter 1 for a discussion of these enzymes that convert the respective nucleosides to the nucleotides.

acid is converted into nucleic acids via adenylic acid, adenylic acid and adenosine are closer to final synthesis of nucleic acid than inosinic acid and inosine, respectively. It therefore follows that adenosine deaminase is probably a catabolic enzyme that has no direct utility for nucleic acid biosynthesis; it is therefore not too surprising that adenosine deaminase detoxifies a number of adenosine-like cytoxic agents such as 9-(β-D-xylofuranosyl)-adenine (III),[3] 9-(β-D-arabinofuranosyl)-adenine (IV),[3] 3'-deoxyadenosine (V),[4] and 3'-amino-3'-deoxyadenosine (VI).[4] A tissue-specific blockade of adenosine deaminase could be of chemotherapeutic utility when it is used in conjunction with cytotoxic agents such as III–VI.

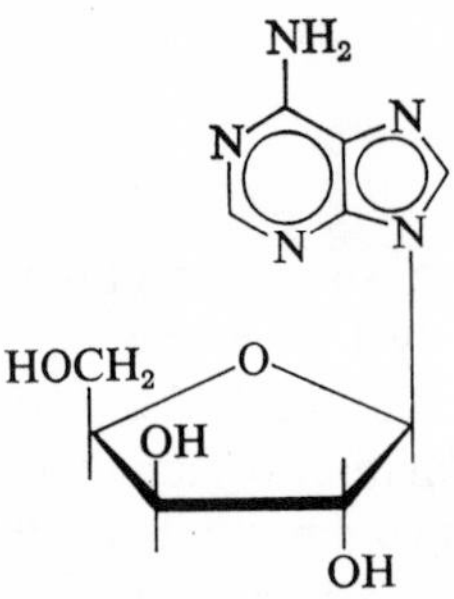

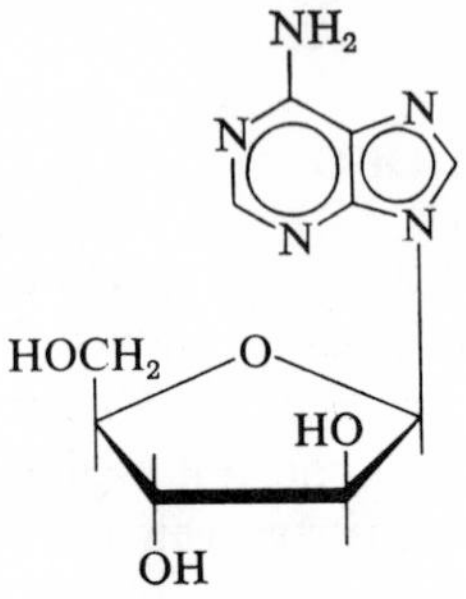

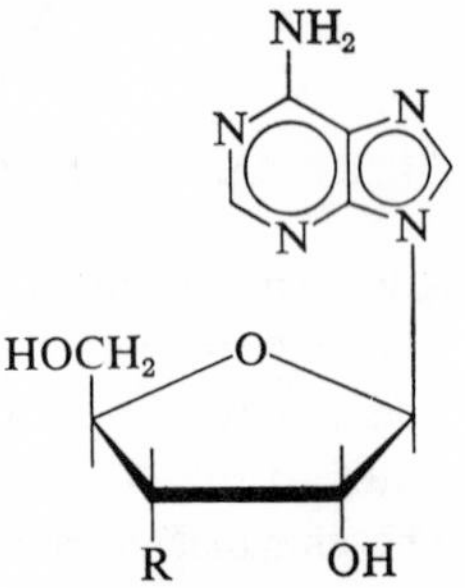

Because there seem to be differences in binding to adenosine deaminase from different sources, the binding measurements will be limited to those determined with the enzyme from calf intestine.

RIBOFURANOSE BINDING

In Table 12–1 are listed the results with some deoxy derivatives of adenosine. It is noteworthy that 2'-deoxyadenosine (VII) complexes about 2.8 times tighter than adenosine (I) and VII has a V_{max} slightly greater than I[5]; thus the 2'-hydroxy contributes neither to binding nor to substrate properties. This is further verified by the 2'-methyl ether (XI) of adenosine, which is complexed about 1.5 times better than adenosine and is still a substrate.

That the 3'-hydroxyl group is not needed for substrate properties is indicated with 3'-deoxyadenosine (V), which appears to be almost as good

[3] G. A. LePage and I. G. Junga, *Cancer Res.*, **25**, 46 (1965).
[4] J. G. Cory and R. J. Suhadolnik, *Biochemistry*, **4**, 1729 (1965).
[5] See Reference 4.

Table 12–1. Binding to Adenosine Deaminase by

No.	R	$K_m \times 10^5\ M$	$K_i \times 10^5\ M$	Reference
I		4.2[a] 8.3[a] 7.3		b c d
VII		1.5[a]		b
V		Substrate		c
VIII		8.5		e
IX		No	~50	f
X		No	>65	e
XI		4.7		e

(continued on next page)

No.	R	$K_m \times 10^5 M$	$K_i \times 10^5 M$	Reference
XII		640		*g*

Enzyme from calf intestine at pH 7.6 in phosphate buffer was employed, unless otherwise indicated.

a pH 7.0; the enzyme has a pH maximum at 7–7.5 (see Reference *b* below).
b O. P. Chilson and J. R. Fisher, *Arch. Biochem. Biophys.*, **102**, 77 (1963).
c J. G. Cory and R. J. Suhadolnik, *Biochemistry*, **4**, 1733 (1965).
d H. J. Schaeffer, S. Marathe, and V. Alks, *J. Pharm. Sci.*, **53**, 1368 (1964).
e H. J. Schaeffer, unpublished.
f H. J. Schaeffer, D. D. Godse, and G. Liu, *J. Pharm. Sci.*, **53**, 1510 (1964).
g R. H. Shah, H. J. Schaeffer, and D. H. Murray, *J. Pharm. Sci.*, **54**, 15 (1965).

a substrate as adenosine, but neither K_m nor V_{max} were measured.[5] This result is confirmed with 2′,3′-dideoxyadenosine (VIII), which is a substrate and binds as well as adenosine. Thus, neither the 2′- nor 3′-hydroxy group of adenosine is needed for binding or substrate properties.

That the 5′-hydroxyl group is needed for both substrate properties and binding is shown by comparing 2′,3′-dideoxyadenosine (VIII) with 2′,3′,5′-trideoxyadenosine (X); the latter has a greater than eightfold loss in binding compared to VIII.

The cyclopentane analog (IX) of 2′,3′-dideoxyadenosine (VIII) is not a substrate and suffers a sixfold loss in binding to the enzyme compared to VIII. This result could be interpreted to indicate that the furanose oxygen is necessary for binding and substrate properties; but this interpretation is highly equivocal for several reasons. As will be discussed later, hydrophobic bonding with 9-alkyl groups—including cyclopentyl—has been observed with adenosine deaminase; in fact, 9-cyclopentyladenine complexes as well as IX,[6] so that the binding observed with the side chain of IX may be primarily hydrophobic bonding. Furthermore—as we observed previously with the cyclopentane analog of thymidine and its binding to thymidine kinase and thymidine phosphorylase[7]—the replacement of the furanose oxygen by a methylene group could lead to a binding loss for two other reasons other than the necessity for furanose oxygen binding, namely, (a) the methylene is larger than oxygen and (b) the ground-state conformations of VIII and IX may differ.

[6] H. J. Schaeffer, S. Marathe, and V. Alks, *J. Pharm. Sci.*, **53**, 1368 (1964).
[7] See Chapter 4.

In summary (a) the 5'-hydroxyl group of adenosine is needed for binding and substrate properties; (b) the furanose oxygen is needed for binding, steric, or conformational reasons; (c) neither the 2'- nor 3'-hydroxyl groups are necessary for binding and (d) the β-configuration is necessary.[8] It is therefore not surprising that small structural changes at the 2'- and 3'-positions, such as the changed configuration at 2' (IV), or 3' (III), or the replacement of the 3'-hydroxyl by 3'-amino (VI), or conversion to the 2'-methyl ether (XI) do not affect substrate properties. However, a highly polar ionized group such as a phosphate ester at 2'- or 3'- leads to loss of substrate properties[9]; the loss of binding with the 5'-phosphate of adenosine[9] can be accounted for by either the necessity of the 5'-hydroxylic hydrogen for binding or the repulsion of the ionized phosphate group or both.

A special case meriting discussion is 9-(5'-deoxy-β,D-xylofuranosyl)-adenine (XII), which is a substrate. Note that XII does not have the 5'-hydroxyl necessary for binding the *ribo* configuration; also note that neither the 2'- nor 3'-hydroxyls of adenosine contribute to binding. Shah et al.[10] pointed out that the 3'-hydroxylic hydrogen of XII can approach in space some of the conformations of the 5'-hydroxylic hydrogen of adenosine [or 2',3'-dideoxyadenosine (VIII)]. Note that the 5'-hydroxylic hydrogen conformation VIII*A* is in about the same position as the 3'-hydrogen of XII in conformation XII*A*; that the enzyme or XII or both probably have to undergo an energetically unfavorable conformational

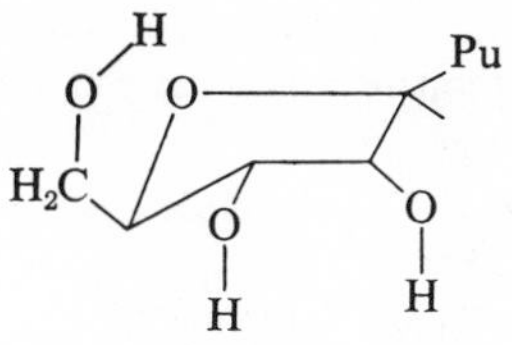

VIII*A* 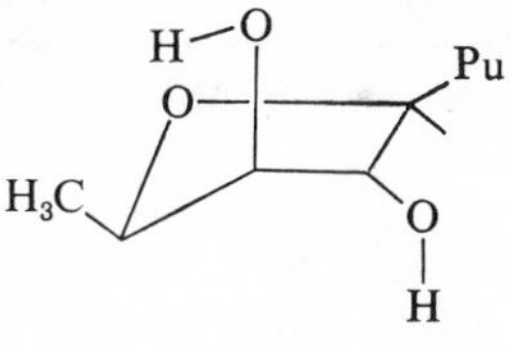   XII*A*

change in order to complex XII*A* is indicated by the 75-fold loss in binding of XII*A* compared to VIII*A*, a matter of 2.6 kcal/mole.

PURINE BINDING

Some structural changes in the purine ring and the resultant effects on binding are listed in Table 12–2. It should be noted at the outset that

[8] See Reference 3, p. 286.
[9] See Reference 4, p. 286.
[10] R. H. Shah, H. J. Schaeffer, and D. H. Murray, *J. Pharm. Sci.*, **54**, 15 (1965).

interpretation of structural changes on a purine ring is difficult, for these changes can affect other nitrogens in the purine by changing their basicity[11] and hence their ability to bind. For example, replacement of the 6-amino group of adenosine (I) by hydrogen (XIV) gives nearly a 10-fold tighter binding; it appears quite certain from this result that the 6-amino

Table 12–2. Binding to Adenosine Deaminase by

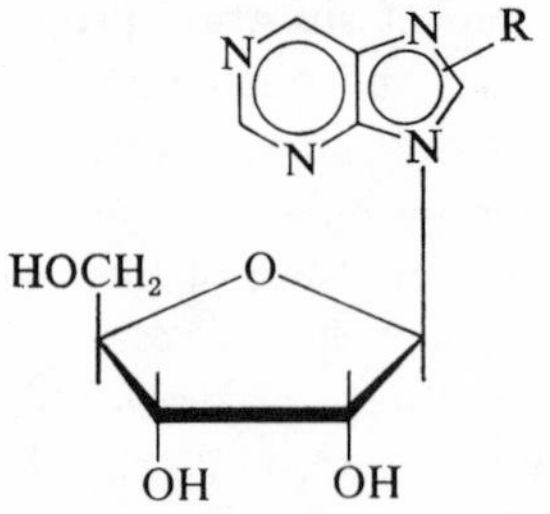

No.	R	$K_i \times 10^5\ M$	Reference
I	6-NH$_2$	8.3[a]	[b]
XIII	2,6-(NH$_2$)$_2$	3.0	[c]
XIV	H	0.88	[b]
XV	6-CH$_3$NH	0.53	[b]
XVI	6-SH	37	[b]
XVII	6-Cl	64[a]	[d]
XVIII	6-NH$_2$-7-deaza	> 40	[b]

Enzyme from calf intestine at pH 7.6 in phosphate buffer was employed.

[a] K_m.
[b] J. G. Cory and R. J. Suhadolnik, *Biochemistry*, **4**, 1729 (1965).
[c] O. P. Chilson and J. R. Fischer, *Archiv. Biochem. Biophys.*, **102**, 77 (1963).
[d] J. G. Cory and R. J. Suhadolnik, *Biochemistry*, **4**, 1733 (1965).

group is not complexed to the enzyme, but why removal of this group affords 10-fold better binding is indeed puzzling. First, removal of the 6-amino group changes the basic pK_a from 3.45 to 2.05, a considerable weakening; therefore, the remaining nitrogens would be weaker bases than those in adenosine. This result is *not* due to any of the following.

1. Less hindrance to binding because the 6-methylamino nucleoside (XV) is even more effectively complexed than XIV.

2. Decreased basicity because the 6-chloropurine nucleoside (XVII) is an

---

[11] For a similar difficulty with the interpretation of purine binding see Chapter 5; similar difficulties were encountered in interpreting the mode of binding pyrimidines to dihydrofolic reductase (Chapter 10) and thymidylate synthetase (Chapter 11).

even weaker base than XIV, but XVII is bound only one eighth as well as adenosine (I).

3. An effect on charge transfer as a donor or acceptor because there is no consistency with the electron-releasing or withdrawing properties of the purine substituents.

Removal of the 7-nitrogen of adenosine, as in tubercidin (XVIII), leads to a loss in binding and substrate properties; to attribute this result to the loss of a binding point is fraught with uncertainty because the antibiotic formycin (XIX) is a substrate even though it has an acidic 7-NH (purine

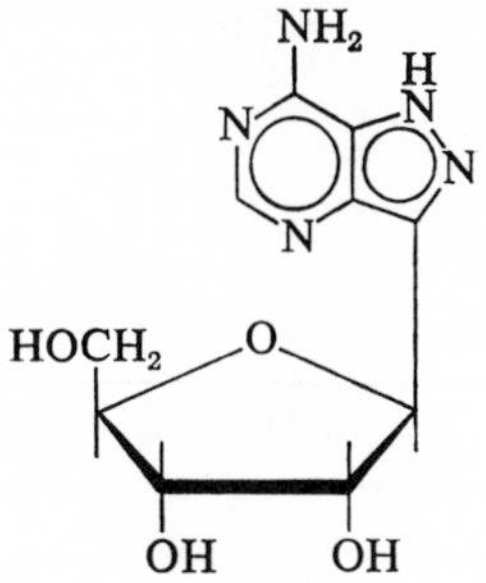

numbering) in place of the normal basic 7-N of adenosine.[12] 7-(β,D-Ribo-furanosyl) adenine (XX) is neither a substrate nor an inhibitor[13]; thus the adenine moiety cannot be turned over and still give proper binding.

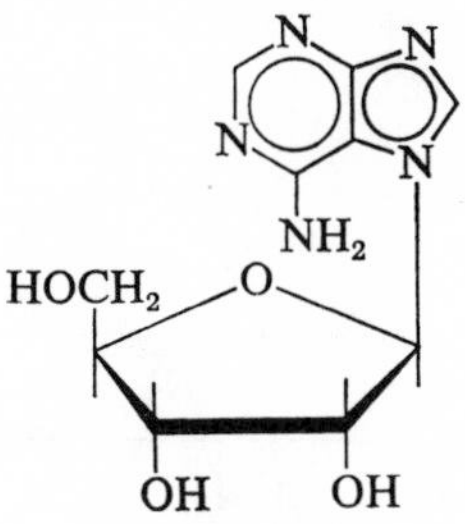

The most important point that emerges on purine binding is that removal of the 6-amino group (as in XIV) or mono-N-methylation (as in XV) of the amino group gives a 10–16-fold increment in better binding; as will be noted later in the section on binding of 9-alkyl and 9-(hydroxyalkyl)-purines, the 6-amino derivatives bind as well as or better than the 6-methylamino derivatives, indicating that the mode of purine binding is not the same with 9-alkyl purines as with adenosine.

HYDROPHOBIC BONDING

9-Alkyladenines show hydrophobic bonding to adenosine deaminase[14] (Table 12–3). The maximum hydrophobic bonding per methylene is observed between three and seven straight-chain carbons with an average

[12] R. K. Robins, L. B. Townsend, F. Cassidy, J. F. Gerster, A. F. Lewis, and R. L. Miller, *J. Heterocyclic Chem.*, 3, 110 (1966); H. Umezawa et al., *J. Antibiotics* (Tokyo), Ser. A, **18**, 175, 178, 191 (1965).

[13] See Reference 4, p. 286.

[14] H. J. Schaeffer and D. Vogel, *J. Med. Chem.*, **8**, 507 (1965).

of 350 cal/mole/CH_2; between methyl and ethyl and between n-heptyl and n-octyl the hydrophobic bonding is only 100 and 170 cal/mole/CH_2, respectively. Inhibition by n-nonyl and n-decyl could not be determined because they are insoluble.[15] Although the increment per methylene is not as large as that observed with dihydrofolic reductase,[16] the total hydrophobic bonding energy between methyl and octyl is large, namely 2 kcal/mole; the total hydrophobic bonding of n-alkyl groups to dihydro-

Table 12–3. Inhibition of Adenosine Deaminase by

No.	R	$[I/S]_{0.5}$[a]	$\Delta \Delta F$[b]	Reference
XXI	CH_3	7.3		[e]
XXII	C_2H_5	6.2	100	[e]
XXIII	n-C_3H_7	3.3	460	[e]
XXIV	n-C_4H_9	2.3	680	[e]
XXV	n-C_5H_{11}	1.4	970	[e]
XXVI	Cyclopentyl	6.8	50	[f]
XXVII	n-C_6H_{13}	0.70	1380	[e]
XXVIII	cyclohexyl	> 5[c,d]		[g]
XXIX	n-C_7H_{15}	0.32	1830	[e]
XXX	$C_6H_5CH_2$	1.5	960	[h]
XXXI	n-C_8H_{17}	0.24	2000	[e]

Adenosine deaminase from calf intestine was assayed at pH 7.6 with 0.066 mM adenosine in the presence of 10 per cent dimethyl sulfoxide.

[a] The ratio of concentration of inhibitor to substrate giving 50 per cent inhibition.

[b] Difference in free energy of binding between compound and 9-methyladenine (XXI).

[c] No inhibition at 0.13 mM concentration of adenosine and inhibitor; because 10 per cent inhibition is readily detected, the concentration for 50 per cent inhibition is estimated at greater than five times the substrate concentration.

[d] No dimethyl sulfoxide present.

[e] H. J. Schaeffer and D. Vogel, *J. Med. Chem.*, **8**, 507 (1965).

[f] H. J. Schaeffer, S. Marathe, and V. Alks, *J. Pharm. Sci.*, **53**, 1368 (1964).

[g] J. G. Cory and R. J. Suhadolnik, *Biochemistry*, **4**, 1729 (1965).

[h] H. J. Schaeffer and E. Odin, *J. Med. Chem.*, **9**, 576 (1966).

[15] H. J. Schaeffer, unpublished.

[16] B. R. Baker, B.-T. Ho, and D. V. Santi, *J. Pharm. Sci.*, **54**, 1415 (1965); see Chapter 10.

folic reductase between methyl and *n*-octyl was as high as 3.8 kcal/mole, most of it occurring between methyl and *n*-butyl.

That certain conformational restrictions of the alkyl group exist in hydrophobic bonding can be gleaned by comparing the 9-cyclopentyl-(XXVI) and 9-cyclohexyladenines (XXVIII) with the other *n*-alkyl adenines. Cyclopentyladenine (XXVI) showed considerably less binding than *n*-pentyl adenine (XXV), being more effective by 920 cal/mole; thus the cyclopentyl (XXVI) was between methyl (XXI) and ethyl (XXII) in hydrophobic bonding ability. Second, *n*-hexyl (XXVII) was complexed at least sevenfold better than cyclohexyl (XXVIII). Third, benzyl (XXX) complexed less effectively than *n*-heptyl (XXIX) by about 870 cal/mole; benzyl (XXX) was about equivalent to *n*-pentyl (XXV) in binding capacity. It would thus appear that the *n*-alkyl groups are complexed in the hydrophobic region in a conformation not too different from the ground-state staggered conformation. A study of branched-chain alkyl and unsaturated alkyl on the 9- position of adenine as performed with dihydrofolic reductase,[17] would be necessary to verify this tentative conclusion.

HYDROXYALKYL BINDING

In Table 12–4 are listed the inhibition results of Schaeffer et al. achieved by using a series of 9-(hydroxyalkyl)-adenines on adenosine deaminase, along with data on appropriate related compounds. Of the ω-hydroxyalkyl adenines, including the unlisted 9-(5-hydroxypentyl)-adenine, the 3-hydroxypropyl (XXXVII) and 2-hydroxyethyl (XXXV) were the most effective inhibitors, being bound about twice as well as adenosine. For some time these results were confusing, for neither the 2'- nor 3'-hydroxyl groups of adenosine are complexed to the enzyme. A solution to this enigma arises when we compare the mode of purine binding.

Note that N^6-methyl adenosine (XV) (Table 12–4) is bound 16 times tighter than adenosine; in contrast, with the 2-hydroxyethyl or 3-hydroxypropyl side chains at the 9- position a ninefold (XXXVI) and threefold (XXXVIII) *loss* in binding occurs by N^6-methylation, a 50–150-fold difference. Other compounds in Table 12–4 have a loss in binding from N^6-methylation that varies from no loss to a ninefold loss, but in no case is there better binding, as is noted with N^6-methyl adenosine (XV). It follows that the purine ring is not complexed in the same fashion with nucleosides on the one hand and 9-hydroxyalkyl, alkyl, or aralkyl groups on the other. In fact, the variation between 9-(*p*-nitrobenzyl)- (XLIV) and

[17] B. R. Baker and G. J. Lourens, *J. Heterocyclic Chem.*, **2**, 344 (1965); see Chapter 10, p. 214, for a discussion of conformational aspects.

Table 12–4. Inhibition of Adenosine Deaminase by

No.	R_6	R_9	$K_i \times 10^5\ M$	$[I/S]_{0.5}$ [a]	Ratio: $\dfrac{R_6}{6\text{-}NH_2}$ [b]	Reference
XV	$NHCH_3$	Ri[c]	0.53	3.3	0.064[a]	f
XXIII	NH_2	$n\text{-}C_3H_7$—		7.0		g
XXXII	$NHCH_3$	$n\text{-}C_3H_7$—		0.25	2.1	g
XXXIII	NH_2	DL-$CH_3CHOHCH_2$—		1.3		g
XXXIV	$NHCH_3$	DL-$CH_3CHOHCH_2$—		1.1	5.2	g
XXXV	NH_2	$HO(CH_2)_2$—	3.8^e	5.3		h
XXXVI	$NHCH_3$	$HO(CH_2)_2$—	34^e	0.70	9.0	h
XXXVII	NH_2	$HO(CH_2)_3$—	3.0^e	1.9		h
XXXVIII	$NHCH_3$	$HO(CH_2)_3$—	9.8^e	1.9	3.3	h
XXXIX	NH_2	$HO(CH_2)_4$—	10^e	2.6		h
XL	$NHCH_3$	$HO(CH_2)_4$—	12^e	0.15	1.2	h
XLI	NH_2	L-$CH_3CHOHCH_2$—		1.4		i
XLII	NH_2	D-$CH_3CHOHCH_2$—				i
XLIII	NH_2	$p\text{-}NO_2C_6H_4CH_2$—		3.6		f
XLIV	$NHCH_3$	$p\text{-}NO_2C_6H_4CH_2$—		4.1	1.1	f

Enzyme from calf intestine assayed at pH 7.6 in phosphate buffer was employed.

[a] Ratio of concentration of inhibitor to 0.066 mM adenosine giving 50 per cent inhibition.

[b] Ratio of concentrations of R_6-R_9-purine to 6-amino-R_9-purine giving equal binding.

[c] Ri is β,D-ribofuranosyl.

[d] Compared to adenosine with $K_m = 8.3 \times 10^{-5}\ M$.

[e] Schaeffer (see footnote h below) has recorded $K_m = 7.3 \times 10^{-5}\ M$ for adenosine, which should be used for comparison.

[f] J. G. Cory and R. J. Suhadolnik, *Biochemistry*, **4**, 1729 (1965).

[g] H. J. Schaeffer, D. Vogel, and R. Vince, *J. Med. Chem.*, **8**, 502 (1965).

[h] H. J. Schaeffer and P. S. Bhargava, *Biochemistry*, **4**, 71 (1965).

9-(2-hydroxyethyl)-adenine (XXXVI) indicates that even these unnatural side chains cause varying effects on the ability of the N^6-methyl group to hinder binding. These results give an indication of why it may have been difficult to interpret purine binding in the earlier section; it may be possible for a number of rotomers of the purine to bind as observed with pyrimidine binding to dihydrofolic reductase.[18] Whether a particular rotomer would allow the hydroxy group of XXXVI or XXXVIII to complex at the same point the 5'-hydroxyl group of adenosine is complexed is purely speculative and requires more work to clarify.

Regardless of how these 9-(hydroxyalkyl)-adenines complex to adenosine deaminase, the results which have emerged with these "competitive" inhibitors are both interesting and useful. That the hydroxylic hydrogen of XXXVI and XXXVIII may be complexed to the enzyme is indicated by a loss in binding on O-methylation or O-acetylation[19]; such a result could also be a steric effect on binding.[19] Of considerable interest is the threefold stronger binding by 2-hydroxypropyl (XXXIII) compared to 3-hydroxypropyl. Resolution showed that the L isomer (XLI) was a sevenfold better inhibitor than the 2-hydroxyethyl group (XXXV), but the D isomer (XLII) was about the same as the 2-hydroxyethyl; these results indicate that good hydrophobic bonding can be obtained with an L isomer, but not the D isomer. Because this sevenfold increment is considerably larger than the twofold increment between ethyl (XXII) (Table 12–3) and *n*-propyl (XXIII), some effects on changes from the ground-state conformation of the inhibitors in the complex are also probably involved.

ACTIVE-SITE-DIRECTED IRREVERSIBLE INHIBITION

Because adenosine deaminase could tolerate bulky groups at the 9- position of adenine, Schaeffer and Odin[20,21] selected 9-benzyladenine for further structural modification towards an active-site-directed irreversible inhibitor. The *p*-bromoacetamido derivative (XLV) was investigated first and found to be an active-site-directed irreversible inhibitor of adenosine deaminase. Later investigations showed that the *o* isomer (XLVII) could also inactivate the enzyme by the active-site-directed mechanism, but the *m* isomer (XVI) gave barely perceptible inactivation.[22] Figure 12–1 shows the rate of inactivation of adenosine deaminase by XLV, the half-life being

[18] See Chapter 10, p. 239.
[19] H. J. Schaeffer, C. F. Schwender, and R. N. Johnson, *J. Pharm. Sci.*, **54**, 978 (1965).
[20] H. J. Schaeffer and E. Odin, *J. Pharm. Sci.*, **54**, 1223 (1965).
[21] H. J. Schaeffer and E. Odin, *J. Med. Chem.*, **9**, 576 (1966).
[22] H. J. Schaeffer and R. N. Johnson, *J. Pharm. Sci.*, **55**, 929 (1966).

about 90 minutes at 37° with 0.015 mM XLV; because XLV had $K_i = 1.3 \times 10^{-5}$ M, 54 per cent of the total enzyme was in the form of a reversible complex.[23]

Iodoacetamide showed no inactivation at 12 times the concentration of

NH₂ structure

XLV, *p*-isomer
XLVI, *m*-isomer
XLVII, *o*-isomer

XLV, thus eliminating the possibility of a random bimolecular mechanism for inactivation.[23] When the concentration of irreversible inhibitor was doubled to 0.03 mM, the rate of inactivation increased only 1.27-fold; it

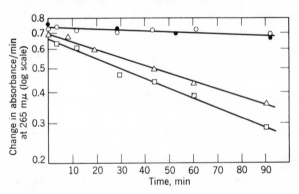

Fig. 12–1. Comparison of the irreversible inhibition of adenosine deaminase by 9-(*p*-bromacetamidobenzyl)adenine (XLV) and iodoacetamide: ○, enzyme control; △, 0.015 mM XLV; □, 0.030 mM XLV; ●, 0.18 mM iodoacetamide. From H. H. Schaeffer and E. Odin, *J. Pharm. Sci.*, **54**, 1223 (1965).

can be calculated from K_i that the rate should have increased by a factor of 1.30 if a reversible complex was an intermediate in the inactivation.

That complexing by a 9-benzyladenine did not expose an enzymic group to bimolecular attack by conformational change of the enzyme—as was

---

[23] See Chapter 8, Kinetic Parameters.

noted with methylguanidine on trypsin[23,24]—was eliminated by incubation of 9-benzyladenine and iodoacetamide with the enzyme; no inactivation occurred above the normal small thermal loss.

In the presence of the reversible inhibitor, 9-(3-hydroxypropyl)-adenine (XXXVII) at 0.12 mM, the rate of inactivation by 0.015 mM XLV was slowed by a factor of 2.4-fold. If inactivation by XLV occurs through a reversible enzyme-inhibitor complex, it can be calculated[23] from the respective K_i's of XXXVII and XLV that the rate of inactivation should have been slowed by a factor of 2.8, for only 19 per cent of the enzyme is in a complex with XLV under these conditions.

In an elegant series of experiments Schaeffer and Odin[25] determined the rate constants for the enzyme inactivation by the p (XLV) and o isomers (XLVII); they measured the change in the rate of inactivation at varying concentrations of inhibitor. If the inactivation proceeds by the mechanism in Equation 12–1

$$E + I \underset{k_2}{\overset{k_1}{\rightleftharpoons}} E\cdots I \xrightarrow{k_3} \widehat{E\cdots I} \qquad (12\text{–}1)$$

where E is the active enzyme, I is the inhibitor, $E\cdots I$ is the reversible complex and $\widehat{E\cdots I}$ is the inactivated enzyme, then the velocity of inactivation V is expressed by Equation 12–4 where [EI] is the concentration of reversible complex and E_t is the total enzyme concentration[26]:

$$V = k_3[\text{EI}] \qquad (12\text{–}2)$$

Because[26]

$$[\text{EI}] = \frac{E_t}{1 + (K_i/\text{I})} \qquad (12\text{–}3)$$

then,

$$V = \frac{k_3 E_t}{1 + (K_i/\text{I})} \qquad (12\text{–}4)$$

Because the inhibitor is present in a large excess over the enzyme concentration, the reaction is first order with respect to the enzyme as presented in Equation (12–5). Therefore Schaeffer and Odin[25] derived Equation (12–7).

$$k_{\text{obs}} = \frac{V}{E_t} \qquad (12\text{–}5)$$

[24] T. Inagami, *J. Biol. Chem.*, **240**, 3453 (1965); see also Chapter 8, p. 151.
[25] H. J. Schaeffer and E. Odin, in press.
[26] See Chapter 8, Kinetic Parameters.

Combine Equation (12–4) with (12–5). Then

$$k_{\mathrm{obs}} = \frac{k_3}{1 + (K_i/\mathrm{I})} \qquad (12\text{–}6)$$

which can be arranged to Equation (12–7):

$$\frac{1}{k_{\mathrm{obs}}} = \frac{K_i}{k_3} \cdot \frac{1}{\mathrm{I}} + \frac{1}{k_3} \qquad (12\text{–}7)$$

A plot of $1/k_{\mathrm{obs}}$ against $1/\mathrm{I}$ should give a straight line where the intercept is $1/k_3$, the slope $= K_i/k_3$, and $K_i = $ slope/intercept if the inactivation operates by the mechanism depicted in Equation (12–1). The results of such experiments are found in Fig. 12–2; the data are also listed in Table 12–5.

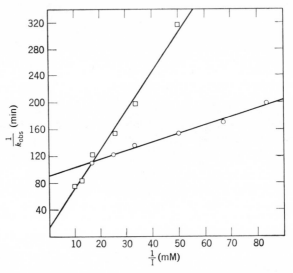

Fig. 12–2. Variation in the rate of inactivation of adenosine deaminase with concentration of inhibitor at 37°; □ 9-(o-bromoacetamidobenzyl)adenine (XLVII); ○ 9-(p-bromoacetamidobenzyl)adenine (XLV). From H. J. Schaeffer and E. Odin, in press.

It should be noted that bimolecular inactivation with self-protection[27] would give the same kinetics; this mechanism is inoperative because iodoacetamide does not inactivate.

The agreement in the K_i's obtained for the p-bromoacetamido purine (XLV) and the o-bromoacetamido purine (XLVII) by the reversible and irreversible experiments is a brilliant achievement that must be gratifying to these investigators and certainly is gratifying to this author. The

[27] See Chapter 8, Kinetic Parameters.

information in Table 12–5 and Fig. 12–2 beautifully confirms some of the complaints the author has had about the comparisons some investigators have made on rates of inactivation of enzymes by active-site-directed irreversible inhibitors where the amount of enzyme in the reversibly bound enzyme-inhibitor complex was not considered.[28]

Table 12–5. Kinetic Parameters of Inactivation of Adenosine Deaminase by

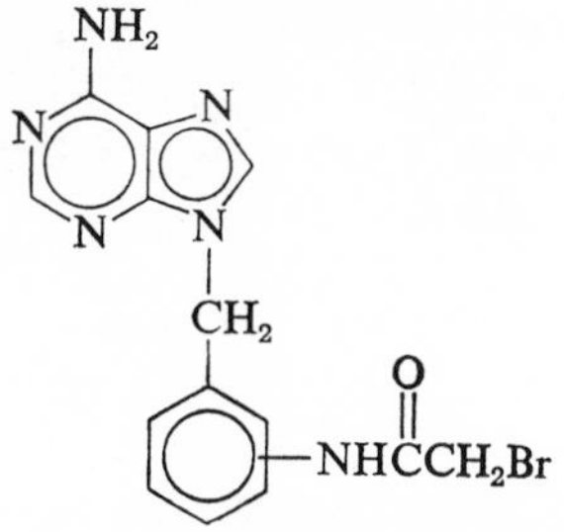

No.	Isomer	$K_i \times 10^5$ M by reciprocal plot[a]	$K_i \times 10^5$ M by inactivation[b]	$k_3 \times 10^3$ (min^{-1})[b]
XLV	*para*	1.3 ± 0.1	1.4	11
XLVI	*meta*	3.6		very slow
XLVII	*ortho*	44	50	70

Data from H. J. Schaeffer and E. Odin, unpublished.
[a] By the Lineweaver-Burk plot of $1/V$ vs. $1/S$ for reversible inhibition.
[b] From Fig. 12–2 and Equation 12–7.

Suppose an investigator arbitrarily chose a concentration of $\frac{1}{17}$ mM, where the two lines cross in Fig. 12–2. He would have observed that both the *o* and *p* isomers inactivated the enzyme at exactly the same rate and would have concluded that the two isomers gave identical inactivation rates. If an investigator arbitrarily chose a concentration of $\frac{1}{10}$ mM, he would have concluded that the *p* isomer was a poorer irreversible inhibitor than the *o* isomer, for at this concentration, the *o* isomer inactivates more rapidly than the *p* isomer. Suppose an investigator chose a concentration of $\frac{1}{40}$ mM; he would have concluded that the *p* isomer was a better irreversible inhibitor than the *o* isomer. To emphasize the point again, inactivation rates must consider the relative amounts of reversible enzyme-inhibitor complex; it is clear that it takes a concentration of 50×10^{-5} M of the *o* isomer to give 50 per cent enzyme-inhibitor complex but only 1.4×10^{-5} M of the *p* isomer to give 50 per cent complex. With an equal

[28] See Chapter 8.

amount of reversible enzyme-inhibitor complex, the *o* isomer inactivates the enzyme seven times as fast as the *p* isomer, which in turn is about 25 times as fast as the *m* isomer. Therefore, a definition of how "good" an irreversible inhibitor is must take into consideration *the concentration necessary to give 50 per cent* E····I *complex* (K_i) *and the rate of inactivation*, k_3.

Further work with these active-site-directed irreversible inhibitors of adenosine deaminase for "labeling" specific amino acids of the enzyme will be awaited with interest; also work with appropriate analogs that may give a species-specific blockade of adenosine deaminase that can be used chemotherapeutically in conjunction with such cytoxic adenine nucleosides as III–VI will hopefully emerge.

13 | Enzyme-specific Columns

The use of carboxymethyl cellulose, diethylaminoethyl cellulose (DEAE cellulose), and related modified celluloses bearing anionic or cationic groups have been used for some years for column purification of enzymes[1]; these operate on the principle of the difference in charge on the various enzymes, the more basic enzymes being retained longer on an acidic column support or vice versa. As he reported in a classical paper in 1953, Lerman[2] attached a molecule to cellulose that could complex with the active-site of the enzyme, thus being far more specific than mere charge difference on the column. He had noted that p-phenylazophenol was an inhibitor of the enzyme tyrosinase that normally uses tyrosine as a substrate.

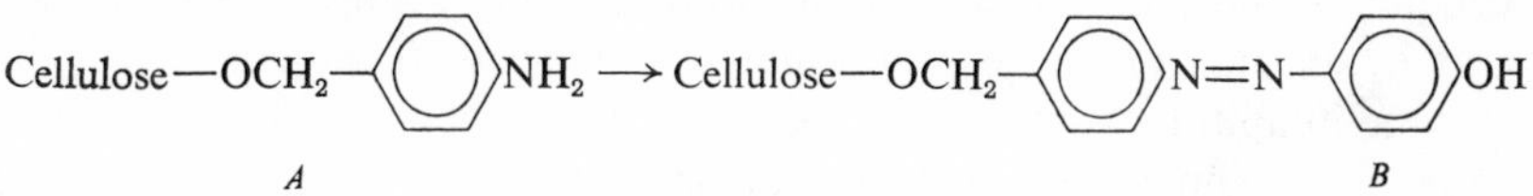

$$\text{Cellulose}-\text{OCH}_2-\langle\bigcirc\rangle-\text{NH}_2 \rightarrow \text{Cellulose}-\text{OCH}_2-\langle\bigcirc\rangle-\text{N}{=}\text{N}-\langle\bigcirc\rangle-\text{OH}$$

A B

By diazotization of p-aminobenzyl cellulose (A), which has about one benzyl unit per 13 glucose units of the cellulose, then coupling with phenol, the modified cellulose (B) was obtained. This modified cellulose (B) will have a higher affinity for enzymes that can complex phenols than enzymes that do not; therefore the enzymes that can complex phenol come off the column later than those enzymes that cannot. Thus, one pass of a crude enzyme extract gave 60–100 purification—much higher than that obtained with cationic or anionic celluloses. The same principle was also used for fractionation of antibodies; if diazotized A is coupled with antigen, the

[1] E. A. Peterson and H. A. Sober in *Methods in Enzymology*, S. P. Colowick and N. O. Kaplan, eds., Academic Press, New York, 1962, Vol. V, pp. 3–26.
[2] L. S. Lerman, *Proc. Natl. Acad. Sci.* (*U.S.*), **39**, 232 (1953).

modified cellulose has higher affinity for the specific antibody of the particular antigen. Not only was purification achieved, but heterogeniety in antibodies for a single antigen was noted.[3,4] Similarly, carboxymethyl cellulose can be coupled to the antigen with dicyclohexylcarbodiimide.[5] A hapten coupled to cellulose can also be utilized for fractionation of antibodies to the haptenic determinant attached to serum albumin.[6,7] Covalent attachment of nucleic acids to cellulose can be used to fractionate other nucleic acids.[8]

Lerman's principle was certainly an attractive one for purification of antibodies or nucleic acids, but it appeared to lie dormant for over ten years for purification of enzymes; this dormancy was due to failure of proper utilization by investigators rather than lack of interest in the principle. Superficially this elegant principle seems simple, but it suffers one of the same pitfalls inherent in the principle behind the design of active-site-directed irreversible inhibitors; if the solid support, such as cellulose, is inadvertently attached to the inhibitor in such a way that complex formation between the supported inhibitor and the enzyme cannot take place, then there will be no more affinity between the inhibitor-modified cellulose and the enzyme than with unmodified cellulose.

In 1962 the author had the opportunity to present a lecture on active-site-directed irreversible inhibitors at Cornell University at the invitation of Professor D. B. McCormick; as a result of mutual discussion on the similarity in binding problems for design of an active-site-directed irreversible inhibitor and an enzyme-specific column, McCormick was successful in ending the dormancy of the Lerman principle. Note in Fig. 1–3 and in Chapter 7 that bulk tolerance areas on the inhibitor must be determined; that is, an area on the inhibitor not in contact with the enzyme in the enzyme-inhibitor complex must be located (Fig. 13–1a). Similarly, it is necessary to know where such an area is located on an inhibitor in order to attach it properly to the solid support, as indicated in Fig. 13–1b; if the

[3] N. Weliky, H. H. Weetall, R. V. Gilden, and D. H. Campbell, *Immunochemistry*, **1**, 219 (1964).

[4] For related examples see D. H. Campbell, E. Luescher, and L. S. Lerman, *Proc. Natl. Acad. Sci. (U.S.)*, **37**, 575 (1951); P. Bernfeld and J. Wan, *Science*, **142**, 678 (1963); A. Hagiware, *Nature*, **202**, 1019 (1964); H. Tuppy and E. Küchler, *Biochim. Biophys. Acta.*, **80**, 669 (1964); N. R. Moudgal and R. R. Porter, *Biochim. Biophys. Acta.*, **71**, 185 (1963).

[5] H. H. Weetall and N. Weliky, *Nature*, **204**, 896 (1964).

[6] L. S. Lerman, *Nature*, **172**, 635 (1955).

[7] For a related study with a differently prepared hapten-cellulose see H. H. Weetall and N. Weliky, *Science*, **148**, 1235 (1965).

[8] A. J. Adler and A. Rich, *J. Am. Chem. Soc.*, **84**, 3977 (1962); S. Erhan, G. L. Northrup, and F. R. Leach, *Proc. Natl. Acad. Sci. (U.S.)*, **53**, 646 (1965).

support is attached in the binding area indicated by the "X" marks, then no complex formation can take place.

In his studies on the inhibition of flavokinase, McCormick[9] had found that the known inhibitor, lumiflavin (I), could be modified with bulky

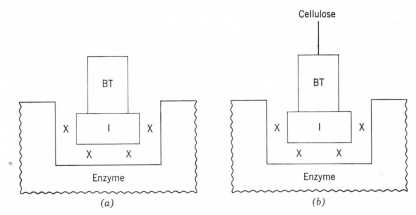

Fig. 13–1. (*a*) A schematic representation of an enzyme-inhibitor complex in which the X's are the points of complex formation between the inhibitor, I, and the enzyme. BT represents a bulk tolerance area on the inhibitor not in contact with the enzyme. (*b*) The proper positioning of a solid support, such as cellulose, for the inhibitor. If the solid support were placed in an X area, no complex formation could take place.

groups at R_1 and R_2 without decreasing affinity with the enzyme; furthermore, the amino derivative (II) was a good inhibitor. It follows that the cellulose should be attached to the R_2 position, which could be conveniently done with the aminoflavin II. Coupling of II with carboxymethyl

I, $R_1 = R_2 = CH_3$
II, $R_1 = CH_3, R_2 = NH_2$

cellulose via conversion of a portion of the carboxyl groups to the acid chloride gave a flavin cellulose that had retention properties for flavokinase. A 100-fold purification could be obtained by one pass through the column; of key importance was the ready separation from the phosphatase acting on riboflavin phosphate, the product of the kinase enzyme, because these two enzymes could not be separated by column chromatography on

[9] D. B. McCormick, C. Arsenis, and P. Hemmerich, *J. Biol. Chem.*, **238**, 3095 (1963).

anionic or cationic celluloses.[10] Although this column material demonstrated the principle of the needed bulk tolerance, it suffered by still having ion-exchange properties from unreacted carboxyl groups; this difficulty will be amplified later.

One of the mose selective columns yet constructed is the biotin cellulose column for purification of avidin.[11] Avidin, a protein usually isolated from egg white, complexes with biotin (III) with an estimated dissociation constant of 10^{-15} M. The complexing apparently does not depend upon a free carboxyl group because biotin methyl ester (IV) and biocytin (V) also complexed effectively. McCormick therefore reasoned that biotin attached

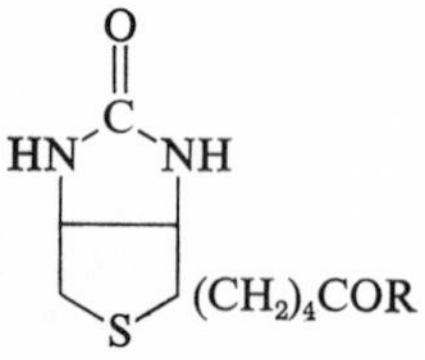

III, R = OH
IV, R = OCH$_3$
V, R = NH-(CH$_2$)$_4$CH(NH$_2$)COOH
VI, R = —cellulose

through its carboxyl group to cellulose should be a specific absorbent for avidin. By reaction of 1 g of biotinyl chloride with 10 g of cellulose suspended in pyridine, a biotin cellulose linked through an ester group (VI) was obtained. The amount of esterification was low, for only one out of fifteen hundred glucose units of the cellulose had an attached biotin even though sufficient biotinyl chloride for one out of fifteen glucose units was employed.

Crude avidin of 10 per cent purity was readily brought to 100 per cent purity with a ratio of 10 g of biotin cellulose to 1 mg of pure protein, which is a ratio of 10 mg of biotin to 1 mg of pure protein. Optimal conditions for the avidin-biotin complex are pH 8.9 and the moderate ionic strength afforded by 0.2 M ammonium carbonate. Under these conditions all of the protein other than avidin is washed through the column; the avidin is then eluted with a reverse linear gradient from 0.2 M ammoniun carbonate to pure water. The results are shown in Fig. 13–2 where pure avidin is eluted after the protein impurities near the front. It should also be noted that the modified cellulose can be reused after washing.

An important contrast between the flavin-cellulose column for flavokinase and the biotin-cellulose column for avidin is that the latter is pre-

[10] C. Arsenis and D. B. McCormick, *J. Biol. Chem.*, **239**, 3093 (1964).
[11] D. B. McCormick, *Anal. Biochem.*, **13**, 194 (1965).

pared from neutral cellulose with no ion-exchange capacity. In the case of the flavin-cellulose column, the linkage is formed from carboxymethyl cellulose through an amide linkage; thus any unreacted carboxyl groups have ion-exchange properties that interfere in the separation of the proteins by retaining more basic proteins as well as flavokinase.

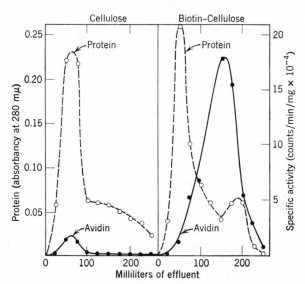

Fig. 13–2. Column chromatography of crude avidin on cellulose and biotin-cellulose. Commercial 10 per cent pure avidin (10 mg) in 5 ml of 0.225 M ammonium carbonate was poured over each 1.5 by 25 cm column containing 10 g of cellulose or biotin cellulose. Ten 25 ml fractions were collected by reverse gradient elution. The avidin content of each fraction was measured by its ability to complex C^{14}-biotin as counted after dialysis. From D. B. McCormick, *Anal. Biochem.*, **13**, 194 (1965).

Riboflavin phosphate monomethyl ester can act as a substrate in place of the usual riboflavin phosphate (FMN) with several enzymes. Therefore McCormick[12] investigated a column of FMN cellulose; the latter was prepared by coupling FMN with cellulose by dicyclohexylcarbodiimide. The most satisfactory results were obtained with glycolate apoxidase; one pass on the column led to 400-fold purification to essentially pure enzyme with no loss. With TPN-cytochrome *c* apoxidase, a 65-fold purification with no loss was obtained.

An interesting modification of the investigation described above is the fractionation of adenine-containing polynucleotides on a cellulose coupled with thymidylate by dicyclohexylcarbodiimide[13]; the separation is

[12] C. Arsenis and D. B. McCormick, *J. Biol. Chem.*, **241**, 330 (1966).
[13] E. G. Sander, D. B. McCormick, and L. D. Wright, *J. Chromatog.*, **21**, 419 (1966).

based on base pairing the thymine on the cellulose with the adenine in the polynucleotide.

The success of McCormick and his coworkers in designing relatively enzyme-specific columns was not based on good luck. They carefully considered the point where the cellulose should be attached to the substrate or inhibitor by at least placing a small group on the functional group to be bound to cellulose to show that loss of this functional group would have a minimal detrimental effect on binding. However, a small group does not necessarily indicate bulk tolerance. Note that FMN cellulose worked best where the K_m of the FMN methyl ester was fortuitously poorest, indicating that there was less binding by FMN to the glycolate apoxidase; a possible explanation may be that the phosphate group of FMN does not bind at all to the enzyme—accounting for its higher K_m—which would also indicate a greater bulk tolerance in the area of the phosphate group of FMN. Thus, a better complex between FMN cellulose and glycolate apoxidase may form than between FMN cellulose and the cytochrome c apoxidase, even though the reverse was true for the binding of FMN monomethyl ester.

In studies of bulk tolerance aimed at designing active-site-directed irreversible inhibitors,[14–17] structures were encountered that would be useful for enzyme-specific columns—particularly after a covalent-forming

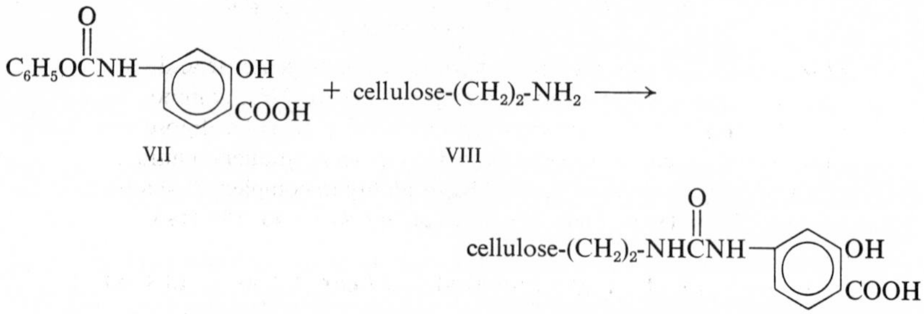

group had been placed in the bulk tolerance area. For example, 4-(carbophenoxyamino)-salicylic acid (VII) is a good reversible inhibitor of lactic dehydrogenase[15]; when excess VII is reacted with aminoethyl cellulose (VIII) in dimethyl sulfoxide, all of the amino groups of VIII are reacted to give the modified cellulose (IX). This modified cellulose had an affinity

[14] See Chapter 7.
[15] See Chapter 9, p. 156, 160.
[16] See Chapter 10, p. 244.
[17] See Chapter 11, p. 281.

for heart lactic dehydrogenase; the enzyme was not eluted with buffer but could be eluted with lactate.[18]

Compounds such as X–XIII that were synthesized as potential active-site-directed irreversible inhibitors of dihydrofolic reductase[19] could presumably be attached to cellulose or its derivatives, such as aminoethyl-, aminobenzyl, etc., or to other polymeric carriers in order to obtain enzyme-specific absorbents for dihydrofolic reductase. Similarly, a molecule such as

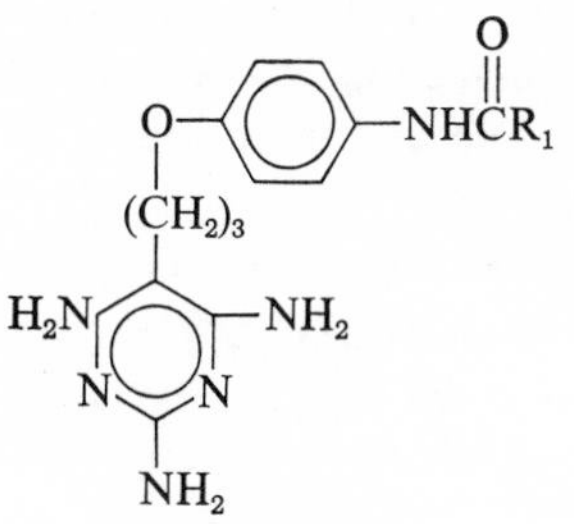

X, R_1 = —CH_2Br
XI, R_1 = OC_6H_5
XII, R_1 = —$(CH_2)_2COOH$

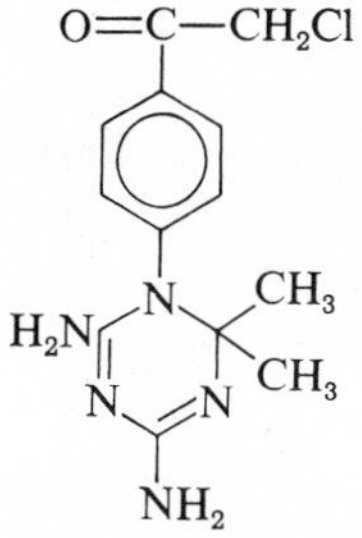

XIII

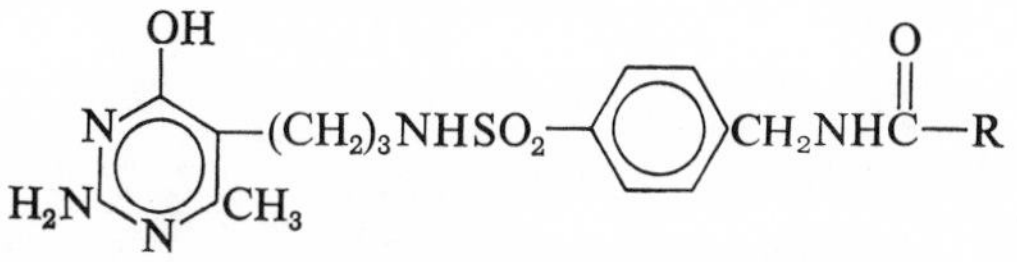

XIV

XIV with a proper R group[20] could be attached to a polymeric support for the purification of thymidylate synthetase.

There are a number of parameters yet to be studied in the design of enzyme-specific columns; it should theoretically be possible to get sufficiently tight absorption that only a substrate or inhibitor will elute the enzyme, thus resulting in a more facile or higher degree of purification. The following parameters should be studied:

1. The type of polymer to be condensed with substrate or inhibitor should either have no ion-exchange properties initially or all of the ionic groups should be reacted with the modifier so that no ion-exchange properties remain. Thus studies on complete reaction of the ionic group on cellulose and on other polymers would be useful.

[18] B. R. Baker and R. P. Patel, unpublished.
[19] See Chapter 10, p. 243.
[20] See Chapter 11, p. 283.

2. The more that is known about bulk tolerance areas on the inhibitor, the better are the chances for synthesis of an efficient column material.

3. Nothing is known about the optimum distance for complexing groups along the polymer chain; if the groups are too close, then efficiency may be lost due to a second complexing group getting in the way of the enzyme complex with the first complexing group. If the complexing groups are too far apart, then larger amounts of column material must be used, which, in turn, means larger elution volumes.

4. Can polymers soluble in dimethylformamide or dimethylsulfoxide—but insoluble in water—be employed so that cleaner and faster reactions with the inhibitor molecules can take place? Cellulose and its derivatives such as carboxymethyl are quite insoluble and therefore react slowly and sometimes ineffectively in suspension.

Such modified polymers with groups for complexing with specific enzymes should ultimately even have industrial application, for these polymers could be reused in the same way that ion-exchange resins are reused for isolation of rare earths.

Notation

DFP	Diisopropyl fluorophosphidate
DPN	diphosphopyridine nucleotide
DPNH	reduced diphosphopyridine nucleotide
dTMP	5′-thymidylate
dUMP	2′-deoxy-5′-uridylate
E. coli	*Escherichia coli*
FA	folic acid
FAH_2	7,8-dihydrofolic acid
FAH_4	5,6,7,8-tetrahydrofolic acid
FU	5-fluorouracil
FUDR	2′-deoxy-5-fluorouridine
FUDRP	2′-deoxy-5-fluoro-5′-uridylate
GDH	glutamic dehydrogenase
GTP	guanosine-5′-triphosphate
4-ISA	4-(iodoacetamido)-salicylic acid
IMP	5′-inosinate
K_i	enzyme-inhibitor dissociation constant
K_m, K_s	enzyme-substrate dissociation constant
LDH	lactic dehydrogenase
M	molar
mM	millimolar
TPCK	1-chloro-4-phenyl-3-(p-tolylsulfonamido)-buten-2-one
TPN	triphosphopyridine nucleotide
TPNH	reduced triphosphopyridine nucleotide
V_{max}	Maximum velocity of enzyme reaction when saturated with substrate
μM	micromolar
π	Hantsch hydrophobicity constant
σ	Hammett electronegativity constant

Author Index

Subject Index

317